D1489301

THE SPIRIT OF MAN

GREAT STORIES AND
EXPERIENCES OF
SPIRITUAL CRISIS,
INSPIRATION, AND
THE JOY OF LIFE
BY FORTY FAMOUS
CONTEMPORARIES

THE SPIRIT OF MAN

edited by Whit Burnett

HAWTHORN BOOKS, INC., PUBLISHERS, New York

FIRST EDITION

ACKNOWLEDGMENTS

The editor and his publisher wish to thank all those who have contributed to this volume, some with material that had not hitherto been published:

Sherwood Anderson, reprinted by permission of Harold Ober Associates, Inc., New York, from *The Sherwood Anderson Reader*, edited by Paul Rosenfeld; copyright 1947 by Eleanor Anderson, published by Houghton, Mifflin Co.

N. J. Berrill, reprinted by permission of Dodd, Mead & Company from *Man's Emerging Mind*; copyright © 1955 by N. J. Berrill.

William Bridgeman and Jacqueline Hazard, reprinted by permission of Henry Holt & Co., from *The Lonely Sky*; copyright 1955 by Henry Holt & Co.

Heywood Broun, reprinted by permission of Harcourt, Brace & Company, Inc., from *Collected Edition of Heywood Broun*; copyright 1941 by Heywood Hale Broun.

Pearl S. Buck, reprinted by permission of Harold Ober Associates Inc., New York, from *The First Wife and Other Stories*; copyright 1933 by Pearl S. Buck, published by The John Day Company.

Hallie Burnett, reprinted by permission of Hallie Southgate Burnett, from *The Seas of God*, edited by Whit Burnett; copyright 1944 by Whit Burnett, published by J. B. Lippincott Co.

John Cheever, reprinted by permission of John Cheever from *The Reporter*, Dec. 29, 1955; copyright by *The Reporter*.

Philippe Diolé, reprinted by permission of Julian Messner, Inc., from *Sahara Adventure*; copyright 1956 by Julian Messner, Inc.

Allan Dowling, reprinted by permission of Allan Dowling from *New Directions No. 8*; copyright by New Directions.

Elisabeth Elliot, reprinted by permission of Harper & Brothers from *Through Gates of Splendor*; copyright by Harper & Brothers.

Etienne Gilson, reprinted by permission of Henry Regnery Company from *Héloïse and Abélard*; copyright 1952 by Henry Regnery Company.

Victor Gollancz, reprinted by permission of Simon and Schuster, Inc., from *My Dear Timothy*; copyright 1953 by Simon and Schuster, Inc. Canadian permission from Victor Gollancz.

To Hallie Burnett

CONTENTS

THE SPIRIT OF MAN

FOREWORD

*Every spirit makes its house, but afterwards
the house confines the spirit.*

Conduct of Life: *Fate*, Ralph Waldo Emerson.

The duty of an anthologist, after the pieces have all been assembled, is to say, finally, what makes his book hold together, to explain the unity he hopes has been created out of diversity. An anthology is a little like a stained glass window, except that the separately shining bits are not all stained in the same studio nor by the same artist. These pieces have come from many quarters of the globe. But there is, for all their differences, a singleness of subject. The subject is the spirit, or the soul, of man.

By the spirit of man is not meant simply the conquering spirit, which triumphs over all and comes through resplendent. Man has, at times, a doubting spirit, of very great depth and interest. He has a questing spirit, a wondering spirit, a playful spirit, and even, now and then, a spirit of purest joy. For the spirit of man, as we see it in this book, is a various thing; it exists in the simplest and most honest man (a poor thing but his own) and it abounds in the rich, inspiring personality-in-thought-and-deed of the saint and sage.

For an anthologist in a field as wide as this, it is easier to gather up the fragments of the mosaic—the bright particular manifestations of the thing itself—than it is to sit down, at the end, which is this beginning, and define the terms.

We say a fine horse has spirit, and we seem to see at times a kind of spiritual quality shining in the loving eyes of a dog. This book, however, deals with the spirit of man of the genus homo, "the highest type," in Webster's definition, "of animal existing or known to have existed . . ." man, as a member of the human race, with human force and nature as a mode of being, man as spiritual existence, as inward man. "How like a god," cried Hamlet, "the beauty of the world, the paragon of animals, the quintessence of dust!" And Job: "Man is of few days, and full of trouble. He cometh forth like a flower and is cut down; he fleeth also as a shadow, and continueth not." Both are man. And both are here.

What does it mean to be, as Thomas Wolfe was, forever lonely in this world? To face death, as Sidney Stewart did, as a prisoner, tortured, starving, in war? To regain one's sight after many years, as John Howard Griffin did, and for the first time gaze upon the face of the woman you have married, and your child's face, and find them almost unbearably beautiful? What does it mean to feel at peace with the world, confident of a kind of rightness in it all, to come back from death, as Jesse Stuart did, and feel man is not a lost creature, but that in him and in him only, by the grace of something, lies all the past and future?

Various are the states and conditions of man, and various is the spirit with which he meets the trials of his living and his dying.

In this book forty different personalities, ranging from desert naturalists to priests and philosophers, from airplane pilots and explorers to teachers and scientists, set forth their most intense personal observations, experiences and crises in their lives and thought. In fact, fiction and in reflection, forty different human beings react in their own private, personal and spiritual way to what for them is the deepest mode of life.

Definitions of the "spirit" of man may have come a long way since the days of the Greeks, or the Medieval scholars, when the spirit was the "breath of life" in three separate kinds of degrees: "(1) *the natural spirit*, a vapor rising from the blood and having its seat in the liver, governing nutrition, growth and generation; (2), *the vital spirit*, transformed from the natural spirit, in the heart, by mixture with the air of respiration, conveying heat and life through the arteries to the whole body; and (3) *the animal spirit*, converted in the brain from the vital spirit and including the rational principle, and having the animal function of distributing the power of motion and feeling through the nerves."

To the man of the Middle Ages the spirit of man was the life principle viewed as the "breath" or gift of deity; hence the agent of vital and conscious functions in man; the soul.

We are less specific today.

"Spirit," writes Edmund W. Sinnott, the American botanist and biologist, "is first of all a questing and aspiring thing, seeking in the world outside for something to satisfy its inner longing. That there exists a means by which this satisfaction can be gained—a reservoir of spirit on which a man may draw—is suggested by the very longing itself. Nature is not frustrating. For every goal that draws us on, the thing desired exists. That we are hungry or cold implies that food and warmth are to be had. Sometimes it may be that we cannot reach them, but they are there. All lower goals set up in protoplasm can be attained. It would be strange indeed if *men* were continually tantalized by urgent desires within them which could never be fulfilled. . . .

"It is in the goal-seeking character of protoplasm that matter and spirit meet. Whether spirit is born here from the complexities of matter or whether spirit at this critical point becomes associated with it and directs the course that matter takes is an important question of philosophy. No one has yet an answer to this problem. . . . (But) the case for spirit as a specific reality is stronger than has generally been admitted. It need not rest alone on inner conviction, faith and the authority of revelation, important though these may be, but can look to the basic fact of biology—goal-seeking—for evidence of something that may truly be called spiritual. This position, to be sure, must assume that life and at least the rudiments of spirit are coextensive; that life, mind and spirit essentially are one. To understand the nature of life, we shall never succeed . . . by seeking to interpret it solely through the laws of physics and chemistry which we now know, but we shall need to discover new laws, perhaps a new kind of law, for life. When we find these, we shall not only solve the deepest problem in biology and the ancient enigma of the relation between mind and body but shall also dimly begin to understand how spirit, mysterious as it now seems to be, can come to dwell in the flesh."

How the spirit has come to dwell in the flesh we may never know, but that it does and that at times it "flashes man into an existence beyond his ordinary self"* we see from countless observations and experiences. Spirit, Dr. Sinnott concludes, is but the "highest expression of life, and life is still as unexplained as spirit is. . . ."

And here, of course, is where philosophers go out, and scientists too, and the artist and the lover and the mystic walk in. If life is unexplainable, and love is a feeling which to define must first be felt, such limitations are but challenges to those who seek the universal in the bright particularity of their art, in the poem or character or experience plumbed creatively and with the gift of the artist's imagination. It is no accident that fourteen of the contributors to this book are first and foremost authors. And while thirty-three are men, it does not mean that men are alone in preoccupation with the spirit of man. Seven are women, and each, with her own insight and intuition, has probed some further depth and come back with treasure.

It has been the editor's pleasure in the last fourteen years to have approached the spirit of man in other volumes somewhat on the fringe of this one. One book, *This Is My Philosophy*, comprising twenty of the world's greatest living thinkers who sought to give expression to the deepest meanings they had found in life, was mainly by philosophers. It was the test of the spirit in thought.

Another aspect was treated in *The Spirit of Adventure*, in which explorers, scientists, travelers and plain "goal-seekers" or adventurers, moved by their own mysterious impulse, tested the human spirit in terms of action, and came back to set it down, "putting aside modesty without becoming vain, so that an advance of the spirit might be recorded."

* *The Seas of God*, Lippincott, 1944.

But the first and earliest book, and a book most nearly resembling *The Spirit of Man*, was one compiled from the work of purely creative writers, *The Seas of God*, Great Stories of the Human Spirit. That book came out in the war years at a time of universal dying, a book which listened for the voice of life. Curiously its greatest body of readers were soldiers, fliers and sailors.

Today is a day of relative peace and none too relative apprehension. The philosophers saw the shadow in their symposium and warned of mankind's tottering on the brink of either immeasurable grandeur or total extinction. Creative writers are more human and reassuring. *The Spirit of Man* is a volume of many points of view, but each revolves about the dominant note that man is here to stay and stay he will, if he can—and if he thinks he can, he probably will. Two of the writers are priests, several are philosophers, one is a publisher, one a minister, two write as soldiers, one is a statesman, one a botanist, another an embryologist, one a chemist, another an explorer, an archaeologist, a medievalist, a theologian, a psychologist, a poet, naturalist, missionary; two are pilots, three, teachers, and more than a dozen spend their conscious lives delving into the mystery of human character as authors or novelists.

For their contributions the editor is expressly grateful. The world, the flesh and the devil we have always with us. The spirit comes and goes—as this book is a humble testament.

Like *The Seas of God*, which was dedicated to a gracious spirit, this too is for my wife, whose own objective study of a minister is here included (one of the few such studies in short story form in English), and to her is due the choice of the particular letters of Katherine Mansfield, a woman and an artist who seemed, in dying, to be almost pure spirit, whose letters to a husband, who could seem indifferent in his absence and his busyness, are perhaps the most emotional and heart-moving pieces in the book.

Especial thanks are due to Mr. K. S. Giniger, of Hawthorn Books, and to Fred Kerner, for many helpful suggestions.

The Editor

BEING

GOD'S LONELY MAN
Thomas Wolfe

Thomas Wolfe, a child of the century, born October 3, 1900, failed to live his tumultuous, great, consuming half of it, although by the time he died, September 13, 1938, he had left an impress on his readers and his time—a man in a hurry, feeding on books and people, pouring out impressions in welters of rhetoric, steamed up with poetic afflatus, "a whale in the straight jacket of prose." The son of a North Carolina stonecutter and a mother who kept a boarding house, Thomas Wolfe entered the University of North Carolina at 15 and soon became the editor of the college paper and magazine. He was a student of George Pierce Baker's 47 Workshop in the drama at Harvard and later taught English at Washington Square College, New York University. His first book, Look Homeward, Angel established his reputation and was followed by several other books before he died of a cerebral infection two weeks before his thirty-eighth birthday.

Of "God's Lonely Man," Edward Aswell, his last editor, then with Harper and Brothers, has written:

"The first draft of 'God's Lonely Man' was written probably as early as 1930 and was entitled 'On Loneliness at Twenty-Three.' Later versions dropped that title, no doubt because Tom realized by then that loneliness was not a phenomenon confined to youth. The piece does not belong to any one period of his career or writing, but rather to his whole life. Written in the first person, it is straight autobiography. It is a very beautiful and tragic work, and proves, I *think, if further proof is needed beyond his books themselves, that Tom was a deeply religious man in the unconventional and truest sense of the word. Of his profound loneliness, none who knew him well can be in any doubt. But it was at the end a wise and friendly sort of loneliness, a self-contained loneliness, a loneliness that had long since accepted loneliness as the inescapable condition of life. . . ."*

My life, more than that of anyone I know, has been spent in solitude and wandering. Why this is true, or how it happened, I cannot say; yet it is so. From my fifteenth year—save for a single interval—I have lived about as solitary a life as a modern man can have. I mean by this that the number of hours, days, months, and years that I have spent alone has been immense and extraordinary. I propose, therefore, to describe the experience of human loneliness exactly as I have known it.

The reason that impels me to do this is not that I think my knowledge of loneliness different in kind from that of other men. Quite the contrary. The whole conviction of my life now rests upon the belief that loneliness, far from being a rare and curious phenomenon, peculiar to myself and to a few other solitary men, is the central and inevitable fact of human existence. When we examine the moments, acts, and statements of all kinds of people—not only the grief and ecstasy of the greatest poets, but also the huge unhappiness of the average soul, as evidenced by the innumerable strident words of abuse, hatred, contempt, mistrust, and scorn that forever grate upon our ears as the manswarm passes us in the streets—we find, I think, that they are all suffering from the same thing. The final cause of their complaint is loneliness.

But if my experience of loneliness has not been different in kind from that of other men, I suspect it has been sharper in intensity. This gives me the best authority in the world to write of this, our general complaint, for I believe I know more about it than anyone of my generation. In saying this, I am merely stating a fact as I see it, though I realize that it may sound like arrogance or vanity. But before anyone jumps to that conclusion, let him consider how strange it would be to meet with arrogance in one who has lived alone as much as I. The surest cure for vanity is loneliness. For, more than other men, we who dwell in the heart of solitude are always the victims of self-doubt. Forever and forever in our loneliness, shameful feelings of inferiority will rise up suddenly to overwhelm us in a poisonous flood of horror, disbelief, and desolation, to sicken and corrupt our health and confidence, to spread pollution at the very root of strong, exultant joy. And the eternal paradox of it is that if a man is to know the triumphant labor of creation, he must for long periods resign himself to loneliness, and suffer loneliness to rob him of the health, the confidence, the belief and joy which are essential to creative work.

To live alone as I have lived, a man should have the confidence of God, the tranquil faith of a monastic saint, the stern impregnability of Gibraltar. Lacking these, there are times when anything, everything, all or nothing, the most trivial incidents, the most casual words, can in an instant strip me of my armor, palsy my hand, constrict my heart with frozen horror, and fill my bowels with the gray substance of shuddering impotence. Sometimes it is nothing but a shadow passing on the sun; sometimes nothing but the torrid milky light of August, or the naked, sprawling ugliness and squalid decencies of streets in Brooklyn fading in the weary vistas of that milky light and evoking the intolerable misery of countless drab and nameless lives. Sometimes it is just the barren horror of raw concrete, or the heat blazing on a million beetles of machinery darting through the torrid streets, or the cindered weariness of parking spaces, or the slamming smash and racket of the El, or the driven manswarm of the earth, thrusting on forever in exacerbated fury, going nowhere in a hurry.

Again, it may be just a phrase, a look, a gesture. It may be the cold, disdainful inclination of the head with which a precious, kept, exquisite princeling of Park Avenue acknowledges an introduction, as if to say: "You are nothing." Or it may be a sneering reference and dismissal by a critic in a high-class weekly magazine. Or a letter from a woman saying I am lost and ruined, my talent vanished, all my efforts false and worthless—since I have forsaken the truth, vision, and reality which are so beautifully her own.

And sometimes it is less than these—nothing I can touch or see or hear or definitely remember. It may be so vague as to be a kind of hideous weather of the soul, subtly compounded of all the hunger, fury, and impossible desire my life has ever known. Or, again, it may be a half-forgotten memory of the cold wintry red of waning Sunday afternoons in Cambridge, and of a pallid, sensitive, aesthetic face that held me once in earnest discourse on such a Sunday afternoon in Cambridge, telling me that all my youthful hopes were pitiful delusions and that all my life would come to naught, and the red and waning light of March was reflected on the pallid face with a desolate impotence that instantly quenched all the young ardors of my blood.

Beneath the evocations of these lights and weathers, and the cold, disdainful words of precious, sneering, and contemptuous people, all of the joy and singing of the day goes out like an extinguished candle, hope seems lost to me forever, and every truth that I have ever found and known seems false. At such a time the lonely man will feel that all the evidence of his own senses has betrayed him, and that nothing really lives and moves on earth but creatures of the death-in-life—those of the cold, constricted heart and the sterile loins, who exist forever in the red waning light of March and Sunday afternoon.

All this hideous doubt, despair, and dark confusion of the soul a lonely man must know, for he is united to no image save that which he creates himself, he is bolstered by no other knowledge save that which he can gather for himself with the vision of his own eyes and brain. He is sustained and cheered and aided by no party, he is given comfort by no creed, he has no faith in him except his own. And often that faith deserts him, leaving him shaken and filled with impotence. And then it seems to him that his life has come to nothing, that he is ruined, lost, and broken past redemption, and that morning—bright, shining morning, with its promise of new beginnings—will never come upon the earth again as it did once.

He knows that dark time is flowing by him like a river. The huge, dark wall of loneliness is around him now. It encloses and presses in upon him, and he cannot escape. And the cancerous plant of memory is feeding at his entrails, recalling hundreds of forgotten faces and ten thousand vanished days, until all life seems as strange and insubstantial as a dream. Time flows by him like a river, and he waits in his little room like a creature held captive by an evil spell. And he will hear, far off, the murmurous drone of the great earth, and feel that he has been forgotten, that his powers are wasting from him while the river flows, and that all his life has come to nothing. He feels that his strength is gone, his power withered, while he sits there drugged and fettered in the prison of his loneliness.

Then suddenly, one day, for no apparent reason, his faith and his belief in life will come back to him in a tidal flood. It will rise up in him with a jubilant and invincible power, bursting a window in the world's great wall and restoring everything to shapes of deathless brightness. Made miraculously whole and secure in himself, he will plunge once more into the triumphant labor of creation. All his old strength is his again: he knows what he knows, he is what he is, he has found what he has found. And he will say the truth that is in him, speak it even though the whole world deny it, affirm it though a million men cry out that it is false.

At such a moment of triumphant confidence, with this feeling in me, I dare now assert that I have known Loneliness as well as any man, and will now write of him as if he were my very brother, which he is. I will paint him for you with such fidelity to his true figure that no man who reads will ever doubt his visage when Loneliness comes to him hereafter.

The most tragic, sublime, and beautiful expression of human loneliness which I have ever read is the Book of Job; the grandest and most philosophical, Ecclesiastes. Here I must point out a fact which is so much at variance with everything I was told as a child concerning loneliness and the tragic underweft of life that, when I first discovered it, I was astounded and incredulous, doubting the overwhelming weight of evidence that had revealed it to me. But there it was, as solid as a rock, not to be shaken or denied; and as the years passed, the truth of this discovery became part of the structure of my life.

The fact is this: the lonely man, who is also the tragic man, is invariably the man who loves life dearly—which is to say, the joyful man. In these statements there is no paradox whatever. The one condition implies the other, and makes it necessary. The essence of human tragedy is in loneliness, not in conflict, no matter what the arguments of the theater may assert. And just as the great tragic writer (I say, "the tragic writer" as distinguished from "the writer of tragedies," for certain nations, the Roman and French among them, have had no great tragic writers, for Vergil and Racine were none, but rather great writers of tragedy): just as the great tragic writer—Job, Sophocles, Dante, Milton, Swift, Dostoevski—has always been the lonely man, so has he also been the man who loved life best and had the deepest sense of joy. The real quality and substance of human joy is to be found in the works of these great tragic writers as nowhere else in all the records of man's life upon the earth. In proof of this, I can give here one conclusive illustration:

In my childhood, any mention of the Book of Job evoked instantly in my mind a long train of gloomy, gray, and unbrokenly dismal associations. This has been true, I suspect, with most of us. Such phrases as "Job's comforter," and "the patience of Job," and "the afflictions of Job," have become part of our common idiom and are used to refer to people whose woes seem uncountable and unceasing, who have suffered long and silently, and whose gloom has never been interrupted by a ray of hope or joy. All these associations had united to make for me a picture of the Book of Job that was grim, bleak, and constant in its misery. When I first read it as a child, it seemed to me that the record of Job's tribulations was relieved only by a kind of gloomy and unwilling humor—a humor not intended by the author, but supplied by my own exasperation, for my childish sense of proportion and justice was at length so put upon by this dreary tidal flood of calamities that I had to laugh in protest.

But any reader of intelligence and experience who has read that great book in his mature years will realize how false such a picture is. For the Book of Job, far from being dreary, gray, and dismal, is woven entire, more than any single piece of writing I can recall, from the sensuous, flashing, infinitely various, and gloriously palpable material of great poetry; and it wears at the heart of its tremendous chant of everlasting sorrow the exulting song of everlasting joy.

In this there is nothing strange or curious, but only what is inevitable and right. For the tragic writer knows that joy is rooted at the heart of sorrow, that ecstasy is shot through with the sudden crimson thread of pain, that the knife-thrust of intolerable desire and the wild, brief glory of possession are pierced most bitterly, at the very instant of man's greatest victory, by the premonitory sense of loss and death. So seen and so felt, the best and worst that the human heart can know are merely different aspects of the same thing, and are interwoven, both together, into the tragic web of life.

It is the sense of death and loneliness, the knowledge of the brevity of his days, and the huge impending burden of his sorrow, growing always, never lessening, that makes joy glorious, tragic, and unutterably precious to a man like Job. Beauty comes and passes, is lost the moment that we touch it, can no more be stayed or held than one can stay the flowing of a river. Out of this pain of loss, this bitter ecstasy of brief having, this fatal glory of the single moment, the tragic writer will therefore make a song for joy. That, at least, he may keep and treasure always. And his song is full of grief, because he knows that joy is fleeting, gone the instant that we have it, and that is why it is so precious, gaining its full glory from the very things that limit and destroy it.

He knows that joy gains its glory out of sorrow, bitter sorrow, and man's loneliness, and that it is haunted always with the certainty of death, dark death, which stops our tongues, our eyes, our living breath, with the twin oblivions of dust and nothingness. Therefore a man like Job will make a chant for sorrow, too, but it will still be a song for joy as well, and one more strange and beautiful than any other that man has ever sung:

Hast thou given the horse strength? hast thou clothed his neck with thunder?

Canst thou make him afraid as a grasshopper? the glory of his nostrils is terrible.

He paweth in the valley, and rejoiceth in his strength: he goeth on to meet the armed men.

He mocketh at fear, and is not affrighted; neither turneth he back from the sword.

The quiver rattleth against him, the glittering spear and the shield.

He swalloweth the ground with fierceness and rage; neither believeth he that it is the sound of the trumpet.

He saith among the trumpets, Ha, ha; and he smelleth the battle afar off, the thunder of the captains, and the shouting.

That is joy—joy solemn and triumphant; stern, lonely, everlasting joy, which has in it the full depth and humility of man's wonder, his sense of glory, and his feeling of awe before the mystery of the universe. An exultant cry is torn from our lips as we read the lines about that glorious horse, and the joy we feel is wild and strange, lonely and dark like death, and grander than the delicate and lovely joy that men like Herrick and Theocritus described, great poets though they were.

Just as the Book of Job and the sermon of Ecclesiastes are, each in its own way, supreme histories of man's loneliness, so do all the books of the Old Testament, in their entirety, provide the most final and profound literature of human loneliness that the world has known. It is astonishing with what a coherent unity of spirit and belief the life of loneliness is recorded in those many books— how it finds its full expression in the chants, songs, prophecies, and chronicles of so many men, all so various, and each so individual, each revealing some new image of man's secret and most lonely heart, and all combining to produce a single image of his loneliness that is matchless in its grandeur and magnificence.

Thus, in a dozen books of the Old Testament—in Job, Ecclesiastes, and the Song of Solomon; in Psalms, Proverbs, and Isaiah; in words of praise and words of lamentation; in songs of triumph and in chants of sorrow, bondage, and despair; in boasts of pride and arrogant assertion, and in stricken confessions of humility and fear; in warning, promise, and in prophecy; in love, hate, grief, death, loss, revenge, and resignation; in wild, singing jubilation and in bitter sorrow—the lonely man has wrought out in a swelling and tremendous chorus the final vision of his life.

The total, all-contributary unity of this conception of man's loneliness in the books of the Old Testament becomes even more astonishing when we begin to read the New. For, just as the Old Testament becomes the chronicle of the life of loneliness, the gospels of the New Testament, with the same miraculous and unswerving unity, become the chronicle of the life of love. What Christ is saying always, what he never swerves from saying, what he says a thousand times and in a thousand different ways, but always with a central unity of belief, is this: "I am my Father's son, and you are my brothers." And the unity that binds us all together, that makes this earth a family, and all men brothers and the sons of God, is love.

The central purpose of Christ's life, therefore, is to destroy the life of loneliness and to establish here on earth the life of love. The evidence to support this is clear and overwhelming. It should be obvious to everyone that when Christ says: "Blessed are the poor in spirit: for theirs is the kingdom of heaven," "Blessed are they that mourn: for they shall be comforted," "Blessed are the meek: for they shall inherit the earth," "Blessed are they which do hunger and thirst after righteousness: for they shall be filled," "Blessed are the merciful: for they shall obtain mercy," and "Blessed are the pure in heart: for they shall see God"—Christ is not here extolling the qualities of humility, sorrow, meekness, righteousness, mercy, and purity as virtues sufficient in themselves, but he promises to men who have these virtues the richest reward that men were ever offered.

And what is that reward? It is a reward that promises not only the inheritance of the earth, but the kingdom of heaven as well. It tells men that they shall not live and die in loneliness, that their sorrow will not go unassuaged, their prayers unheard, their hunger and thirst unfed, their love unrequited: but that, through love, they shall destroy the walls of loneliness forever; and even if the evil and unrighteous of this earth shall grind them down into the dust, yet if they bear all things meekly and with love, they will enter into a fellowship of joy, a brotherhood of love, such as no man on earth ever knew before.

Such was the final intention of Christ's life, the purpose of his teaching. And its total import was that the life of loneliness could be destroyed forever by the life of love. Or such, at least, has been the meaning which I read into his life. For in these recent years when I have lived alone so much, and known loneliness so well, I have gone back many times and read the story of this man's words and life to see if I could find in them a meaning for myself, a way of life that would be better than the one I had. I read what he had said, not in a mood of piety or holiness, not from a sense of sin, a feeling of contrition, or because his promise of a heavenly reward meant very much to me. But I tried to read his bare words nakedly and simply, as it seems to me he must have uttered them, and as I have read the words of other men—of Homer, Donne, and Whitman, and the writer of Ecclesiastes—and if the meaning I have put upon his words seems foolish or extravagant, childishly simple or banal, mine alone are not different from what ten million other men have thought, I have only set it down here as I saw it, felt it, found it for myself, and have tried to add, subtract, and alter nothing.

And now I know that though the way and meaning of Christ's life is a far, far better way and meaning than my own, yet I can never make it mine; and I think that this is true of all the other lonely men that I have seen or known about—the nameless, voiceless, faceless atoms of this earth as well as Job and Everyman and Swift. And Christ himself, who preached the life of love, was yet as lonely as any man that ever lived. Yet I could not say that he was mistaken because he preached the life of love and fellowship, and lived and died in loneliness; nor would I dare assert his way was wrong because a billion men have since professed his way and never followed it.

I can only say that I could not make his way my own. For I have found the constant, everlasting weather of man's life to be, not love, but loneliness. Love itself is not the weather of our lives. It is the rare, the precious flower. Sometimes it is the flower that gives us life, that breaches the dark walls of all our loneliness and restores us to the fellowship of life, the family of the earth, the brotherhood of man. But sometimes love is the flower that brings us death; and from it we get pain and darkness; and the mutilations of the soul, the maddening of the brain, may be in it.

How or why or in what way the flower of love will come to us, whether with life or death, triumph or defeat, joy or madness, no man on this earth can say. But I know that at the end, forever at the end for us—the houseless, homeless, doorless, driven wanderers of life, the lonely men—there waits forever the dark visage of our comrade, Loneliness.

But the old refusals drop away, the old avowals stand—and we who were dead have risen, we who were lost are found again, and we who sold the talent, the passion, and belief of youth into the keeping of the fleshless dead, until our hearts were corrupted, our talent wasted, and our hope gone, have won our lives back bloodily, in solitude and darkness; and we know that things will be for us as they have been, and we see again, as we saw once, the image of the shining city. Far flung, and blazing into tiers of jeweled light, it burns forever in our vision as we walk the Bridge, and strong tides are bound round it, and the great ships call. And we walk the Bridge, always we walk the Bridge alone with you, stern friend, the one to whom we speak, who never failed us. Hear:

"Loneliness forever and the earth again! Dark brother and stern friend, immortal face of darkness and of night, with whom the half part of my life was spent, and with whom I shall abide now till my death forever—what is there for me to fear as long as you are with me? Heroic friend, blood-brother of my life, dark face—have we not gone together down a million ways, have we not coursed together the great and furious avenues of night, have we not crossed the stormy seas alone, and known strange lands, and come again to walk the continent of night and listen to the silence of the earth? Have we not been brave and glorious when we were together, friend? Have we not known triumph, joy, and glory on this earth—

and will it not be again with me as it was then, if you come back to me? Come to me, brother, in the watches of the night. Come to me in the secret and most silent heart of darkness. Come to me as you always came, bringing to me again the old invincible strength, the deathless hope, the triumphant joy and confidence that will storm the earth again."

AN ASIDE ON CONSCIOUSNESS

Jacquetta Hawkes

Now the wife of J. B. Priestly, the British writer, Jacquetta Hawkes is the younger daughter of Sir Frederick Gowland Hopkins, OM., who was a first cousin of the poet Gerard Manley Hopkins. Growing up at Cambridge, she determined to become an archaeologist and after her research scholarship work she excavated at a number of sites in England and elsewhere. Her first husband was Christopher Hawkes, professor of archaeology at Oxford. "An Aside On Consciousness" is taken from her book on England, A Land.

Proust holds himself like a naked nerve at the center of a trembling web of remembered consciousness. No sound or smell or physical detail of his surroundings escapes him; his awareness of the complexity of emotion, thought and association in himself and in others is almost too sensitive to be endured.

Newton and Einstein drive their minds into regions untouched by experience; Mozart appears as a man born without some obstruction that prevents ordinary people from communicating with a stupendous world of understanding. All of them represent the furthest achievements of an evolutionary process which relates them to the chemical constituents of the planet.

It has been thought that solar radiation acting upon sea water first enabled matter to reproduce itself and life thus to begin. Now it seems that drying mud is a more likely cradle. I had always imagined that the earliest essays in life would be microscopically small, but, on the contrary, it was probably in quite large masses of matter that reproduction began. Whatever the size of these first pieces of life, whether they preferred sea water or mud, nothing but some fifteen hundred million years separate them from their outcome in Proust. They have grown also into butterflies, into the elaborate lobster and the simple worm. But the dominant, the significant process in those millions of years has been the heightening of consciousness. It remains the only visible opening for significant development in the future. Among the earliest creatures known from the Cambrian rocks are the trilobites, a large family of primitive crustaceans, which for an immense span of time were the aristocrats of life. Today the lobster is a very fine fellow whether he promenades the sea-floor in flashing blue or lies pink and opulent in an entrée dish; whether he eats men under water or is eaten by them in their world of air. But he has gone too far. Imprisoned in his splendid, his fantastic external skeleton, he has no expanding future. If man leaves the feast he will not rise from the dish to make himself master of some new region of life. It is no better with the birds. Though in their isolation the wrens of St. Kilda may have grown longer tails than the wrens of the mainland, they cannot achieve anything much more significant. The birds burnt all their boats when they left the ground; so it has been with all our fellow creatures—they have committed themselves too far. The gazelle is given over to fleetness, the rhinoceros to strength, the giraffe, though he can reach the topmost leaves, already looks impossible.

It seems, although certainly it is only we in our ignorance who say so, that our minds alone are free to go forward to something significantly new. There may be a time when all school teachers can expect to have sitting before them children of the capacities of Newton and Einstein, Mozart and Proust, while the men of genius move in a country far beyond our present guessing. There may be, or it may prove that brain development must be likened to that of the horn of *Synthetoceras*.

It has been a diverse yet constant process, this heightening of consciousness. I shall not attempt to interpret the experiences of the first cells when they suffered fission, but will begin with the trilobites that represented the most complex and shapely form life had achieved by the end of Cambrian times. To secure food was the first duty of consciousness, and the trilobites, some of which had as many as three eyes of a rough and ready sort, were sufficiently aware of matter looming toward them through the water to move in pursuit. For the first time an image, however blurred, was being received by a living organism.

This most vital faculty was advanced by the fishes who must have seen a dim, flat world but one that contained distinct shapes, and shapes that were related to one another. When the reptiles left the water life in the air was a tremendous stimulus toward the refinement of the senses. *Diplodocus* was ninety feet long and had a brain the size of a small kitten's; nevertheless the brain was there in the heavy skull and, helped out by a smaller nerve center above the hips, controlled the vast, straggling nervous system. The toed feet could feel the ground, be aware of the different texture of sand, wet stone or slime as they waded into the water. The lidless eyes as they swung at the end of a neck as long as a crane recorded bright, meaningless pictures of lagoons and fern trees. The nose, too, was sensitive, and made its own arrangement of the smells coming from mud, from crushed vegetation and from animals dead and living.

It was among the early reptiles that consciousness gained a new incentive and a tremendous new agency for its own perfection. For the first time the male had to seek and take the female. Perhaps it is too gross, too crude a piece of sensationalism, to claim for those reptilian couplings, all slime or scale, some part in the creation of Héloïse and Abelard, yet it is the truth. There is something more here than sexual selection, immensely powerful as that has been in the evolution of life. The forces of attraction and repulsion, of mutuality, in all their forms, have acted like some universal, instinctive artistic genius, creating all that is most highly formed, most brilliantly colored in the world; all that is furthest from the drab equality of chaos. Insects have intensified the colors of flowers, fighting has set delicate antlers on the stag, courtship has given birds their brightest plumage. Love refines and sharpens human personality and provokes poetry and music.

Before the great reptiles had disappeared, the mammals were there with their keener senses and their far more complex brains. They experienced fear and anger, and, beyond reptilian sex, they knew family life. Even the nest of a tree shrew can do much to incubate consciousness. Before long the small tarsier appeared with his forward-looking eyes—eyes so disproportionately large that he seems still startled by the stereoscopic vision that made the seen world one and gave it a third dimension. The nut was seen to be plump, the receding glade asked to be explored.

And so to apes and men. A long-drawn effort to correlate hand and eye and brain in non-instinctive movement; a complication of emotion tending towards refinements of love and hate; a widening separation of the self from its surroundings. Then, suddenly, the bison painted on the cave wall. What has happened since then but fifty thousand years of the accumulation of experience and an erratic but pitiless sharpening of thought and feeling?

This gathering up of consciousness during time can be followed also through space. It stretches up through time from the placid mass of cells on the drying mud, through reptiles browsing on the branches of trees and the little mammals peeping on them through the leaves, up to Proust in his exquisite, agonizing web. So, too, at this one moment of time I can feel consciousness stretching from the crystalline virus that blights tomato plants, through fish, reptiles and mammals to the minds of men. Indeed, it is obviously only an expedient convention to stop with the forms of life that are earliest in time, or the simplest in space. Consciousness must surely be traced back to the rocks—the rocks which have been here since life began and so make a meeting place for the roots of life in time and space, the earliest and the simplest. Why, indeed, stop with this planet? Even if nothing like the human psyche and intellect have developed elsewhere, it is necessary in an indivisible universe to believe that the principle of consciousness must extend everywhere. Even now I imagine that I can feel all the particles of the universe nourishing my consciousness just as my consciousness informs all the particles of the universe.

At this my own flesh should be clamoring. Why go so far afield when here in the ball of your thumb, in the muscle of your thigh, is unconscious life. Every cell that makes this "me" has its individual life, and if skilfully transplanted to another medium can grow and multiply—might even be made to outlive "me." Similarly I have rehearsed the story in time. Starting from a single cell, I passed one period of my life with gill slits inherited from my fishy ancestry, then for a few weeks sported a tail and was hard to distinguish from an unborn tree shrew. The protest of the flesh is reasonable. Why think of viruses or pre-Cambrian organisms when inside this delicate membrane of my skin, this outline of an individual, I carry the whole history of life. I am a community of countless units, from cells to complex organs, living unconscious lives, yet supporting as their kind the invisible power that is enthroned in the brain.

As in the physical being the foetus recapitulates episodes in the history of life, so each individual consciousness, that most fleeting manifestation, carries beneath it, far out of reach of normal memory, episodes in the history of consciousness back to its remotest origins.

Because mind, like the matter in which it is immanent, seeks to continue itself, it suffers the strange pangs of love, love which can serve its end in two ways. Either it leads mind to strive for union with another and so to continue its existence in a new creature, or excites it to creative activity of all kinds, and above all to project itself through the arts. Whereas the new physical creature represents the prolongation of consciousness in the stream of time, these projections—pictures, poems, symphonies—are the perpetuation of a phase of consciousness motionless within the stream. Fossils of the psyche. So might a dinosaur either lay its leathery eggs and so secure posterity, or allow its own dying body to roll down to the sea bed to be preserved through all time.

We have become very conscious of the individual being, apparently neatly enclosed by its covering of skin, recognizable as "me," a being to be disliked or desired but certainly a distinct and particular entity. It is the natural tendency of our mode of perception. Even a fire we contrive to see as a separate thing rather than as a chemical process affecting a wide area round the visible flames and smoke. A human being is hardly more cut off from its surroundings than is a naked fire. It is continuously exuding gas and moisture and consuming other gas; a variety of waves can pass through a wall, through air and through a human body almost without interruption. It seems that the mind itself can issue waves, or something akin to them, that can penetrate and be received by other minds. Every being is united both inwardly and outwardly with the beginning of life in time and with the simplest forms of contemporary life. "Me" is a fiction, though a convenient fiction and one of significance to the consciousness of which I am the temporary home.

I think that we are returning to an awareness of our unity with our surroundings, but an awareness of a much more exalted kind than anything that has existed before. The primitive tribesman, to go no further back than the early days of our own species, was still so deeply sunk in nature that he hardly distinguished himself from his environment or from his fellows. This sense of oneness shows itself in totemism and in many forms of magic. In the identification of the name or image with the living person; in summoning rain by spitting water, or in the belief that a man by leaping into the air can make the corn grow tall. In this, just as in the foetal gills, the child repeats the development of the species, he does not distinguish—" 'Tis the eye of childhood that fears a painted devil."

It is in this natural unity that the savage may truly be said to be happy. Certainly civilization must always destroy it. In urban, literate surroundings self-consciousness becomes a sharp knife cutting man away from his matrix. It was early sharpened among the Greeks, but the collapse of the classical world before Christianity and tribal barbarism brought a respite. For another thousand years the mind of an agricultural society was rocked by the comforting seasonal rhythm.

If the East threw the knife away, the West retrieved it. After the Renaissance its possession became the mark of Western civilization —*la volonté de conscience et la volonté de découverte*. It was not hard to bear, indeed it could be exhilarating, for man to feel isolated if he also felt important in his isolation. But, needlessly perhaps, man allowed himself to be dwarfed by his own discoveries, by his recollection of evolutionary processes and of the humble place of the earth in the material universe. He was left not merely naked and lonely, but apparently insignificant. Perhaps this condition reached its most terrible pitch of sensitivity in the present century with those who, like Proust, accepted it, and those who, like D. H. Lawrence, tried to retreat. Even for the mass of people for whom the knife was not so finely sharpened, the god who died and was resurrected in the spring had deserted them.

Yet I believe that those who have had the courage to suffer *la volonté de conscience et la volonté de découverte* are now already half assuaged. Mind, which at first denied men their instinctive sense of wholeness, is at last returning such a sense, but on its own mental level. Consciousness is melting us all down together again— earth, air, fire and water, past and future, lobsters, butterflies, meteors, and men.

APRIL-MAY
Jesse Stuart

Jesse Stuart, probably the best loved literary son of the state of
Kentucky, a farm lad who wrote his first poems on leaves in the
woodlots of his parents' farm, a man who became a school teacher,
principal, fighter for a wider and better education in his communi-
ties, an author who has written hundreds of stories and a score of books,
and who at 46 could cut eighty-seven logs in a short winter day,
collapsed on October 8, 1954, at the age of 47, after a lecture before
a group of school teachers of Western Kentucky on his way from
the auditorium to an airplane scheduled to rush him to another
lecture. A coronary occlusion, from which he had one chance out of
a thousand to recover, immobilized him in an oxygen tent for several
months, but the will to live kept him alive, and the experience of
his first year of recuperation he has recorded in a lyrical book The
Year of My Rebirth, from which these extracts are taken.

1. April: Man, the Seed of God

The idea of resurrection is a most fascinating one. I am glad that
Christ's resurrection came in spring. It couldn't have happened
in a more likely month than April, judging from the part of
the earth where I was born and grew to manhood. I do not know
about the Holy Land, where Christ was born, lived, and was crucified, whether there are four distinct seasons or not. I doubt it. I
have been in Istanbul, Turkey, which is not a great distance away,

and they do not have our four distinct seasons there. Yet this spring month of April is beautiful in almost every part of the world.

Since I have grown up in this valley on little farms, helped my father plow the creek bottoms and the steep slopes on the hillside, hoe the plants, and later harvest the crops in autumn, I cannot doubt resurrection. How can any farmer ever doubt resurrection? Though there have been periods that I didn't go to church, often when I was away a year or more at a time, there was never a time when I doubted the resurrection of Christ. He was the seed of God planted in the earth, the Son of God sent to show us the way. Only after death, the kind of death we know, He was called by God and came from the tomb and ascended into Heaven. It is a beautiful idea.

The man who has never planted a seed in the ground would be the first to doubt the story of the resurrection. One of the first things we have always planted in the spring has been our Irish potatoes. We plant them on Good Friday, the day of Christ's crucifixion. I have seen snow fall on our potatoes and the ground get cold. I have seen it freeze. The potatoes would lie lifeless in the cold ground. Then suddenly the crumpled dark-green leaves would peep up through the rough dark crust of earth. The potato seed had resurrected. And through the spring and early summer we hoed these potatoes and kept the weeds cut down. In autumn, after their summer's growing season was over and their vines had withered, we dug our potatoes. We put them in the cellar and the next spring planted from our own seed. Here was the process of eternal life—growing, living, dying, and rebirth.

In the same manner we have planted peas, sugar corn, beets, radishes, carrots, and lettuce. We have planted seed almost too small to see. But from that seed came the identical plant that gave birth to the seed. This is birth and rebirth. The month of April is the time of our greatest resurrection.

Before I ever entered a church, I had read the story of Christ's death and resurrection. I liked it so well that each year I read and reread it in early April before Easter Sunday. This is the time when God's world has resurrection going on every place.

Now there is another part of this resurrection. It is faith. Do we have faith and do we believe? I never had any trouble having faith. I know I have faith when I see one of the first wild flowers, trailing arbutus, emerge from the cold sod above the rock cliffs. When I see this exquisite flower and the little sweet-potato leaves on its stem, I know that this is trailing arbutus. I am sure of myself. I am positive. I know who I am, where I am, why I am. This is positive identification, and this is positive faith.

When I have sown Korean clover on a cold snow in February over fields I planned to pasture, I never had any doubt that these seeds would reach the earth as soon as the snow melted. I sowed them on snow because I could see how many of the tiny seeds I was sowing. And I knew, when the snow melted, that the seeds dropped down to the soft, warm earth and sank therein and that the late winter rains fell and buried them and that in middle March or early April, when warm suns and rains came, these seeds sprouted and grew. How can I possibly doubt the resurrection of Almighty God's Son when every spring I have seen the process of resurrection in the laws of Almighty God.

I have planted seeds in the garden and broadcast them on the slopes. I have planted seeds in the creek bottoms. I have sowed seedbeds to take up plants to reset again. Maybe this is the reason there are so many believers in resurrection among farmers and people who live on the land, who keep their feet on the ground and their eyes on the stars. In ancient times, shepherds with their flocks under the stars saw miracles come to pass, saw great visions open up. They dreamed dreams and wrote poetry. And why not? There are more true poets where people plow the land, work with animals under the sun and stars, feel the rain and wind in God's world, than there are in city apartments.

History records that for nearly 2,000 years there have been Easter celebrations in God's churches. If people have believed for nearly 2,000 years, then who am I, a small man from W-Hollow in the Kentucky hills, to dispute the greatest event of all times? Each spring I shall plant seeds into the earth and in a few days they will sprout and in a little more time I shall see the green

bodies reaching up through the ground for the su
I am no longer able to plant fields of my own,
planted so I can watch, or I shall watch other

In the woods the process is the same, but r
to do with it. The walnut drops from the trees.
same tree and cover this walnut. Then snows fall on ...
leaf loam is created. In the spring the walnut germinates and a
sprout comes forth and a new walnut tree is born. The same is
true with the acorn from the oak, the pine cone, the hickory nut,
seeds from the berries, wild plums, crab apples.

Where God is Scientist, I see resurrection with my own eyes. I
feel confident—I have faith—that when man, the seed of God, is
planted in the ground, though his husk will go back to the earth,
he will be resurrected into a new life, for this is the law of God.

2. May: The Kind of Bed to Lie On

Though I am still required to take bedrest every day, there was
never anything said about the kind of bed I am to lie on. So instead of going to my room this afternoon, getting into my pajamas,
and climbing into bed, I took a walk. Carrying a combination
topcoat and raincoat and walking alongside W-Branch, I reached the
mouth of Byrnes Hollow and stepped over the gnarled roots of the
tall trees. Finally, I came to the right place. Here, I found a
carpet of last year's leaves on the ground. Around me, in a small
area, grew a variety of trees with leaves of different shapes and
colors. This was Nature's room, and I had selected it for my bed. I
spread my raincoat upon the leaves. I unlaced my shoes to make
my feet comfortable, but left them on for warmth. I unfastened my
belt, untied my tie, removed my hat, and lay down.

There was enough softness for comfort lying there on my back,
which is the only way I can rest. The bed was not as soft as a
good mattress, but it was what I wanted. If a draft blew over my
body and I needed more cover, I could use half of my raincoat. I
lay there and looked up through the green roof of leaves at the

blue May sky. Everything was quiet on this Sunday afternoon, and I was at peace with the world.

I didn't go to sleep. Everything was so new about me and in such contrast to the plain, barren, and ugly walls of the hospital room that I had known a few months ago. This spacious room filled with trees, singing birds, and talking ground squirrels was highly decorated. Nature had used a varied color scheme here. Even if it had been possible for me to do so, I would not have changed a single thing.

The star-of-Bethlehem, which grew in white clusters at the foot of a tall beech tree, was not in a vase where it would wilt and have to be replaced with fresh flowers. And there were bluets and white violets growing here, too. My walls were decorated with leaves and flowers, and the ceiling above was the crazy patchwork of many green, gray, and red tints stamped against a deep, distant blue. I had found the perfect recuperating room. I knew that, if the weather permitted, I would be back here each afternoon for my "bedrest."

The purpose of taking rest is to relax, to get away from stress and strife, which, though I have never been conscious of it, my doctors say is within me. If it weren't for these inner tensions, they tell me, my defective heart muscle and circulatory system wouldn't be forcing me to take bedrest each afternoon, something I hate violently to do.

Now, on my new bed of leaves beneath the beeches in this little valley between the hills, I don't hate it any more. I don't lie staring at a blank ceiling. I don't go back and recount my little accomplishments and failures, month by month, year by year, wondering what I could have done differently. Those days are as dead leaves of other autumns. That was life lived, life to be remembered for its pleasures and forgotten for its heartaches.

The mind is a most peculiar part of a man's being. It is a part that he should keep happy. The mind controls the body, it tells the body what to do. Put the mind in a hospital room with plain and ugly walls and it will go out and hunt for something beyond.

Perhaps it will take one back through his lifetime to pleasanter scenes, or forward to bright hopes and plans. The mind has wings and it can soar.

But in the hospital, and even in my room at home, my mind recounted the past. And this was a renewal of the old stress and strife. I wanted to get away from worry. I didn't have a lot to worry about, but when I thought, *I will not worry, I will put worry away, I will not think of the old things that trouble me,* right then, the rebellious mind betrayed me. It did worry.

One has to control the mind gently by offering it something new, something better, to make it swing naturally and easily away from the old distressing thoughts.

Lying here on my bed of old leaves, with a new growth of soft green about me to shade my face from the sun, it suddenly was easy. My world was a different one. My thoughts didn't go back, they were of the present. My mind was not under strict control, but was pleasantly relaxed. It wasn't girding my body to fight some ambitious battle. For I lay flat on my back and looked up through an opening in the beech leaves at the afternoon sun. Then, when the wind barely moved the beech tree's branch of trembling leaves, the hole was covered over and I couldn't see the sun. It was a simple change, a soothing movement, and I loved it.

In my new resting place I shut out a past world. My present world became a very small one. I didn't think about ideas for poems. I didn't take paper from my pocket and jot down thoughts. I didn't sweat over lectures and trouble about the right end for a novel. I had much that was new to see in a new world of ground, tree, leaf, stream, flower, wind, and sky. And I was in complete agreement with my surroundings. I didn't think of the short stories I was going to write this month. Characters for these didn't start kicking up their heels in my mind.

Leaf and sky were only parts of it. When I was quiet, and when wild birds stopped singing and crows quit cawing and ground squirrels hushed their talking, I could hear the trickle of the little stream down the Byrnes Hollow. I had found the right bed for recovery, so much so that I hated for my period of afternoon rest to end. If I ever went to sleep, I was not conscious of it. There is a deeper rest than sleep, when the mind relaxes in complete harmony with the intimate, known world around it. . . .

I have forgotten old ambitions. I have found a new small world that has subdued them. It has isolated me from a broader world that disturbed me. Just as the dry, parched lips of earth absorb the soft-falling spring rain, this little world has absorbed my thoughts and tensions, like a soft blotter absorbing ink. I am more relaxed in this green room, under this blue sky, than I have been since my first illness.

The beech leaves above and around me have made unnecessary the things I thought I had to do. They have destroyed the habits I thought I had to obey. They have taken away the ten pipes a day I thought I would never be able to do without. In their stead they have substituted clean wind for my lungs. These natural pleasures have been so satisfying that I am left to wonder why man is always burning with his ambitions, his desires to accumulate, his great competitiveness, his wild impulse to excel his fellow man.

Why is one so ambitious? Why have I been all my life? I have been a fiercely competitive person ever since I can remember. If I had two slices of bread, I wanted three. If I had completed my grade school education, I wanted high school, and after high school I wanted college, and after college I wanted graduate work, and then more after that. If I wrote one poem and published it, I could write the second one and the third and publish them, too. And the same held true for the short story and the novel. And as long as I was writing, why shouldn't I write the best?

Now, I wasn't thinking about writing in my new world. I had found one place where I could get away from it. I wasn't hearing about what others were doing, how they might be getting ahead of me. And they certainly weren't hearing from me about what I was doing. For no one knew.

I didn't worry because I wasn't working now and making money. Not when the soft beech leaves moved gently overhead and the May winds blew over me with the scent of burning brush. The winds seemed to whisper to me not to worry. Whether I made money or not I wouldn't starve. Maybe something I had already written would sell. Anyway, there wasn't any rush about it. Not any hurry to write something to sell. If I wrote anything at all, let it be for the joy of writing. Let it come from my heart.

I had been given artificial means of relaxation. Now, I wasn't taking anything to make me relax. Yet every limb in my body seemed rested when I arose from my simple bed. Doctors and others had tried to force me to relax. I had not been able to. But now I had stumbled into the right room at the right place and time.

Not a bad idea Christ had when he went into the wilderness alone to fast for forty days and nights while He thought about many things. Why did He choose the wilderness, a wild country of trees, skies, winds, birds, and animals? And why did He go alone?

He had had a rough time. He was interested in formulating a new philosophy of life on earth. He had promised Man a reward of everlasting, eternal life.

Even one of His stature went into the wilderness instead of the tabernacle or the cathedral with ornaments of glittering gold. He climbed up the rough hillsides. He spent hours deep in the valleys meditating. His thoughts were higher than the winds were high, His soul as clean as wind-touched grass, His dreams big enough to encompass the entire universe.

And, yet, why did He choose the wilderness? Why did He cut Himself off from the small world that He then knew? Why did He get away from His disciples and His friends? There is something that is elevating in being alone with nature. Here is the peace of new perspective for men sick in an uncertain world.

And as I lay on my bed, I thought of the world known to Christ. I thought of Him as He walked away to be alone in the wilderness. What kind of a place was this wilderness that He visited? What did He do there? What were His thoughts? What were His decisions? What did He say in His prayers? Were His days there akin to poetry? Were the torment and anguish eased from His soul?

I know they were.

Because to lie under the green trees beneath an open sky upon a bed of leaves and feel the wind across one's face must summon forth the best in any of us. It brings out the man that is akin to God, the man that is one with nature. To see the beauty of a trembling leaf above one's head is to know that life has meaning. No wonder Jesus chose the wilderness to communicate with His Father.

THE NIGHT SELF

D. H. Lawrence

David Herbert Lawrence, who was born September 11, 1885, and died March 2, 1930, was the son of a British coal miner father and a mother in school teaching—a profession he entered for a time at the age of twenty in an elementary school near London. He spent most of the forty-four years of his life in a struggle with a combative spirit and a frail body and succumbed to tuberculosis in Vence, France. His living and his books were devoted to the "pursuit of a fuller, freer, more intense life." In one of his books, Fantasia of the Unconscious, he attempted to systematize phases of the philosophy implicit in his novels and poetry.

When you go to sleep at night, you have to say: "Here dies the man I am and know myself to be." And when you rise in the morning you have to say: "Here rises an unknown quantity which is still myself."

The self which rises naked every morning out of the dark sleep of the passionate, hoarsely-calling blood: this is the unit for the next society. And the polarizing of the passionate blood in the individual towards life, and towards leader, this must be the dynamic of the next civilization. The intense passionate yearning of the soul towards the soul of a stronger, greater individual, and the passionate blood-belief in the fulfilment of this yearning will give men the next motive for life.

We have to sink back into the darkness and the elemental consciousness of the blood. And from this rise again. But there is no rising until the bath of darkness and extinction is accomplished.

As social units, as civilized men, we have to do what we do as physical organisms. Every day, the sun sets from the sky, and darkness falls, and every day, when this happens, the tide of life turns in us. Instead of flowing upwards and outwards towards mental consciousness and activity, it turns back, to flow downwards. Downwards towards the digestion processes, downwards further to the great sexual conjunctions, downwards to sleep.

This is the soul now retreating, back from the outer life of day, back to the origins. And so, it stays its hour at the first great sensual stations, the solar plexus and the lumbar ganglion. But the tide ebbs on, down to the immense, almost inhuman passionate darkness of sex, the strange and moon-like intensity of the hypogastric plexus and the sacral ganglion, then deep, deeper, past the last great station of the darkest psyche, down to the earth's center. Then we sleep.

And the moon is the tide-turner. The moon is the great cosmic pole which calls us back, back out of our day-self, back through the moonlit darkness of the sensual planes, to sleep. It is the moon that sways the blood, and sways us back into the extinction of the blood. And as the soul retreats back into the sea of its own darkness, the mind, stage by stage, enjoys the mental consciousness that belongs to this retreat back into the sensual deeps; and then it goes extinguished. There is sleep.

And so we resolve back towards our elementals. We dissolve back, out of the upper consciousness, out of mind and sight and speech, back, down into the deep and massive, swaying consciousness of the dark, living blood. At the last hour of sex I am no more than a powerful wave of mounting blood, which seeks to surge and join with the answering sea in the other individual. When the sea of individual blood which I am at that hour heaves and finds its pure contact with the sea of individual blood which is the woman at that hour, then each of us enters into the wholeness of our deeper infinitude, our profound fullness of being, in the ocean of our oneness and our consciousness.

This is under the spell of the moon, of sea-born Aphrodite, mother and bitter goddess. For I am carried away from my sunny day-self into this other tremendous self, where knowledge will not save me, but where I must obey as the sea obeys the tides. Yet however much I go, I know that I am all the while myself, in my going.

This, then, is the duality of my day and my night being: a duality so bitter to an adolescent. For the adolescent thinks with shame and terror of his night. He would wish to have no night-self. But it is Moloch, and he cannot escape it.

The tree is born of its roots and its leaves. And we of our days and our nights. Without the night-consummation we are trees without roots.

IS THIS WHAT IT MEANS TO SEE?

John Howard Griffin

MANSFIELD, TEX. Jan. 10.*—*Still marveling at his newly re-gained eyesight, John Howard Griffin today was anxious to start reading the best-selling novel he wrote during his 10 years of blindness.*

The 36-year-old author of "The Devil Rides Outside" was walking from his parents' home to his workshop near here yesterday when he suddenly regained his vision.

"It was a terrible shock. I received no jar, no bump . . . Suddenly everything looked like red sand in front of my eyes," he said. "Then I saw the outline of the door. I went inside and called a Mansfield doctor who rushed right over. I was near collapse."

Griffin was able to identify the color of the doctor's coat when he arrived. He also was able to read a note the physician pulled from his pocket.

Griffin said an eye specialist told him that a 12-year-old blockage of the circulation of blood to the optic nerve had been broken, enabling him to see again. While serving as an Air Force sergeant in the Pacific during World War II, Griffin suffered a concussion when a B-24, loaded with bombs, exploded. His vision gradually faded until he was totally blind by 1946.

Examinations by specialists in Fort Worth today indicated his vision should clear completely within a month, he said.

* 1957.

The large, husky author saw his wife and two children, Johnny, 1, and Susan, 2, for the first time.

"You don't know what it is for a father to see his children for the first time. They are both much more beautiful than I ever suspected," he said.

Griffin and his wife, Elizabeth Ann, 21, were married in 1953 after he had been blind seven years.

MANSFIELD, TEX., APRIL 6, 1957

Dear Whit Burnett,

Here are the notes, transcribed exactly. What they have in crudeness is perhaps made up for by their immediacy . . . I am still too near this thing, and still under such heavy medication that I have no perspective—not enough to edit these pages at this point in any case. . . .

> Yours cordially,
> John Howard Griffin

MOUNT CARMEL—SUNDAY, JANUARY 13, 1957

Father Patrick came to my cell, awakened me for early Mass. Amazed it is Sunday already. We attended from the little cubicle upstairs, looking down on the chapel.

Extreme clumsiness. I know I am acting in a dream, but I can't help it. The Fathers do not talk about it. They understand that to regain sight after a decade of blindness is not something to realize quickly—that we must think of other things for a time.

I keep these notes, because there is no more memory from one moment to the next. It seems real at the moment, but disappears soon afterward. I cannot read this, but see it as a blurred and jumping line.

There is no sequence to memory, only fragments. I try to put them down.

Wednesday, four days ago, I was walking to the house for lunch. Redness swirled in front of my eyes. Then I thought I saw the back door, cut in portions, dancing at crazy angles. I stood dumb-founded. Angles continued to dance and there was pain in the eyes and head.

I stumbled inside, found the telephone. Somehow I got the number dialed. I heard my wife's voice.

"I think. . . ." I began, and then collapsed into weeping.

"What is it? What's happening?" she asked.

"I think I can see."

I couldn't talk anymore. Only mumblings came out until I managed to say: "Call the doctor. Hurry."

Her voice was quiet, awe-stricken. "All right. Oh, Lord—go lie down. I'll have the doctor there in a minute."

"You come, too."

"Yes . . . yes, I will. Don't move. Don't do anything."

I sat in my chair at the table. The room was broken up. Triangles of color faded and swirled.

Two thoughts overwhelmed me. My blind friends. Was something happening to me that would never happen to them? Emile, Armand, Alfred, Edith and Merrill—all the others; people dear to me. People blind as I had been so many years. Dear God, would this hurt them?—make them feel more lonely?

And my family? Was I really seeing? Would their hopes be built up only to crash when this weird thing passed?

My wife. I'd never seen her or the children. From the swirl of my own confusion, I thought of how she must feel. Should she run immediately to me? Should she take the time to dress, fix herself up, so I could see her first in the best possible light?

The doctor was there. I couldn't see him. Only a splotch of blue. My eyes ached from the effort to focus. But there was no focus, only lights and colors in constant movement.

His voice was calm. He did not believe I could see.

"What color is my suit?"

"Blue, I think." I was trembling violently. He was saying things about how wonderful it was. "You have to give me something. I can't stand it," I said.

He gave me a shot and stayed with me.

The shot had slight effect. I asked him what it was.

"It was a light one—demarol. I want you to be aware of every-thing. This is an experience few men can ever have."

I seemed to withdraw into myself. I didn't try to make him understand that it was too much of a blow. I didn't want to be aware of it. A man's system can't stand up under such a shock. I wanted to sleep, to be unconscious.

The phone rang. I heard my mother's voice asking me what was happening. It was filled with anguish. I couldn't speak. The doctor talked with her. "Yes, Mrs. Griffin. He's seeing enough to make out colors. He's very upset. His wife is on her way over."

My wife and children. Would I know them? Would I know my parents after all these years? Weird and twisted things passed through my mind. My wife, my children and my parents—people who were my life—yet if I saw them in the street, I would not even know them!

Later a car pulled into the drive.

"Tell me who it is."

"Your mother and dad."

Nerves simmered up from numbness. I prayed vaguely, prayed and braced myself, prayed that it not be a deception for them. They had suffered too much, too gallantly on my account.

There was a swirl of movements around me. Faces were close to mine, and words. They were kissing me, talking in low tones. I had to pull out of it, to reassure them some way.

"Can you really see me?" my mother asked.

"I can see you have on a green dress," I mumbled.

I couldn't control my vision enough to see their faces. I would see a portion of their clothes and instantly the ceiling and then a side wall, and then haze.

Another car arrived. I stayed seated at the table. At the door, I heard the voices of my wife and children. I rose to my feet. Susan ran forward and was the first to appear in the kitchen door. I concentrated beyond my strength and saw all the radiant wisdom of her two-year-old face looking up at me, saw it clearly and then saw nothing else.

My wife was in my arms, her face beside mine. I glimpsed black hair.

My son was tugging at my pantlegs. I reached down, felt his short-cropped hair, but could not see him. That first clear view of my daughter had been like looking at the sun—blinding me to everything else. It was there in front of my face during the next dim hours.

I remember then that I was at the eye specialist's, late in the evening. The building was deserted.

Words detach themselves.

"The eyes look fairly good. A brain injury."

"No, doctor—a concussion."

"A concussion is a brain injury . . ."

"Yes, of course."

There were prescriptions. "We'll work on restoring circulation to the eyes."

Then to the pharmacy to buy the medicines. Then to my sister's house in town.

Endless hours with reporters and photographers, and the beginning of nervous rigors that shook me. I concentrated on the blind, knowing I must say nothing to hurt them, nothing to give them false hopes.

Fear of going to sleep. Would I wake up blind again?

I heard my wife talking to my sister. Low voices. We'd better call Sue Turner (my doctor's assistant). She can come over and give him a shot. There was some telephoning.

It was decided Doctor Clayton and Sue Turner's husband would come for me. I would spend the rest of the night at the Turners' where they could watch me, give me a shot if things got worse.

Then I was in a car, between Joe Turner and Dr. Clayton, driving in the night. Lights were flashing past.

"Howard, you're shaking terribly," the doctor said.

"What the hell do you think they called you for?"

At the Turners', they gave me a shot. We sat up. I was afraid to go to bed.

Some day, I told myself, I will do something for these people who sit up with me.

The next morning I was having hard rigors. No recollection of the day. I was virtually unconscious, although I moved and acted and spoke. I recall a hall full of reporters and camera men when Joe took me to the doctor's. I recall they followed me all day.

I said "yes" to everything they wanted to do.

I saw the eye specialist, then went to Doctor Clayton's office. Irene Lang, his therapist, brought a chili dinner in—a celebration dinner. I was afraid it was premature. And I was too sick to eat.

Doctor Clayton was worried. He talked to the reporters. "You'll have to wait. This man's in a state of shock. He doesn't know what he's doing or saying. You must wait a few days."

But they were insistent. I didn't care. I said "yes" to everything. I was feeling nothing except a vague pain in my eyes.

They put me in training glasses, to force my eyes to focus.

Doctor Clayton insisted I stay at the Turners' again that night. The phone rang constantly. Telegrams from all over the world. The news had spread. I sat numb in the midst of a bombardment, vaguely surprised that people should be so interested. It kept swelling. Sue gave me more shots. She began to get tough with people. I was collapsing and didn't know it.

Another day, deep within myself, forced there by shock and hypodermics.

I was being shaken into wakefulness. I was asleep in the Turners' study. Sue was talking to a doctor, an internist. "He's been like that for hours, Doctor. The moment he sits down, he falls to sleep."

I heard kindness and firmness in the doctor's voice.

He had talked with the eye specialist and with Dr. Clayton. He was making tests—blood pressure.

"Yes sir. I'm diabetic."

"No more visitors. No more telephone calls or interviews. You'll have to go to the hospital, or somewhere where no one can get to you."

I asked him if I could go and stay with the Carmelite Fathers.

That would be even better than the hospital, he said.

I got a telegram from the American Foundation for the Blind, congratulating me on the fine interview I gave one of the New York newspapers by telephone. I had no recollection of having given it.

Later, I heard Sue giving Father Augustin, prior of Mount Carmel Seminary, his instructions.

"No telephone calls. No visitors. Here are his medicines. They're dangerous, so you keep them and dole them out to him. No one is to know where he is. If he goes into a rigor, give him 100cc. of this in the muscle."

Then nothing. No recollection of the trip over. Nothing except blankness and a feeling of safety. Surprise when Father Patrick awakened me this morning. Surprise that it is Sunday.

MONDAY

Father Augustin gave me all of my medicines. Then to the kitchen for insulin and coffee and toast. Then the rigors began, shaking me from head to foot. I had to have a shot.

I was dimly delighted only because Father Augustin would have to give it to me, and I knew the size of the needle was terrifying him.

"I hate to do this," he said shakily.

"It's nothing. Just jab me anywhere. But hurry."

"Wait a minute," he said.

He went and called one of the Spanish Carmelite nuns. She came over, a tiny creature. Sister Fernandino.

"Poor thing," I thought. "She'll faint when she sees the size of that needle."

She grabbed a wad of cotton, dipped it in alcohol and rubbed my arm. Then expertly jabbed me.

"She used to be a nurse before she became a nun," Father said.

Lunch: beans, bread, butter and coffee. More rigors but did not take shot. Slept.

Nerves grip and cramp and lock. There is pain. Father Patrick met me in the corridor and told me it was time to take all medicines again. I talk with difficulty. I told him I wondered if there weren't some sort of animal that did nothing but sleep and eat, as I do these days. The name of the animal wouldn't come to me. Finally it occurred to me.

"Father, it's a sloth, isn't it. I know what it feels like to be a sloth."

He was thoughtful for a moment. "I think the sloth moves around a little more than you've been doing."

That broke the tensions.

Strange, strange moments when light is fatigue. Father Patrick brought me to my cell. I got into bed. As he left, he said: "You don't want this light, do you?"

When he turned off the light, I felt as though a burden were lifted from me. I felt safe, at home in the dark. It is hard to explain. All day the light has had this exhausting effect, and now, with it off, things relax back to some semblance of normalcy. I can even type better; and I know it will take time before light is once again natural to me.

TUESDAY AFTERNOON

Become more aware of sights, but I can only absorb a little of them at a time and then something within me clicks off, banishing the rest from awareness.

Father Patrick brought me a book of great paintings this morning, opened to Vermeer's "Woman Weighing Gold." I see her expression—remote, serene; and magnificent light pervades the canvas.

Intense unmoving excitement in this place of polished corridors and silence. Father Patrick took me to look out the windows. A dark, grayish day, hinting snow. Below, a rye field is brilliantly green. Black and white Holstein cattle graze it.

Just talked with mother and then Pi. How excited they all are,

and how strange it becomes when I go outside the quiet of this cell
into the world even by telephone. Happiness mingles with a peculiar depression—that I cannot be with them, that I cannot yet feel
things. Underneath it, I sense their great worry.

LATER

After days of silence, there is music. Father Patrick has broken the
quiet with the music of Bach, and my heart is unable to bear it. It
floats clean—the *Orchestral Suites*—as overwhelming to my ears as
the Vermeer was this afternoon to my sight.

I sit here wondering, seeing light and listening to these magnificent sounds. Will I ever forget the colors of the Vermeer?——the
colors of this music?——these moments in the cloister? I pray not,
pray that they live vividly with me to remind me of the great gift.

Clarity, enthusiasm. I find myself smiling at things brought
gently to life by the Bach. I see many outlines of things, but still I
see things—the clean outlines of this typewriter, the brass doorknob,
the life-sized statue of St. Joseph standing beside my bed, this desk,
the large wooden cross on the wall. Desire to remember first real
views:

1. My daughter's face, and those of my wife and parents.
2. The chapel before dawn with its candles and gold glints.
3. The field of cattle.
4. The Vermeer painting.

And sounds—the silences of rustling robes and whispered voices
and footsteps, and finally tonight the marvelous natural rhythms of
Bach superposed on the natural rhythms of the Carmelite life here
. . .

WEDNESDAY MORNING

Father Augustin took me with him over to say six o'clock Mass in
the chapel of the Carmelite Sisters—a miniature room, Spanish in
that cluttered way that is so typical of them. When we left to return
here, the moon was full behind very thin clouds.

A week today. Sleep and look at the art books.

No rigors today. On a diet of Carmelite silence, interrupted only by Mozart and Bach and occasional voices; in the calm gray light of rains spattering against my window, nerves return perceptibly to health. But there is a great drag of fatigue, a great weight of see-ing, as though my eyes were pulled into shape by these new glasses, and occasional sharp pains when I try to look to the side.

I look out and see a piece of white paper caught in the limbs of a small tree. I am moved to retrieve it, to cleanse the blemish from these orderly grounds.

Father Augustin reads to me, a text on *Pastoral Medicine*, by Father Ruland—an old-fashioned work containing much unintentional humor. For example: "Riding on motorcycles is particularly injurious to pregnant women."

At dinner I realized I was buttering my bread directly from the butter dish. I told Father Vincent to correct me, even though such things are little noticed here. I remembered that you are supposed to put the butter on your plate, and butter it from there, a portion at a time.

I have looked so intently at paintings that now all things look as though they were painted rather than real.

FRIDAY EVENING

Father Patrick brought the phonograph into my cell. Now, the final movement of the *Jupiter* conducted by Beecham. And the rain is coming down in a fine rumble. I think of the dusk of the long corridors here, and of the children and Pi and my parents and brothers and sisters, and long to be with all of them. And for a moment, were it not for the great wash of this envigorating music, I would be embittered that the world, the impatient world of reporters and journalists prohibits my being with the family and forces me to secrete myself here where they cannot reach me. But it is perhaps better. If I were with them, I think I would weep, and now, in this state, one tear would be dangerous. No, I must wait and throw out the burden of shock resulting from my return to a world of sights.

Certainly this adjustment is more difficult than the one to blindness, filled with a thousand clumsinesses, frustrations and complexities never dreamed-of. I cannot remember that I can see. I get around much less-well here than I did when I had no sight and walked by the sound of memory and echoes. Then I was alive to all stimuli. Now, I am blurred to all of them except the one of sight which overwhelms all others even in its imperfection.

But sight—yes, it obsesses me. I squint and concentrate and feel it grow better. I look out to the country and see it with wonder. Now it is the sight of rain glazing the walk leading to the statue of Our Lady of Mount Carmel. In the twilight I see the walk as a silver streak standing out brilliantly against the greens of winter grass.

All sights are like paintings. Surely no one has ever seen the view from atop Chalk Hill in Dallas as a Florentine landscape.

And it is the same with my medicine bottles. Clear, greenish, amberish, in different shapes. They catch dull highlights and they are a painting by Chardin, because this evening the light is Chardin's rather than Vermeer's, the clarity is his rather than Cezanne's, alas. And I end up saying hopelessly in my heart the same old things: "It is too beautiful, too beautiful . . ."

To watch the daylight turn to obscurity of beginning night, and to feel a strange nostalgia for that, and to put off the moment of turning on the lights. And then to see all of this brightness, to see the scene change like a modulation in harmony.

Is this what it is like to see? Is this the way other people see? If not, it is surely the way they were meant to.

A man is alone in himself at such a time, filled with intimate discoveries; reinforced by music and silence and the rhythms of things viewed very still . . .

Viewed from deep within self, from deep into past memories brought to freshness by renewal . . .

Many visits with the doctors. I have new glasses and see well, but with pain. I am doing less well than I thought. Two days at home. A great stack of mail. L. A. Jones offers to answer it for me. I turn it over to her, knowing that I would never get around to it myself—at least not for months.

Then it was learned I was home. The telephone began ringing, day and night. I had to return here to Mount Carmel.

When I walked into my house, a small, blond boy came toddling to me and when I bent down, he put his arms around my neck. What a beautiful, beautiful child! I could not believe he was my own. We sat on the couch and he put his eye against my glasses and stared into my eyes with great curiosity. He realizes, then, that something has changed. All evening I watched them, watched them in all of their moods, watched the play of expressions on their faces and realized that I had before only the palest concept of how my children were. I believe that evening at home was the highpoint in my entire life.

But the doctor ordered me back here, away from telephones and mail.

It is a time of great interior loneliness and dryness, such an experience. I struggle through layers of it, back to realizations. I am not unhappy, God knows, only in a state of constant bewilderment not to feel those things which people think I should be feeling—a sort of bursting joy. Yes, a lonely, terribly private thing, and yet I could not bear to be alone. I need life around me, and still to preserve the illusion of solitude, and both requirements are taken care of here.

A friend called today. No one was here to answer the phone and so finally I did. She told me that there were loud rumors circulating that Griffin saw his wife, didn't like what he saw, and left to become a monk! Poor gossips.

Later, perhaps it can be explained how at such a time love must allow for this privacy—that indeed the granting of it, the encouraging of it—is perhaps the greatest proof of the quality of love. I think of my wife and my mother—the two people who would most want to be with me through such a time; both of whom realized how it is and urged me to go this way. If there had been the slightest reticence on their part, I should not have been able to come here. I should have given in to my desire to be at home, a desire that is almost equally as searing as the one for solitude.

Noonday angelus is ringing. Time to go to lunch.

SATURDAY

I speak to two people on the telephone. Lon Tinkle and Decherd Turner, book editors for the Dallas papers; not because they are book editors, but because they are dear friends and it does good to talk with them. I call home every day.

Decherd indicated he would like to come see me. I told him to come for lunch today. I think it will be all right, though it is against doctor's orders.

Now there is excitement. Yes, it will be all right to receive him upstairs in my room. He is to be my first visitor—the first of my old friends. We make preparations. The Fathers help me. I am dizzy with the prospect, and frightened. Father Patrick brings in a chair for him, and a small wobbly coffee table.

"I don't know how you look at people," I say to him.

"He'll understand."

The room is swept, dusted. The easy chair is in place. A dented metal ashtray is placed on the coffee table. Even though the effect is tawdry, I am touched at the gesture.

Father Augustin, or another—I can't remember—brought him to my cell. He entered, small, dark, smiling, his eyes peering questioningly into mine. And then hands were being shaken. Talk. He was presenting some books to Father Augustin for the Carmelite library.

What did we talk about? Already I have lost it. Saint Augustin,

Vermeer's light—names come back but the words are blocked and the memory stops at the absorbing view of a face with light falling across it from my window.

Intimate constraint. I was deeply moved and feared showing it too much. I wanted to talk but I didn't know how to look at him. Would he think I was staring? Did one look into a person's eyes or glance about the room?—or perhaps at the face without looking into the eyes?

I offered him a cigarette. Did he take it? I can't remember.

A glass of very bad port before lunch? I could not take it because of my medicines, but he had a little, served in a large drinking glass —an inch of the sweetish-smelling stuff which he drank without showing the distaste I knew he felt.

Then lunch. I had promised him there would be nothing special; that I would not even tell the Carmelite nuns, who prepare our meals, that he was coming.

I told them only a moment before we entered the refectory—another plate for the professor. They were horrified. A visitor, and they had prepared nothing special for him. Immediately they set about breaking eggs. I assured them that he expected only what we had, but added that he was "*muy famoso.*" They became more agitated. A distinguished guest, and nothing but Carmelite food.

Lunch was a haze. I was talking, making sense; but mostly I was looking, perhaps staring. Always on his face there was the strange expression, gentle but concentrated—the way one looks at a wounded animal.

LATER

Dusk, gray and iced. In the chapel they are making their evening meditations. We are cloistered in rain that freezes instantly, closing us in, protecting us.

I struggle against the numbness. It is impossible to pray, but tonight I spent a long time alone in the chapel, thinking nothing, feeling nothing, at peace. And then, as I was walking past the recreation room downstairs, I saw the ping-pong table. It occurred to me that now I would be able to do things like that—to play ping-pong. For days I have passed that room and thought nothing of it, so accustomed am I to being unable to do such things.

Father Augustin played with me. The ball was only a white streak at first, but soon I was hitting it. And then we played some billiards. All of the stagnation, the brain-cramping left. It was fascinating. For the first time since this thing happened, I felt real laughter within myself. And too, it is good exercise for the eyes. Perhaps tomorrow I shall try the piano.

SUNDAY

I have waited for the joys of sight, those joys which all have told me I should feel, and which I have felt in smaller measure than expected. But this morning they have come to me; for this morning I picked up the office and began reading those marvelous texts of Matins, Lauds, Prime, Tierce, etc. I have been reciting them aloud here in my cell while the rain mists my windows in the half-light of early morning, with a brilliant ceiling light turned on. And in the recitation there was the intense breaking-through of joy for which sight served as the instrument, allowing me to read such phrases as:

—— *Thou hast made the lips of children, of infants at the breast, vocal with praise* . . .

—— *The Lord's perfect law, how it brings the soul back to life; the Lord's unchallengeable decrees, how they make the simple learned.*

And on and on. The soul's nourishment, the soul's normalcy, sinking beyond the words to their innermost meaning, seeking and thirsting for it . . . feeling it melt away all hardness as it awakens love to its proper dimensions.

If only these clarities could remain always to erase the numbness, the endless pettiness . . .

This morning then, the tired brain, the battered brain conceived the idea of reading the clear black type of the office. And therein found full reason and justification for seeing again.

SHARING

THE YOUNG LINCOLN

Sherwood Anderson

Sherwood Anderson, who was born in Ohio in 1876 and died at 64 while on a semi-official good will trip to South America in 1941, left many revealing lights on his own spiritual struggles in his autobiography, A Story Teller's Story and his Letters and Memoirs. "Obsessed," as Clifton Fadiman once put it, "with the experience of sudden self-discovery," he probed also into the hidden sides of other Americans of his own times and earlier. He was deeply drawn to the struggles and conflicts in the life of Abraham Lincoln and after Anderson's death a long study of the President under the title "Father Abraham: A Lincoln Fragment" was found in his old printing shop in Marion, Virginia, stored away in a box. The entire fragment was included posthumously in The Sherwood Anderson Reader edited by Paul Rosenfeld and part of it is included here.

Nothing could have been more astonishing than that he was to be President. But it was not altogether astonishing when it came. There had been a hint of it in Abraham's mind for a long time. The man had always been, from the first, both proud and humble. Sometimes thoughts within him made him sink into depths, feel himself lower in the mire than the pigs that used to lie in the mud in the streets of Elizabethtown, Kentucky, where he was a child.

At the same time there was something in him that held him

erect. He was like a tree, having its roots in black mire, its upper branches reaching toward the sky.

Sometimes he tried to figure out his own purpose. He had been doing that since he was a boy. It seemed to him he had no purpose. He did not feel himself a leader. He was a questioner, a groper. In those moods, it would have been utterly incredible to him that he was, in fact, to become the hero of his country, the one man of all the men America has produced who was to stay in people's minds as representing something finer in themselves.

It was not that Abraham did not think there was fineness in himself. He was an odd contradiction, knew himself as an odd contradiction.

In the first place, there was no question but that he was coarse. He was the son of a man named Thomas Lincoln, a no-account, a weak, vacillating man. There was nothing in his inheritance to make him feel rich, self-assured, firm on his feet. Perhaps the men with whom he associated, had always associated, had also helped to make him coarse. He was peculiarly subject, in outward things, to the influence of others.

A man with a coarse homely body, legs too long, skin yellow and dry-looking, hair coarse, face too long. It was hard to think he could ever be attractive to women.

A man needs women. He needs to feel that a few women, at least, have found him physically attractive. Such an experience makes a man walk about more firmly. Abraham had thought about women a great deal, more than anyone ever guessed. Before he went up to Springfield to become a lawyer, when he was in the country store at New Salem and later when he was postmaster there, he used to think of women a great deal.

The country and small-town girls of Abe's day were shy and awkward in the presence of young men. Abraham was shy and awkward in their presence.

When he was a storekeeper in Offut's store and later when that fellow Berry ran the store and when a girl came in and after making her purchase went out, he felt intensely relieved. "My God!" he said to himself. Young men who could go freely about with girls, who could laugh and talk with them, aroused in him an intense jealousy. He wanted to hate such young men and, at the same time, he wanted, with all his soul, to be such as they.

There were not many young women about. Well, he was a young man. Since he had been a child, he had always liked being where older women were at work. He liked sitting unnoticed in a room with them. They were sewing or cooking. His stepmother, Sally Lincoln, was cutting bread.

Another woman standing at the door of the Lincoln house, a neighbor woman.

Quiet voices, a sense of well-being in a boy's heart.

When you are older, you begin having another feeling. There is a vague, shadowy hope.

Men were always hanging about the store. They liked Abraham. You know how men are, at least that kind. They were country yokels, hired men working on farms, farmers' sons.

In Abraham's town, no one had any money, no one wore good clothes.

During the evenings, especially on Saturday nights, crowds gathered around the store. The men all chewed tobacco and drank whiskey.

In the wintertime their boots and clothes were covered with mud. The main street of New Salem was deep in mud.

Frozen mud in the streets in the wintertime. Abraham's feet were always cold. His hands were cold. Both his arms and legs were too long. The blood, perhaps, could not get down there.

The store at New Salem was in a cheap frame building and in winter days and nights the cold winds crept in. Men came tramping in out of the deep snow. Hard balls of snow had formed on their boots.

They stood in the store and stamped like horses. They sat on boxes and put their feet against the stove. Steam arose. There was the rank smell of stables and of clothes worn a long time without washing. The stove sat in a box of sawdust. The men spat tobacco juice into the sawdust.

When the men stamped on the floor, everything in the store

shook. There were cups for the whiskey-drinkers on a shelf at the back. They clinked together. The whiskey was in barrels. Abraham was the only man in town who could lift a barrel of whiskey in his two hands and drink from the bunghole.

Wood was cheap. Abraham or some other hanger-on put great chunks of it in the fire. The stove grew red-hot.

The men standing or sitting about chewed tobacco, drank whiskey, and talked. Abraham neither chewed nor drank. There might have been something deep down inside him offended by the sight of the men chewing. The taste of whiskey rather sickened him. He often talked more than any of the others. At other times he was strangely silent.

No one knew it, but once he had been drunk. It wasn't while he was running a store, but afterward, after he had been to the state legislature and to the Black Hawk War. A lot of young men were in the store drinking one night.

They stayed until quite late. It was one of Abraham's quiet times. Usually he was in the forefront of everything, talking politics, telling stories, wrestling with some strong young fellow, taking part in the horse-play that sometimes went on. But that evening he was in another mood.

When he grew silent, you could almost feel his silence.

Sometimes it was a kind of deep discouragement with everything about his life. He became morose. It was as though his own mind plunged deep down into his own long body.

He thought he saw himself as he was.

He was more ambitious than any man in town. There was something in him wanted to rise in the world.

Rising in the world might mean, for one thing, getting rid of the stigma of his family. His father was no good. Abraham had tried to do his duty by his father, he had stayed with him, worked for him without pay longer than most sons, but how glad he had been to get away.

The man, Thomas Lincoln, Abraham's father, was ignorant and shiftless. Even in a poor community he was always the poorest man.

It was all a matter of mismanagement. His father was a visionary, a poor, feeble visionary.

Abraham knew he also was a visionary. The thought frightened him.

The world was the world. You had to study the world. Most of all you had to study men. You found out what men were like. Then you managed them. Abraham already knew he could do that. He had got elected to the state legislature. That meant getting men's confidence, getting them to vote for him.

You don't toady to men to do that, not if you are Abe's kind. You say to them, "Go and vote for me."

No, you don't do it that way either. You make them go and do it without saying anything directly. They are with you, they see you, hear you speak. To themselves they say, "Here is a strong honest man." Say it yourself and they may believe you for a time, but not for long. You have to make them say it, make their hearts say it.

It means not putting yourself up too high or down too low. You have to be patient, have understanding. Understanding comes very, very slowly.

Abraham's mother was what she was, too. There were stories about her. She was said to have been an illegitimate—a bastard.

That meant a lot in the community in which Abraham lived.

He got to thinking about his family sometimes and that led to thoughts of himself. He was so awkward, so ungainly. He would be going along all right, would be quite cheerful in fact, and then some little thing would happen.

It was always connected with people, sometimes with men, more often with women.

A young girl had come into the store that afternoon. She wanted something—a pound of coffee. Abraham gave it to her. They were alone together. He tried to say something. If he could only, for example, make a pretty speech. He tried.

The girl went out laughing. What a come-down. It sent him off into a long period of gloom.

He was in such a period of gloom that night. No one knew. He was alone in the store. There had been a lot of young fellows in that evening and he had been silent and gloomy while they talked.

While they had been talking, he had been sprawling on the counter, his long legs on the floor, his head in his hands. No one had paid much attention to him. Even when he was a young man, he was called "Old Abe."

"Old Abe is in one of his spells, let him alone."

It was a good thing he was physically strong. If he had been a weak man physically, one always having imaginary or real illnesses, like his father . . .

In that community he would have had no chance. New Salem was full of ignorant young men. Ignorant men are likely to be cruel. He already knew that.

Plenty of bullies about. A bully is a cruel man. He likes to see other people suffer.

Perhaps a bully is a weak man. He is ashamed of his own weaknesses. If I can make some other man seem weaker than I am!

The young man had gone out of the store. Sometimes, when men get together like that in a frontier store, things go pretty well. They get to telling stories. Abe was good at that. He could take an old story that had been told over and over and give it a little twist of his own.

He made up stories, too. Sometimes his stories were a little daring. There was a story around town that he, Abe Lincoln, did not believe in God.

What had he to do with God, one way or the other? At that time he neither believed nor disbelieved. He tried to keep out of religious discussions.

The stories about his being an unbeliever had sprung out of his talent for story-telling. Sometimes he just made his stories up. Something happened. A little series of things happened.

There were creeks running down through that part of Illinois to the Sangamon River. In the spring, when the heavy rains came, the creeks were flooded.

A man got two calves drowned.

Abe told the story. He had made it up. He said the man, whose name was Hank Bardshore, stood on the bank of the creek looking at the two drowned calves. They had been washed up against a pile of driftwood. When he told the story, Abe got a little carried away. He said the man, Henry Bardshore, stood on the banks of the creek and saw the two dead calves. There was a neighbor with him.

"Take him up one side and down the other and God Almighty does about as much harm as he does good," Abe said Hank Bardshore had said. He imitated Hank's voice saying it.

Hank hadn't said anything of the kind. It was sacrilegious. When Hank Bardshore heard about it, he was half-mad, half-pleased.

It was funny all right. Everyone laughed when they heard the story. Hank Bardshore got credit for wit he did not have.

Abe, who told it, who really made it up, got credit for being too free with God. He hadn't been thinking about God at all.

There was a man over in the next county, really a sacrilegious man, who spoke of God as "John R. God." Abe heard him do it when he was over there. The man was a natural kind of showman as Abe was himself. He was entertaining some men in a tavern.

He spoke of God that way and it pleased Abe. Afterward in the store he got it off himself. He spoke of God as "John R. God" two or three times, and then afterward spoke of him as old "J. R." A man came and said something about snow. "Do you think it will snow?"

"I don't know," Abe said. "It's up to J. R."

That sort of thing is all right and gets a laugh, but in a community such as Abe lived in, it gets you in bad repute.

People begin to say you don't believe in God. The story that you are an agnostic or an atheist or something of that sort gets around.

There were such stories around about Abe. They came back to him.

The stories made him sad. He wanted to be liked, to be popular, had an intense desire to be popular.

Sometimes he got to thinking. Something happened like the girl laughing at him trying to make a pretty speech.

Or one of the men hanging about the store said something. He made some reference to Abe's long legs, or to the fact that he, Abe, did not believe in God.

The other men paid no attention. The remark was forgotten.

Abe was, however, more sensitive than the man knew. He went into a period of deep gloom. "You could cut it with a knife, like cheese," someone said.

Abe did not hear. He was half-lying with his head in his hands as he was that night when he got drunk.

Suppose you think yourself utterly worthless, low. You come of low people. There is in you an intense desire to rise. You know you can't.

You are too ignorant, too low-down.

You get to thinking about it and fall into a gloom that makes your heart ache.

He was thinking about it that night in the store, at New Salem, when he was postmaster there.

There were some young fellows in the store drinking, chewing tobacco, telling stories, and talking politics and religion.

It got late and they all went home. "Good night, Abe," they said. He did not answer.

They laughed at him and went out.

There was no one in the store but Abe and the storekeeper. He was a small fat man with several days' growth of beard on his face. He started putting out the lights.

Then, when there was but one light left burning, he stood and looked at Abe. Abe did not move. The storekeeper took a key out of his pocket and put it on the counter near him. He might have sensed something of Abe's deep gloom. It was like a disease that numbs all the senses. Nothing touches other men like the sadness of a strong man.

The storekeeper felt something stir within himself. His voice grew gentle, "You lock up, Abe," he said. He went along the street in the darkness to his house feeling oddly tender. "Abe's all right," he said to himself.

Abraham did not know how long he stayed there that night, like that, sunk in gloom.

Later, he aroused himself. He never had drunk whiskey before that night. Whiskey was five cents a drink. He put twenty-five cents on the counter where the storekeeper would find it in the morning. He took one drink and then another and another. When he had taken five drinks, he managed to put out the lights and close the store.

It was snowing outside. The streets were silent and empty. He was drunk.

He was staying, boarding, at a tavern. There was a girl there named Rutledge. Her father owned a mill. They were solid, nice people. The girl, whose name was Ann, had taken his fancy. He thought if he could get her, if she would marry him, it would be like beginning to live. At night he dreamed of it. The girl had never seemed to him to be laughing at his tall awkward body. He was in love with her, but had not told anyone.

He never thought he could get her, that he could get any such woman. He thought Ann was beautiful. What would she be wanting of a man like him?

That night, when he got drunk, the time no one knew about, he got sick. He had walked out of town, not daring to go home in the condition he was in, wading in deep snow. He had stopped by a rail fence.

He was terribly sick, had to hold on to the fence to keep from falling.

He realized that he was near a house out that way. A dog came from the house. Evidently the dog knew him. He came up quite close, smelled of Abe's long, floppy legs—they were surely floppy that night—then went silently away.

Abe thought the dog had contempt for him. He did not blame the dog.

But even when he was drunk, Abe kept his sense of humor. He

never quite lost that. He thought sometimes, if he ever did lose it, he would go insane.

He thought it very silly and foolish for a man, built as he was, with such long ridiculous legs, to get drunk.

There were some men who could do it, while others couldn't. Doing it might be a great relief if it did not make a man sick. It might give a man boldness.

Well, it made Abe sick. It made him more ridiculous than he was when sober.

It was like getting women. Some men can do it, others can't.

Abe could not drink, he could not get any pleasure out of drinking. He found it out that night.

It was a good thing, he thought, that no one knew. He never tried it again.

2

It was late that night when Abe reached the tavern. The cold had sobered him, but his hands and feet were icy cold. The front door of the tavern was not locked.

Abe went in and upstairs to his room. It was a bare little room. He undressed and got into bed.

It was freezing cold in bed too. The night was very silent now. It had quit snowing and the moon had come out. There was one small window in his room. It was covered with frost.

He did not mind the cold too much. If you cover up and are patient, warmth gradually comes. He remembered plenty of other cold nights, heavy snow on the ground, trees in the forest cracking with cold. It was that way when he was a child in Kentucky and later at Pigeon Creek. At Pigeon Creek, the Lincolns lived all winter in a cabin that had only three sides.

Abe had got a sense of something strange and in some way lovely out of many such cold, lonely nights. When he was a small lad at Pigeon Creek, his father went off to Kentucky in the winter, hoping to get him a new wife.

That was shortly after Abe's mother died. The Lincoln children were left alone. When he was a mere child in Kentucky, a neighbor woman had taught him not to be afraid at night in the dark. He and the woman were in a room and the woman hung an old dark dress over a window. "Night is like that," she had said to the child. "Everything is the same as in the day. The whole world is just an enormous room with something hung over the window."

The figure had caught the boy's fancy. It had made him un-afraid in the dark. It had made him able to walk in the forest at night, hearing strange sounds unafraid.

The world was an enormous room, but it was too empty. That was why he wanted someone in the room with him.

He wanted someone to lie close beside him at night, feeling the warmth of that other person.

He was cold, cold. It wasn't just physical cold.

He lay in the room in the tavern thinking. After he had been in one of his depressed times, his head was particularly clear. The drinking he had done that night had also done something to him.

It had made him desperately sick, but after such a sickness sometimes an odd clearness comes. The mind is like a cool running stream.

He was in the room in the tavern, the cold moonlight coming in, and his mind was like the moonlight. He was too much alone, had always been too much alone. He was too cold.

The men, the young men about the store and on the streets of New Salem, warmed something in him sometimes, but they froze it too.

The young men were like himself. Most of them constantly got drunk. Abe had tried that, had tried it that very night.

With the young men he talked, wrestled, and told stories. Some-times when he was with them a sudden warmth of companionship seemed to well up out of them and out of himself.

They all became a little excited. Stories were told. Abe could outdo them all in story-telling.

Everything seemed to get warmer and warmer. There was a kind of mutual excitement. Abe broadened his stories. He had made the others laugh. He would make them laugh harder.

All the others felt what Abe felt.

There was something fine going on. There was something coarse and ugly going on.

It was inside Abe. It was inside all the others.

It was like a white boy running a race with a beast.

You get odd notions in your head, living a long winter alone in a lonely cabin, with other children. Sometimes at night you lie awake. You can't get warm enough to sleep. You get odd notions later when you are a young man and in particular if you are a young man different physically from all the others about.

You have longer legs, longer arms, you are stronger. Without your exactly intending it, things center about yourself. It is like being the tallest tree in a forest. Thousands of other trees standing there. Everyone looks at the tall tree.

You have to be careful not to be self-conscious, not to be always showing off.

You have constantly, every minute of the day, to fight something in yourself.

It was the race between the white boy and the beast, between what is fine and what is ugly, pretentious, evasive.

Profanity in the air.

Abe told stories. He had pride in his story-telling—to make every story have a nub.

Sometimes he got too eager, wanting perhaps to be liked, to keep everyone laughing.

His stories grew coarser. He told stories without point—just to be telling them.

There was a word on his lips, on the lips of the others.

A moment of abandon. Some grip Abe was always trying to keep on himself was gone.

He was a horse that had run away, a strong horse. His laughter became horse laughter—his words horse words.

He who loved to give a story a certain delicate twist of his own had lost his power.

He became ashamed, deeply ashamed. Where there had been a warmth of companionship, there was now but coldness. It was a familiar coldness to Abraham.

Voices of other men drifting away from him. He got sometimes in the midst of other men feeling as alone as though he were in a vast desert or at the North Pole.

Or in the forest.

The race with the beast.

Others perhaps feeling the same thing. That might be why so many young men in New Salem got drunk. They lived as Abe did, in ugly rooms in ugly little houses. They were poor as he was. Drinking carried them off into a world of illusion. They became in fancy mighty men.

The man who was naturally weak and afraid became strong. Then he lied and boasted. Fights started among the young men. Sometimes they cut each other with knives.

Blood on the floor of one of the stores, or the tavern floor, in the dirt of the road before some store.

But no, loneliness in the forest was somewhat different. Something besides yourself was living there. Trees that stand up above other trees as you, physically, stood up among men.

He remembered once, when he was in the war—the Black Hawk War that wasn't a war—he left the men of his company and went into the dense forest.

He went to a tall tree, taller than any other tree in sight. There was no one there. He patted the rough bark of the tree as though it had been a friend.

"You are all right," he said to the tree.

It was a childish thing to do. He laughed to himself.

In the bed that night, after he had been drunk, he was not laughing.

He was in love, had been dreaming dreams. If he could marry Ann Rutledge, if she would have him, he would have all his life a companionship that would destroy his inner loneliness.

He would have someone warm and close to himself, a part of himself and yet not himself.

Ann Rutledge was gentle, she was quiet.

He was terribly afraid she would not have him. He had been afraid that evening in the store, had been seized with fear, while the others were talking.

The fear had grown stronger and stronger. It had become a kind of ecstasy of fear. If he could not get Ann Rutledge, he would be alone always. In the end, the coarser side of his own nature would come more and more to the surface. He would sink to the level of the men about him. Perhaps he had already done that.

Abe Lincoln was a man of his generation. There was a sensual side to his nature, but he was afraid of it. Sometimes he thought of Ann in a very intimate way. His imagination ran away with him. In fancy he saw her beside him in bed. She was naked. His hands touched her body.

He was greedy. It was the same feeling he had when, with men, he was too greedy to make them laugh, to make himself the central figure.

Greediness leading to what he felt was vileness, emphasizing the wrong thing.

It was because he was at bottom vile.

He sank into one of his periods of deep gloom. Perhaps his drinking alone that night had come about because he hoped, through drinking, to surrender to his own greediness.

He might even have thought that, through drink, he would find courage to creep into Ann Rutledge's room. If she would not have him as a husband, he would take her, anyway. He was physically strong, could do what he pleased. After he had taken her, she would have to marry him.

"Do I want her for just that purpose, to satisfy the greedy, lustful side of myself?"

Abe Lincoln asked himself that question that night in the room in the tavern. It was almost morning. His body had grown almost warm.

He got out of bed and stood on the floor in the little room.

Ann Rutledge was asleep in another room upstairs in the tavern.

He knew where her room was. He went out into a little hallway. The floors were very cold. When he had gone to bed, he was still weak from the illness brought on by his drinking. He had merely taken off his long trousers and his huge socks.

He had got into bed in his shirt. Now he made a ridiculous figure in the moonlight, with his long bare legs, his head almost touching the ceiling.

When he went outside the room into the hallway, he had to stoop. He went to Ann's door, stood by her door, he wanted to be closer to her.

His legs and feet were freezing. He began to shiver. His teeth chattered.

What would happen if Ann came out at the door? He had a moment of fancying he might have courage to take her into his arms. She might be clad in her nightgown.

Her warm body, fresh from sleep against his cold body. Something flamed up in him—desire, blind greedy desire, he thought it.

Once he even raised his right hand to knock on her door, perhaps to knock the door down. He was strong enough. Well, he knew himself better than that. There never was a chance he could do it.

In the forest that time, in the presence of the tallest tree in the forest, he had patted the tree with his hand.

"You are all right," he had said to the tree.

"Abe Lincoln, you are a fool, you are an old fool," he said to himself that night in the tavern.

He said the words to himself softly as he went back into his own room and got again into his bed.

He was icy cold again and would have to wait a long time to get warm.

Well, he had been cold before. He knew how to wait. He was conscientious, some men thought childishly conscientious. The storekeeper had left the key to the store in his possession; had asked Abe to lock the store.

He began wondering if he had locked it. Getting up again, he put on his clothes and went through the icy streets to the store door.

It was locked all right. He would have to get up early to return the key. It was already so late that there was no use going to bed again.

There was a stove downstairs in the cabin. He lighted a fire. When at last he grew warmer, he slept a little, sitting upright in the chair with his mouth open.

He was dreaming of Ann. It was a good thing for his suit she did not see him then. When he had been ill he had made a mess on the front of his coat. It had frozen there.

3

It was the spring of 1837 when Abraham Lincoln moved to Springfield, Illinois. Birds were singing in the town, farmers were planting crops. In new cleared land, the logs and bushes cleared during the winter were being piled in great piles and fired. The smoke curled up through the low branches of trees. On some of the trees the green had begun to show. Lincoln rode to Springfield on a borrowed horse. It wasn't a very good one. The better horses were all at work in the fields.

Lincoln had been studying law. When he and Berry had the store at New Salem, he had, by a lucky accident, got hold of a copy of Blackstone. He had read it as though it were the most absorbing book in the world.

It was not that he was a student or had the student's type of mind. He had just passed through a dark time, one of the darkest times of his life. Studying had been an intense relief. He had been at it hard all that winter. He thought it had helped to keep him from going insane.

After all his doubts of his own courage, he had, during the summer before, asked Ann Rutledge, of New Salem, to marry him and she had said she would.

Almost immediately after she became ill. She died. Her death came in the late fall, just as the leaves were dying on the trees.

There had been an hour that to Abe Lincoln was the blackest of his life. Ann Rutledge was dying and he was sent for. He went into the room where she lay.

She was too ill for much talk. In such times of serious or dangerous illness in a frontier community, neighbor women came in. There were several such women in the house. Abe always remembered sharply one of the women. She was an extraordinarily tall woman with a peculiar mouth. The mouth was like the mouth of a squirrel. The teeth, not white like a squirrel's, little but long and discolored, protruded over her lower lip. The teeth were wide apart. She might have been a woman of thirty-five or even forty. No doubt she was the wife of some man of the town.

She was in the room where Ann lay when Abe went in. Everyone in town knew that Ann and Abe were engaged. The woman was standing near Ann's bed. She was like Abe in that she was so tall; her head almost reached to the low ceiling. There was a strand of yellow hair hanging down over her face. Her hands were large, like Abe's hands.

Perhaps he had noticed her particularly because he had been told that Ann was dying. He looked at the strange woman because he did not dare look at Ann.

The woman had passed silently out of the room. As she went out, she laid one of her large hands on Abe's shoulder.

It might have been the touch of the strange woman's hand that had saved him from insanity.

Abe's despair that day did not come from the belief that the woman he was losing was the most lovely of women. Since he had loved Ann, he had never compared her with other women.

She was his woman. To him she had become a thing of utter loveliness, of infinite sweetness.

Whether or not she was all he then thought her, Abe later did not know. She was that to him. She and Abe had talked but little. During the summer they had walked out together a few times. When they came together they were often silent—two dumb young things under the summer trees, under the summer moons.

To Abe, her interest in him, her consenting to be his wife, had been enough. One evening he had been with her and suddenly had got courage to ask the question.

Perhaps she was somewhat like himself. There was something reticent in her nature. She had not answered for what had seemed a long time and then had said simply that she would marry him.

He hadn't even kissed her. It was Sunday evening and she had been to church. Abe hadn't been. He had met her at the church door and had asked if he could walk home with her.

They had gone directly home, walking very slowly. He had asked her and had been answered.

Afterward he had to ask her people. That wasn't so hard.

It had been for him a joyous quiet time. After he knew he was to have her, a passionate longing to hurry up the day of their marriage crept over him. He held it down, said nothing. He would let her fix the time. His reticence was due to the feeling that had come to him that night in the winter as he lay in the cold bed.

He wanted possession of her body and was afraid of the feeling. He was afraid because he wanted something else now. There was a dreadful responsibility in marriage. What was it? He could not give it a name.

It was a possibility of long, quiet possession. He had kept pushing his passions back and back. Ann Rutledge might have been doing that with herself. She might have loved him, wanted him, as he did her.

He was sure of one thing. If he were loved as he wanted to be, the realization of it would have to come slowly.

More and more, as the time for marrying her drew nearer, he had held something within himself back and back. No other woman in his life ever aroused his passions as Ann Rutledge had. Indeed, there was no other woman he could not have lived without. Later, he knew that, had he never got another woman afterward, his life, the tone of his life, would not have been much changed. But, had Ann lived and had he not gotten her, he would have gone to pieces. He knew that.

It was because his passions were so thoroughly aroused at the time that he wanted to hold them down. On some nights he could not sleep for wanting her. He got out of bed and read law, made himself read law.

When he had been with her, usually on Sunday evenings, and there were others about, other young men and women, he stayed with the young men, talking with them. He had been ashamed that anyone should see how much he cared for Ann, ashamed even that she should see.

And now she would never see.

When he went into the room where she lay dying, it was late in the afternoon.

He knew she was going to die as soon as the other woman, the tall one with the squirrel-like mouth, had gone away.

Ann must have known, too. He sat in a chair beside her bed. They did not talk. She might have been too ill for words. Perhaps she did not know him.

He took her hand. They were alone. He wanted to crush the hand—it was a small plump hand—in his own big one, but didn't. He held it lightly.

Ann moaned a little, said a few incoherent words. Time passed. To Abe it seemed he might have been sitting like that for days. As a matter of fact, he was in the room with Ann but twenty minutes.

Then the doctor came for his visit. He was a heavy-looking short man with gray whiskers growing on each side of his face. He wore a fancy vest. There were stains on his vest. No doubt he was a tobacco-chewer, a slovenly man. Two women came into the room with him.

Abe got up out of his chair. It was the most painful thing he ever did. When he raised a leg to walk, it was as though the doctor standing there were cutting the leg from his body.

On such occasions everyone is polite, everyone is kind.

Abe knew, a long time afterward, that, had Ann Rutledge lived, had he married her, the marriage might well have been like any other marriage. Life with her might have killed the ambition in him that later made him rise in the world.

Although he was then but young, he had always been a shrewd observer of people. He knew how marriages usually turn out.

In every marriage there is, however, a chance. Men like Abe Lincoln are after something in marriage. It is a plunge into the dark, deliberately taken on the chance of coming out into the light.

Something Abe wanted, that he always wanted and never got.

He went out of Ann Rutledge's living presence and into the streets. It was late summer. Already the days were growing short. Abe walked down through the little main street of New Salem and into the country.

He did not stay in the road, but climbed a fence and crossed a field.

He thought of suicide. He went into a wood and stood with his back to a tree.

The black hour had come. Ann was dying in the room in the house in town. She might already have died. A man with a mind like that of Abraham Lincoln's must sometimes let it have play. He can hold on to himself most of the time, but sometimes he lets go.

He began thinking about himself and his chances in life. If he had got Ann, he might have settled down in New Salem. The town was small, a mere backwoods settlement. However, life could be lived there as it could in any other place.

You live your life in your own house, in a few people about you. A man who is really married lives in his wife. She lives in him.

Before marriage he has seen life through his own eyes. Afterward he must see it through two people's eyes. He is no longer a solitary thing walking around. He is two people.

Thinking Ann Rutledge beautiful and having always, since he had grown up out of boyhood, having thought of himself as physically ugly, he was to have shared in Ann's beauty.

It would have become his beauty, a part of himself.

What he was losing in her death was an abstract thing.

Losing her would be like losing the sense of truth, of God. He put it to himself that way.

It seemed to him that without her, he would always be a crippled man. He grew desperate. "I can't! I can't!" he cried aloud.

His shrill voice rang out in the silent wood. There was no one else there. He had walked a long way from the road. It was the same shrill voice that was always making men laugh in the town and in the store.

The forest in which he stood was not empty. There was a waiting kind of silence down within himself that was unfathomable. There was a stillness, an emptiness that hurt. His long body ached with it. Had he had a knife with him or a gun, he might have shot or stabbed himself. The physical pain of a knife or a gun wound would have been a relief. Once he even felt in his pocket, hoping to find a pocket knife.

"If I had one, I would open a vein in my arm. I could die quietly here, bothering no one. The blood would come slowly out of my body."

There were noises outside himself, the little noises of nature. A man on horseback passed on the distant road. He heard the clatter of the horse's hooves on the hard road.

He heard a little wild animal run through the forest.

It was quite dark outside Abe and within. He did not know how long he stayed in the wood that night.

There was a man named Bowlin Green who lived on a farm near New Salem with his wife. It was a house he had often visited. The Bowlin Greens were gentle people, friends of Ann Rutledge. They were simple good people who had come out into the new country and settled on a little farm near Clary's Grove. They hadn't fitted in there, being unable to swear, drink whiskey, take part in the rough-and-tumble political meetings with which the community entertained itself. They had settled down on their small farm and planted flowers all about the house, and Ann had found out about them. She had taken Abe there two or three times.

He went that night to Bowlin Green's house, stayed there all that fall and a part of the winter. They were glad to have him. Bowlin Green would not take any money for his board.

It was Bowlin Green's wife who had told him when Ann died.

He had not shed any tears. When she told him, his body did not even tremble.

He had renounced something, the hope of Ann's living, that night in the wood, and with it something else.

He had renounced the hope of the life of direct personal love. Abe did not put that thought into words then or later. He was to marry and have children.

It did not matter. He was to live his life without direct personal love. The woman he might have loved was dead. Abe knew it that night in the woods. He knew it when he went from the woods to Bowlin Green's house. To keep the thought from growing too strong in him, he spent all that winter studying. . . .

THE DEVIL'S NIECE: HÉLOÏSE

Allan Dowling

Allan Dowling was born in New York on July 4, 1903, but lives a good deal of his time in Europe. From 1927 to 1933 France was his home, but in 1935 he returned to New York and went into the real estate business. After ten years of business he left it to become the owner and publisher of Partisan Review. He is still one of the advisory editors. He produced three feature films in Hollywood and last year collaborated with George Antheil in a cantata entitled "Cabeza da Vaca," now on the schedule of the Indianapolis Symphony. He is the author of three books of verse, two fantasies and a book of fiction, The Swimmer.

The Devil is the uncle of all beautiful women. Once he lived in Paris and called himself Canon Fulbert of Notre Dame, and he chose a brilliant dialectician and philosopher to instruct his niece, Héloïse. The name of the dialectician was Pierre Abélard, and the Devil chose him because he was making a success.

But Héloïse, unknown to her uncle, had an angel who stood behind her and kept setting parts of her on fire; and Abélard, while instructing her, saw the flames, now in her hands, now in her face, and now in different parts of her body, obscured by the clothes she wore. He was seized by a desire to remove the clothes and see the flames in all their purity; and when they were alone in a room together, he did so, and the flames burst out all over them both, and they were terrified at the impossibility of not loving.

Then Abélard became confused. He did not realize that the pleasure of love, which is the pleasure of dying, must be deliberately isolated and divorced from all usefulness, or else we become the dupes of life and are tricked into reproduction.

So Héloïse bore him a child, and the great games of love, which are the supreme masterpieces of art, were spoiled for them. The fact that Abélard then married Héloïse in secret, and immediately afterwards sent her to a nunnery, is proof that he was confused. But the Devil, who can never think clearly and even makes a mess of hell, was confused also. The idea took hold of him that his niece had been betrayed and abandoned, and the most fiendish revenge he could think of was to have a gang of ruffians set on Abélard and castrate him. He thus destroyed the reproductive principle in Abélard, which to the Devil was the most precious thing he possessed; but of course in so doing the Devil destroyed himself, and the lovers, liberated from reproduction, and freed from all brief intercourses, became united forever in the Human Imagination, which is God.

THE MYSTERY OF HÉLOÏSE
Étienne Gilson

Étienne Gilson, who was born in 1884 in Paris, and has taught at the Universities of Lille, Strasbourg and Paris, is a member of the French Academy, and since 1929—when he founded it—the director of the Pontifical Institute of Mediaeval Studies at Toronto, Canada.

It is not too difficult to extract from the texts a picture of Héloïse that is at one and the same time simple and clear. But the Héloïse thus discovered, though possibly historically real and certainly consistent with documentary evidence, is most improbable. The evidence points to a Héloïse who is all lover, who is an incarnation of the pure essence of love to the exclusion of everything else. We can add, however, that if she is the great lover, she is so in the French manner, with that strange yearning for rational or sophistical justification to be encountered in Chrétien de Troyes, in Corneille, and even, alas, in Rousseau. If this demands further testimony, we have the word of Henry Adams, whose perspicacity borders on genius: "The twelfth century, with all its sparkle, would be dull without Abélard and Héloïse. With infinite regret, Héloïse must be left out of the story, because she was not a philosopher or a poet or an artist, but only a Frenchwoman to the last millimeter of her shadow. Even though one may suspect that her famous letters to Abélard are, for the most part, by no means above scepticism, she was, by French standards, worth at least a dozen Abélards, if only because she called St. Bernard a false apostle. Unfortunately, French standards, by which she must be judged in our ignorance, take for granted that she philosophized only for the sake of Abélard, while Abélard taught philosophy to her not so much because he believed in philosophy or in her as because he believed in himself. To this day, Abélard remains a problem as perplexing as he must have been to Héloïse, and almost as fascinating. As the west portal of Chartres is the door through which one must of necessity enter the Gothic architecture of the thirteenth century, so Abélard is the portal of approach to the Gothic thought and philosophy within. Neither art nor thought has a modern equivalent; only Héloïse, like Isolde, unites the ages."

That a woman should rival a myth in sheer realism is, indeed, a remarkable occurrence! Proof is not wanting that Héloïse was much like this, and no one will insist upon more. Nevertheless, what remains to be noticed is essentially different from what we have seen hitherto. For it will not hereafter be a question of a learned young woman seduced by the famous master, but of something far more significant, the Abbess of the Paraclete. When we read her letters, we hear the voice of a woman, still young, to be sure, yet one to whom has been entrusted the important spiritual offices of prioress and abbess in two Benedictine houses. But reading her letters, one is struck immediately by the omnipresence of Abélard and the total absence of God. Nor can this fact be passed off by merely saying that God is absent from the letters. He is continually being expelled from them. How are we to explain an attitude like this?

We know from Abélard himself that when he sought refuge in the monastic life, neither fervor nor religious vocation played a very large role in his decision. He was obeying neither God's call nor the command of Héloïse. He wanted to hide his shame; and this was about all. Héloïse's entry into religion, if externally like Abélard's, was basically very different. No more, of course, than he, was she answering an interior call. She was acting out of deference to Abélard's orders. When formerly she had offered to be his mistress and he had preferred that she become his wife, she had done as he wished. Now, when he wanted her to become a religious, she

became this too, simply because it was a further mark of the love
he expected of her and which she was powerless to refuse. Again,
her sacrifice was immediate and without reservation either in
thought or act. Her action here was the more meritorious in that
Abélard, if he had not actually misjudged it, had at least found
means to render it odious. For he was not satisfied that she should
merely enter religion, but he insisted that she enter before he did.
He was not, in his heart, even then sure of her! She did as he
asked and submitted to the outrage, but she was never able to forget it.

On this important point, as indeed on all the others, the testimony of both Abélard and Héloïse is in complete accord. "She,
however, spontaneously took the veil first, at my command" (*illa
tamen prius ad imperium nostrum sponte velata*), says Abélard, in-
dicating that before he himself entered Saint-Denys, Héloïse had
promised to take the veil *at his command*. Several, he adds, tried
vainly to frighten her, depicting the monastic rule as too heavy a
yoke for youth to bear. But in vain. Their pity could not break
her resolve. "Mingled with tears and sobs, the lament of Cornelia
escaped as best it could from her lips: 'Illustrious spouse, for whom
my bed was unworthy, what rights did destiny possess over your
noble head? How great was my sin in marrying you, if I was to
make you so miserable? Accept this day my expiation, for it is of my
own accord that I offer it.'" "Saying these words" (*in his verbis*)
"she rushed towards the altar, accepted unflinchingly the veil
blessed by the bishop, and consecrated herself publicly to the religious life." When this scene took place, Héloïse could hardly have
been twenty years old.

Abélard's account is of capital importance because its every
word is full of significance. Even the apparent contradiction in its
first phrase is significant: *At the command* of Abélard, Héloïse
spontaneously took the veil. When it was Abélard who commanded,
immediate obedience was her only course. But her reasons for obeying Abélard's command were supremely personal. Héloïse knew
only too well what lay behind Abélard's decision. When we examine his reasons, we see that they do him little honor. In demand-

ing that Héloïse enter religion, Abélard was depriving her of the only consolation remaining to her—expiation for her crime of marrying him. Thus Héloïse accepts Abélard's order; but only for her own reasons will she do what he asks. The action to which he forces her will have no other significance than she chooses to give it. And this significance has no religious character whatsoever. The verses of Lucan's *Pharsalia* which she stammers out as she hastens towards the altar are too expressive for one to misunderstand the exact value she was assigning her act. There would be something naïve in believing that she could really have recited these verses, if it was not still more naïve to doubt it. They express her intentions so perfectly that one wonders if it was not the intentions which suggested the verses. The idea of renouncing the world, not for God, not even to expiate the offenses committed against God, but for Abélard and to expiate the crime which she had committed against Abélard, assuredly indicate in Héloïse a singular indifference to the Christian sense of the act which she is performing. But if the sentiment motivating her is not Christian, it is completely Roman and not at all unworthy of Cornelia from whose words she borrows. If we must believe what Abélard indicates, Héloïse regarded her religious profession only as an expiatory sacrifice to the hero whom she had destroyed by marrying him.

One is forced to believe this because what Abélard suggests so precisely and discreetly, Héloïse later affirms with all the force and insistence of which she was capable, when it was a question of removing all equivocation as to the "purity" of her sentiments. "Since at your command I changed at once both dress and mind to show you to be *sole* possessor of both my body and my soul . . ." Since Abélard is the *sole* possessor of Héloïse's soul, God has then no part in this religious profession—"Not devotion to religion but your command alone drew me, young as I was, to embrace the severities of monastic life." It is only Abélard's command, and no devotion whatsoever, which determined this taking of the veil. And as if these statements were still not sufficiently clear, Héloïse goes so far as to state precisely that God owes her no recompense for what she has done, because from the time of her entrance into religion she has done nothing out of love for Him: "Over and above this [that is, any favor Abélard might show her] I can expect no reward from God, for I am sure that up to now I have done nothing out of love for Him." It is not then for God but for Abélard that the Abbess of the Paraclete works; for just as he alone can make her suffer, so *he alone* can console her: "For you alone can make me sad, you alone can make me happy or bring me consolation." How could Abélard have doubted for an instant one who, at a word from him, had preceded him when he was going to God? This cruel want of confidence filled her with such sorrow and shame, that the very memory of the affront is enough to send Héloïse into a raging passion. To follow him into the convent or to precede him there, what difference to her? "God knows, I would not have hesitated to follow you or to precede you into hell itself (ad Vulcania loca) if you had given the order. My heart was not my own, but yours. Even now, more than ever before, if it is not with you it is nowhere, for you are its very existence. So, I pray you, let my poor heart be happy with you. And it will be happy with you if it finds you gentle, if you render it grace for grace, little things for great, words for things. Remember, I beg you, everything I have done; and weigh out all that you owe me. When I delighted with you in carnal pleasures (libido), many wondered why I did it, whether it was for concupiscence or for love. But now my last state shows my true beginning, and I now forego all pleasures only to obey your will. Truly, I reserved nothing for myself but to be yours before everything, and such I am to this very moment."

Such words are too clear for any mistaking of the true nature of Héloïse's feelings. The seventeenth century will know women ready to endure hell for the love of God, but the love of Abélard is quite enough to make Héloïse willing to seek the realm of Vulcan. He speaks, his servant listens. Of old, at a word from him, she gave herself up to the most violent carnal pleasures. Now, at another word from him, she condemns herself to the severest rigors of the monastic life. She not only thinks of it this way, but writes to him to this effect, for she wishes him to know it. He must know it,

indeed, lest he come to think that Héloïse had found in the cloister the calm, the peace, and the consolations of divine love. No
doubt, it was that she might find these things that Abélard gave her
up. But he simply must know that it is not for God but for him
that she is in the cloister. What does it really matter where she is?
She would go to hell itself at his bidding. Only Abélard must know
that she has become a religious for the same reason that she had
become his mistress. What others call giving themselves to God was
for her but another way of giving herself to him.

It has been necessary to examine all these minute details to understand the terrible anguish that lies behind Héloïse's first letter.
It is literally the distress of a worshipper forsaken by her god. The
comparison is not too strong, for although Héloïse never dared
write it, she never ceases to suggest it. The least love of God, so it
seems to her, would be a theft from the exclusive love vowed forever to Abélard and reserved exclusively for him. In consterna-
tion at these sentiments, Abélard undertakes the impossible in
trying to make her renounce them. His efforts were put forth in
vain. Neither God nor Abélard could ever make Héloïse deny the
reality of her passion. Save to reproach him, Héloïse speaks of God
only to call Him to witness that she does not think first of Him,
do anything first for Him, nor hope for anything first from Him.
"Whatever the state of my life, God knows I still fear more to offend you than to offend Him. It is you rather than He that I desire to please. It is not out of love of God, but at your request that
I entered religion." Abélard got Héloïse to do everything, save to
pretend to love God a little more than him.

It has been necessary to push things thus far in order to discover
the full sense of certain expressions which Héloïse employs in
speaking of her taking of the veil. Even Abélard, in the few gripping lines he devotes to this scene, carefully notes the tragic out-
burst with which Héloïse undertook her sacrifice. "Thereupon she
rushed to the altar and quickly took the veil" (*Mox properat, con-
festim velum tulit*). Clearly, she threw herself passionately into
the cloister. At no moment in her life, indeed, did she give herself
quite so passionately to Abélard. Of old, at a word from him, she

agreed to lose herself for his sake. But this was still just a matter
of love because Abélard was only asking for what she desired
herself. Her entry into religion was quite another thing. It was no
longer love, but madness, because in her very excess of love she
separated herself forever from the one being she loved. Here are no
conventional formulas, but the plainest conceivable expression of
the most genuine feelings and the most incontestable facts. If Héloïse's taking of the veil was not her tenderest and most passionate
sacrifice for the love of Abélard, one wonders what more she could
possibly have given him.

It is true, of course, that Abélard was giving a command. But
by no divine law was it her duty to obey. Abélard's mutilation, his
decision to hide his shame in a cloister were certainly not for Héloïse
the equivalent of a religious vocation. Fifteen years later, as Abbess
of the Paraclete, she still felt the want of this. All she really wanted—
quod solum appetebat—as we already know, was what she was
actually giving up, Abélard himself In his ruin, she loves him more
than ever, and never for an instant dreams of being separated from
him. What matter the pleasures lost? She has told us clearly enough
that it was not the pleasures but himself she loved. It is enough for
her that he still lives, provided that a long life of happiness by his
side is still possible. This happiness he could not take from her save
by her own consent. If Héloïse were to refuse to enter religion,
Abélard himself could not enter either. He was her husband, she
his wife, and even leaving out of consideration their child (who never
seems to be considered in this affair), it was only the mutual consent
of the spouses that could separate them. We can well imagine what
spirit of sacrifice it required for her to become a religious before
Abélard and to forego all that was left to her of a love to which she
had already sacrificed everything.

When we follow Héloïse to this point, to the very core of her
conscience, remarks which might otherwise have struck us as cyn-
ical and even blasphemous, are redeemed by a basic truthfulness
and simple honesty. To say that they are only human is not to
make them less true or less honest. We see here, more than
anywhere else, how much better it is to read the story in its basic

texts than simply to imagine it. When all is said, what has Héloïse actually told us? That she entered religion without a religious vocation? Certainly. That at the moment of writing the letters, this vocation had not yet come? She seems to think so, in any case, and it may well be true. That as Abbess of the Paraclete, she had never found the strength to love God above all things else, because Abélard was still her first love? Perhaps she was far closer to divine charity than many others who dethrone God for a great deal less than Abélard, or who do not even so much as recall what is the greatest and the first commandment.

Historians, treating of Héloïse, ought never to forget a cautionary remark of Ste. Teresa of Avila, which might well have had her in mind: "I am surprised at your saying you know this young woman merely from having seen her. We women are not easy to know. Even when you have been their confessor for many years, you are surprised yourself to have understood them so badly. They do not, in exposing their faults, give an exact account of themselves, and you are wrong to judge them only from what they tell you." What exactly was the spiritual life of Héloïse? Since she perhaps never knew this herself, I willingly admit that we will never know either. Still it is true to say that Héloïse's confidences are not those of a religious who has failed in her vocation or who is in revolt against the divine summons, but rather the plaints of a simple woman forced by the despotic will of her lover to tackle an insoluble problem. Her problem is to find in the passion this man inspires the strength required for a life of sacrifice which is both meaningless and impossible save on the level of the love of God. Such is the crisis through which the Abbess of the Paraclete is struggling. Nothing could be more poignant than this spiritual misery. The whole thing is so cruelly clear to her that she prefers to put up with it rather than lie about it, even if lying about it could help her to forget it.

—TRANSLATED BY L. K. SHOOK

MY DEAREST OWN

Katherine Mansfield

Katherine Mansfield, born in New Zealand, but a writer who made her name in England with her first short stories published in the magazines run by John Middleton Murry, died in her 34th year of a pulmonary disease in 1923 at the height of her career. Married to Murry, from whom her health forced frequent long separations, she wrote him hundreds of letters which were finally, under his editorship, published in unexpurgated form only a few years ago, forming an incomparable documentation of a woman's love. The husband to whom she addressed them died at 67 in March, 1957. He was married three times and the author of some forty books.

MONDAY, MAY 27, 1918

While you read this feel that my arms are round you and your head is hidden—and I'm telling you it all—with every part of me.

My dearest own,

I think, reading your three letters this morning, I suffered every atom that you suffered. Nay more, because it was I who inflicted it on you—you who came crying to me and saying "This is what you have done to me! This!" Even now I can't get calm and I am all torn to pieces by love and hideous remorse and regret. I must try to explain all this away and it's so difficult—so difficult—with these great clumsy words. I could do it were I to see you in a moment—in a breath. Only *one thing*. Never, never have I ever said to myself "Shut up shop and take your love away." If you ever feel that, don't tell me until you do take it away. It really nearly killed me. The sky—the whole world—fell. Before I begin to speak—you must know that you're all life to me. God! haven't my letters said just that? Hasn't all my suffering and misery been just because of that—because of my terrible—exhausting—utterly IN-TENSE love? But you must have understood that. That was the whole why and wherefore.

You see, I was in the S. of F.* from December till April. What was it like on the whole? Just HELL. As you know it nearly killed me. Then I came back to rest with you. All my longing, all my desires, all my dreams and hopes had been just to be with you, and—to come back to my home. Bien! I came. Heard how ill I was, scarcely seem to have seen you, except through a mist of anxiety, felt that *all* your idea was for me to get away into the country again. Well, I understood that—although, please try to realise the appalling blow it was to me to uproot again—and so soon—with hardly a word spoken. Please do try and realise that. Plus the knowledge that I was more ill than I'd thought, and that all my precious "privacy," my love of "self-contained" life, doing all for myself in my own way, doing all *enfin* for YOU, was to be taken away from me, was "bad" for me, *enfin*.

However, it was only for a month or six weeks that I was to be alone. Then you came down for your holiday and we went back together. I arrived, and found I was to be here (without a word explaining why this change had been) at *least* 4 months, until the *late* autumn. No word of your coming, no word of anything else. It was a sort of ultimate *comble*. It knocked me back on to my own lonely self. I was in despair, as you know, and I saw Life quite differently. I felt that if all I had oh so passionately pleaded and protested without shame or fear about my love—my longing for married life—as soon as possible—was to be just delayed, not understood—I could endure no more, and I fell into the dark hollow which waits for me always—the old one—and I wrote from

* South of France.

there. I felt he has not this same great devouring need of me that I have of him. He *can* exist apart from me. I have been in the S. of F. nearly four months and here is another four. He will never realize that I am only WELL when we are "together." All else is a mockery of health. I depend on him as a woman depends on a man and a child on its little playfellow, but he, as long as he knows I am all right, he can play "apart." Now, do you see a little bit? Is it a little bit clearer? But there is more to say.

Our marriage. You cannot imagine what that was to have meant to me. It's fantastic—I suppose. It was to have shone—apart from all else in my life. And it really was only part of the nightmare, after all. You never once held me in your arms and called me your wife. In fact, the whole affair was like my silly birthday. I had to keep on making you remember it. . . .

And then—all the L.M. complex is—taking the reins out of my hands. I am to sit quiet and look at the country. I can't—I can't. Don't you know that LIFE—married life with you—co-equal—part-ners—jealously alone—jealous of every other creature near—is what I want. I am jealous—jealous of our privacy—just like an eagle. If I felt that you and she discussed me even for my own good—I'd have to fly out of the nest and dash myself on the rocks below.

My little Boge-husband, you don't know me even yet. I adore you and you only. I shall not take my love away ever—not even long after I am dead. Silly little button flowers will grow out of my grave with Bogey written on the petals. . . .

Do you understand now? (*Maintenant, c'est moi qui pleure.*)

There is my answer for ever to you.

Now about the Elephant. Get it if you can, and we will make it a Singing Elephant with all our hearts.

As I wired you this morning, I am not going to leave this hotel after all. I cannot explain to another landlady that my lungs is weak. Also the fag of wondering what I shall order to eat would mean I'd order nothing. Here, it comes, and one eats it, and it's over. And they know me here, now, and are more than kind to me. The old 'un, Mrs. Honey, is "pure Heron." Bless her! I can always hear her and my Gran'ma talking as they put the linen away. So here I shall remain, and I will take your money, please—unless it leaves you short. I will take it from you. You must try to come here, as we did once arrange, even for a week, and we'll have a sail-boat and go "whiffing for pollocks." I am working hard and Pagello says I have made remarkable great strides.

So now, please God, let us be calm again. *I will not be sad.* Let us be calm. Let our love keep us quiet and safe—like two children in a great big quiet field—sitting there hidden in the flowers and grasses.

O thou who hast all of my heart. Accept me.

I am simply for ever and ever your own little

Wig

I have told the manageress I am staying for the whole of June— *at least.*

The books came and the cigarettes—thank you, love.

Tell me all the practical things. Don't spare me. Tell me all the worries. They are my RIGHT. I must have them and discuss them. You are NOT to have any worry unshared.

MONDAY MORNING, NOVEMBER 10, 1919

My own dear Love,

Here is another Monday. They do seem to come round so fast, like the horses we saw at the fair—no, the *roosters*—that was our one, wasn't it? Do you remember those little Princesses who went round for ever? They wore cotton frocks and tiny leather belts.

It's a chill, strange day. I breakfasted in Valhalla—cracks of lightning, thunder, tearing rain. Now I'm on the verandy and the clouds are immensely near and distinct like mountains.

Will you please say if my Dosty is all right? I sent it rather in fear and trembling, but I meant it. I am doing Virginia for this week's novel. I don't like it, Boge. My private opinion is that it is a lie in the soul. The war never has been: that is what its message is. I don't want (G. forbid!) mobilisation and the violation of Belgium, but the novel can't just leave the war out. There must have been a change of heart. It is really fearful to see the "settling down" of human beings. I feel in the *profoundest* sense that nothing can ever be the same—that, as artists, we are traitors if we feel otherwise: we have to take it into account and find new expressions, new moulds for our new thoughts and feelings. Is this exaggeration? What *has* been, stands. But Jane Austen could not write *Northanger Abbey* now—or if she did, I'd have none of her.

There is a trifling scene in Virginia's book where a charming young creature in a light fantastic attitude plays the flute: it positively frightens me—to realise this *utter coldness* and indifference. But I will be very careful and do my best to be dignified and sober. Inwardly I despise them all for a set of *cowards*. We have to face our war. They won't. I believe, Bogey, our whole strength depends upon our facing things. I mean facing them without any reservation or restraints.

I fail because I don't face things. I feel almost that I have been ill so long for that reason: we fear for that reason: I mean *fear* can get through our defences for that reason. We've got to stand by our opinions and risk falling by them.

Oh, my own Bogey, you are the only one in the world for me. We are really absolutely alone. We're a *queer couple*, you know, but we ought to be together—in every sense, really. We, just because we are "like this," ought not to be parted. We shall not be after May. I'll come home then.

Do you want to know how I am? Yesterday, upstairs in my room I suddenly wanted to give a small jump—I have not given a small jump for two years—you know the kind, a jump-for-joy. I was frightened. I went over to the window and held on to the sill to be safer. Then I went into the middle of the room and *did* jump. And this seemed such a miracle I felt I must tell somebody. There was nobody to tell. So I went over to the mirror—and when I saw my excited face I had to laugh. It was a marvellous experience.

Blessed little Wing! Kiss his nose for me and whistle in his ear and say "Your gan'ma loves you." She does. I wish he would have one kitten in May. Has he grown very big? And how is Athy? And how does the house look? Does it shine? And do you have nice food? Why can't we meet in dreams and answer all each other's questions? Our nights are wasted.

The sea is up to the brim of the world today.

Your own

Wig

SUNDAY, 8 A.M., NOVEMBER 16, 1919

My own Bogey,

It was a fearful *blow* to get no letters yesterday again. I shall never understand it. When L.M. came back after the last chance, I *hid* for a moment or two upstairs, just to delay the "No letters— nothing." Perhaps my luck will turn today and the sea have a pearl.

Such a night! Immense wind and sea and cold. This is certainly no "pensive citadel." This morning the storm still rages. It's a blow. I long to go out and have a walk, but I daren't face the wind.

What is this about the novel? Tell me, thou little eye among the blind. (It's easy to see who my bedfellow has been.) But seriously, Bogey, the more I read the more I feel all these novels will not do. After them I'm a swollen sheep looking up who is not fed. And yet I feel one can lay down no rules. It's not in the least a question of material or style or plot. I can only think in terms like "a change of heart." I can't imagine how after the war these men can pick up the old threads as though it had never been. Speaking to you I'd say we have died and lived again. How can that be the same life? It doesn't mean that life is the less precious or that "the common things of light and day" are gone. They are not gone, they are intensified, they are illumined. Now we know ourselves for what we are. In a way it's a tragic knowledge: it's as though, even while we live again, we face death. But *through* Life: that's the point. We see death in life as we see death in a flower that is fresh unfolded. Our hymn is to the flower's beauty:

we would make that beauty immortal because we *know*. Do you feel like this—or otherwise—or how?

But, of course, you don't imagine I mean by this knowledge let-us-eat-and-drink-ism. No, I mean "deserts of vast eternity." But the difference between you and me is (perhaps I am wrong) I couldn't tell anybody *bang out* about those deserts: they are my secret. I might write about a boy eating strawberries or a woman combing her hair on a windy morning, and that is the only way I can ever mention them. But they *must* be there. Nothing less will do. They can advance and retreat, curtsey, caper to the most delicate airs they like, but I am bored to Hell by it all. Virginia*, *par example*.

Here is the sun. I'll get up. My knees are cold, and my feet swim between the sheets like fishes.

Si tu savais comme je t'ai. . . . me! Oh, Bogey, darling heart, I shall never reconcile myself to absence from you—never. It's waste of life. But be happy, my precious.

Wig

NOVEMBER 17, 1920

Thank you for the flower. Yes, it *did* touch me.

No, darling. If I let this letter go I shall repent it. For it is not all.

It's true I am hurt as I've never been. Perhaps it is your carelessness. But then carelessness in love is so dreadful. And yet what else can it be? Even after getting my present which I tried to make perfect for you in a case which I chose awfully carefully *and you never even gave one word to*, you didn't mention this other photograph. And to talk about too much fragility and so on —I hang my head. I feel timid and faint. I am not an ox. I *am* weak; I feel my hold on life is fainting-weak. But that is ME—the real me. I can't help it. Didn't you know? And then when you toss off my letter about "passports, kisses, O.B.E."—oh, I am so ashamed. Was that what I wrote about? Let me creep away and fold my wings. They quiver—you hurt me.

* Virginia Woolf.

I must tell you; no one else will. I am not that other woman. I am not this great girl. Whether you did tell Sadler it was precious or not, I don't know. I scarcely hear you saying that to him.

But I must tell you something else. I have been ill for nearly four years—and I'm changed, changed—not the same. You gave twice to your work (which I couldn't see) what you gave my story. I don't want dismissing as a masterpiece. Who is going to mention "the first snow?"* I haven't anything like as long to live as you have. *I've scarcely any time, I feel.* Richard will draw posters 100 years. Praise him when I'm dead. Talk to ME. I'm lonely. I haven't ONE single soul.

SUNDAY, OCTOBER 15, 1922

I have opened my letter, darling, to add something. It's this. Darling Bogey, in your spare time, however little that is, get nearer the growing earth than that wheelbarrow and spade. *Grow things.* Plant. Dig up. Garden. I feel with all the force of my being that "happiness" is in these things. If it's only cabbages, let it be cabbages rather than chess. Sweep leaves. Make fires. Do anything to work with your hands in contact with the earth.

You see chess only feeds your already over-developed intellectual center. And that regular spade-and-barrow becomes a habit too soon, and is likely only to feed your moving center—to exercise your machine. Does that sound awful rot to you?

Why don't you get some animals? I'm not joking. Two hours a day would be enough for them. Birds—rabbits—goats—anything, and live through it or them! I know you will say you haven't the time. But you'll find your work is 100 times easier if you come to it refreshed, renewed, rich, happy. Does this sound like preaching? Don't let it. I am trying to tell you what I feel deep down is your way of escape. It is to really throw yourself into life—not desperately, but with the love you even don't feel yet. People won't do. We know too well that unless one has a background of reality in

* *The Stranger.* "But her words, so light, so soft, so chill, seemed to hover in the air, to rain into his breast, like snow."

oneself, people can't endure in us. When we have a table spread we can afford to open our door to guests, but not before. But enough of this. I am afraid of boring you.

Did you ask L.E. about tulips? Has he got anemones in the garden? You ought to see to them; they are your flowers. Why don't you write to Sutton's and ask their advice?

Oh, if you knew how I believe in Life being the only cure for Life.

Ever your own Wig

K.M.

About being like Chekhov and his letters. Don't forget he died at 43. That he spent—how much? of his life chasing about in a desperate search after health. And if one reads "intuitively" the last letters, they are terrible. What is left of him? "The braid on German women's dresses . . . bad taste"—and all the rest is misery. Read the last! All hope is over for him. Letters are deceptive, at any rate. It's true he had occasional happy moments. But for the last 8 years he knew no *security* at all. We know he felt his stories were not half what they might be. It doesn't take much imagination to picture him on his deathbed thinking "I have never had a real chance. Something has been all wrong."

Le Prieuré,
Fontainebleau-Avon
(Seine-et-Marne)
OCTOBER 18, 1922

My dear, darling Bogey,

I have been through a little revolution since my last letter. I suddenly made up my mind (for it was sudden, at the last) to try and learn to live by what I believe in, no less, and not as in all my life up till now to live one way and think another. . . . I don't mean superficially, of course, but in the deepest sense I've always been disunited. And this, which has been my "secret sorrow" for years, has become everything to me just now. I really can't go on pretending to be one person and being another any more, Boge. It is a living death. So I have decided to make a clean sweep of all that was "superficial" in my past life and start again to see if I can get into that real living simple truthful *full* life I dream of. I have been through a horrible deadly time coming to this. You know the kind of time. It doesn't show much, outwardly, but one is simply chaos within!

So my first Leap into the Dark was when I came here and decided to ask Mr. Gurdjieff if he would let me stay for a time. "Here" is a very beautiful old chateau in glorious grounds. It was a Carmelite monastery, then one of Madame de Maintenon's "seats." Now, it is modernized inside—I mean, *chauffage centrale*, electric light and so on. But it's a most wonderful old place in an amazingly lovely park. About 40 people—chiefly Russians—are here working, at every possible kind of thing. I mean, outdoor work, looking after animals, gardening, indoor work, music, dancing—it seems a bit of everything. Here the philosophy of the "system" takes second place. Practice is first. You simply *have* to wake up instead of talking about it, in fact. You *have* to learn to do all the things you say you want to do.

I don't know whether Mr. Gurdjieff will let me stay. I am "under observation" for a fortnight first. But if he does, I'll stay here for the time I should have been abroad and get really cured—not half cured, not cured in my body only and all the rest still as ill as ever. I have a most lovely sumptuous room—a kind of glorified Garsington—but for the fortnight. As for the food, it is like a Gogol feast. Cream, butter—but what nonsense to talk about the food! Still, it's very important, and I want you to know that one is terribly well looked after, in every way. There are three doctors here —real ones. But these, too, seem details. The chief thing is that this is my Selsfield for the time, the house of *my dreams*. If Mr. Gurdjieff won't let me stay, I shall go to the South, take a little villa and try to learn to live on my own, growing things and looking after rabbits and so on, getting into touch with *Life* again. . . .

Goodbye for now, darling heart.

Ever your own

Wig

SUNDAY (DECEMBER 31, 1922)

My darling Bogey,

My fountain pen is mislaid, so as I am in a hurry to write please forgive this pencil.

Would you care to come here on January 8 or 9 to stay until 14-15? Mr. Gurdjieff approves of my plan and says will you come as his guest? On the 13th our new theatre is to be opened. It will be a wonderful experience. But I won't say too much about it. Only on the chance that you do come I'll tell you what clothes to bring.

One sports suit with heavy shoes and stockings and a mackintosh and a hat that doesn't matter. One "neat" suit with your soft collar or whatever collar you wear and tie (you see you are my husband and I can't help wanting you to look—what shall I say?) slippers and so on. That's all. If you have a cardigan of course bring it and a pair of flannel trousers in case you get soaking wet and want a change.

I am writing to ask Brett to go to Lewis' and get me a pair of shoes. Will you bring them? I may ask her to get me a jacket too. But she will give you the parcel. Will you wire me your reply—just "yes" or "no" and the date, if "yes," of your arrival.

There is a London train that reaches Paris at 4 something. You could then come on to Fontainebleau the same day. Otherwise it's far better to stay the night in Paris as no cabs meet the late train.

You get out of the train at *Avon* and take a cab here which costs 8 francs *with* tip. Ring the bell at the porter's lodge and I'll open the gate.

I hope you will decide to come, my dearest. Let me know as soon as you can, won't you? I hope Tchekhov's wife will be here. I have gone back to my big lovely room, too, so we should have plenty of space to ourselves. We can also sit and drink *kiftir* in the cowshed.

I can't write of other things in this letter. I hope to hear from you soon.

Your ever loving
Wig

I arrived at the Gurdjieff Institute early in the afternoon of January 9, 1923. Katherine was very pale, but radiant. We talked for a while in her room overlooking the garden. She told me that she had wanted me to come very much indeed, because the moment had come for which she had been waiting. She had had to disentangle herself from our love, because it had become an agony of concern for each other which threatened to strangle us. At the Institute, she had worked herself free of it, and from the fear of death, with which it was so deeply entwined. Now she could come to me as a free being, in a love that was purified of all fear.

The greatest obstacle she had to overcome in taking the plunge and making the final decision to enter the Institute had been her fear of losing me. But that fear had been the source of the falsity that had steadily grown upon her since her illness began. Only at rare and terrible moments had she dared—or been driven—to reveal to me the deadly fear that was taking possession of her soul, the blackness that engulfed her; and then I had been dismayed. When she had cried to me to help her out of the gulf, I could do nothing: I almost seemed to turn away as from something intolerable. And so our love had become a dream of happiness to be in some unattainable future. And she had had to pretend, and to go on pretending, to herself and to me that she was not the sick and frightened Katherine that she was, until her own identity was lost and she did not know which was her true self.

Suddenly, she had known that, if she was to escape this living death, she must make a clean sweep of all her fears. The Institute had offered her the opportunity. Even to enter it had been the cause of fear: she had been fascinated by, but afraid of its doctrines. She had been afraid of ignoring her illness. She had been afraid of finally alienating me. By acting in spite of her fears, she had overcome them. By risking losing me, she had found her love for me: it was entire and perfect.

And truly as I looked at her, while I listened, she seemed a being transfigured by love, absolutely secure in love. She had no desire to defend the Institute; as indeed I had none to criticise it. She spoke quite quietly of her feeling that she had perhaps now gained all that it had to give her, and that she might be leaving very soon. When she did, she would like to live with me in extreme simplicity in a small cottage in England, and she would like me to cultivate the land.

It was a great happiness to me to be with her again. She led me out first to her gallery in the cowshed, then to where the company was putting the finishing touches to the dancing hall which had been erected in the garden. Though it was built with trusses, hangar fashion, it immediately impressed me by its likeness to a huge no-mad tent, though I have never seen one. She introduced me to some of her friends—to Hartmann and Salzmann and Dr. Young, to Olga Ivanovna and Adela, a young Lithuanian girl who was de-voted to her. Under instruction I took a hand in painting coloured designs upon the windows of the hall. I met Orage again, for the first time for many years; and he seemed to me a changed man, much gentler and sweeter than I remembered him. Indeed there was a blend of simplicity and seriousness in most of the people I met there, and in the company as a whole, which impressed me deeply.

Many of them were very tired. They had been working against time, and often all night long, to finish the hall in time to open it on January 13. The work appears, in memory, to have gone on un-interruptedly all through that afternoon and evening. I cannot re-member that there was any formal meal. But later in the evening Katherine and I went to sit in the salon. At about 10 o'clock she said she was tired, and began to go to her room. As she slowly climbed the big staircase to the first floor where her room was, she was seized by a fit of coughing. I took her arm and helped her into her room. No sooner were we inside, than the cough became a par-oxysm. Suddenly a great gush of blood poured from her mouth. It seemed to be suffocating her. She gasped out "I believe . . . I'm going to die." I put her on the couch and rushed out of the room calling for a doctor. Two came almost immediately. Wisely, I sup-pose, they thrust me out of the room though her eyes were implor-ing me. In a few minutes she was dead.

She died at the age of 34 and was buried in the communal cemetery of Avon near Fontainebleau. On the stone was carved a sentence from Shakespeare which she particularly loved. "But I tell you, my lord fool, out of this nettle, danger, we pluck this flower, safety."

It is not for me to pass judgment on the Gurdjieff Institute. I cannot tell whether Katherine's life was shortened by her entry into it. But I am persuaded of this: that Katherine made of it an instrument for that process of self-annihilation which is necessary to the spiritual rebirth, whereby we enter the Kingdom of Love. I am certain that she achieved her purpose, and that the Institute lent itself to it. More I dare not, and less I must not, say.

JOHN MIDDLETON MURRY

SOLITUDE AND LOVE

Thomas Merton

A desire to "find his personal salvation" led Thomas Merton, at the age of 26, to give up the prospects of a literary life in metropolitan New York after his years at Columbia University and to enter a monastery. Today he is an ordained priest, Father M. Louis O.C.S.O., in the Trappist order at Gethsemani, Kentucky, where, apart from his duties, he has continued his writings which include his auto-biography The Seven Storey Mountain, Seeds of Contemplation, No Man is an Island, and many other books of poetry and prose. He has been described as "a modern man in reverse"—a mystic, withdrawn into an intensely spiritual and personal world, and his theology "a projection into his writing of a personal experience."

He was born in 1915 in Southern France, the son of an English landscape painter father, and a mother who was an American Quaker. He grew up in France, England and the United States. He studied at Cambridge and at Columbia University where, for one semester, he taught English. In the depression he joined a young Communist group and later worked at a Catholic settlement house in Harlem. In 1938 he joined the Roman Catholic Church and entered the Trappist monastery in 1941.

1. Charity is a love for God which respects the need that other men have for Him. Therefore, charity alone can give us the power

and the delicacy to love others without defiling their loneliness which is their need and their salvation.

2. Do not stress too much the fact that love seeks to penetrate the intimate secrets of the beloved. Those who are too fond of this idea fall short of true love, because they violate the solitude of those they love, instead of respecting it.

True love penetrates the secrets and the solitude of the beloved by allowing him to keep his secrets to himself and to remain in his own solitude.

3. Secrecy and solitude are values that belong to the very essence of personality.

A person is a person insofar as he has a secret and is a solitude of his own that cannot be communicated to anyone else. If I love a person, I will love that which most makes him a person: the secrecy, the hiddenness, the solitude of his own individual being, which God alone can penetrate and understand.

A love that breaks into the spiritual privacy of another in order to lay open all his secrets and besiege his solitude with importunity does not love him: it seeks to destroy what is best in him, and what is most intimately his.

4. Compassion and respect enable us to know the solitude of another by finding him in the intimacy of our own interior solitude. It discovers his secrets in our own secrets. Instead of consuming him with indiscretion, and thus frustrating all our own desires to show our love for him, if we respect the secrecy of his own interior loneliness, we are united with him in a friendship that makes us both grow in likeness to one another and to God. If I respect my brother's solitude, I will know his solitude by the reflection that it casts, through charity, upon the solitude of my own soul.

This respect for the deepest values hidden in another's personality is more than an obligation of charity. It is a debt we owe in justice to every being, but especially to those who, like ourselves, are created in the image of God.

Our failure to respect the intimate spiritual privacy of other persons reflects a secret contempt for God Himself. It springs from the crass pride of fallen man, who wants to prove himself a god by prying into everything that is not his own business. The tree of the knowledge of good and evil gave our first parents a taste for knowing things outside of God, in a way in which they are not known truly, instead of knowing them in Him, in Whom alone we are able to find them and know them and love them as they are. Original justice gave our souls the power to love well: to increase our own heritage of life by loving others for their own good. Original sin gave our souls the power to love destructively: to ruin the object of our love by consuming it, with no other profit to ourselves than the increase of our own interior famine.

We ruin others and ourselves together not by entering into the sanctuary of their inner being—for no one can enter there except their Creator—but by drawing out of that sanctuary and teaching them to live as we live: centered upon themselves.

5. If a man does not know the value of his own loneliness, how can he respect another's solitude?

It is at once our loneliness and our dignity to have an incommunicable personality that is ours, ours alone and no one else's, and will be so forever.

When human society fulfills its true function the persons who form it grow more and more in their individual freedom and personal integrity. And the more each individual develops and discovers the secret resources of his own incommunicable personality, the more he can contribute to the life and the weal of the whole. Solitude is as necessary for society as silence is for language and air for the lungs and food for the body.

A community that seeks to invade or destroy the spiritual solitude of the individuals who compose it is condemning itself to death by spiritual asphyxiation.

6. If I cannot distinguish myself from the mass of other men, I will never be able to love and respect other men as I ought. If I do not separate myself from them enough to know what is mine and what is theirs, I will never discover what I have to give them, and never allow them the opportunity to give me what they ought. Only a person can pay debts and fulfill obligations, and if I am less than a person I will never give others what they have a right to ex-

pect from me. If they are less than persons, they will not know what to expect from me. Nor will they ever discover that they have anything to give. We ought normally to educate one another by fulfilling one another's just needs. But in a society where personality is obscured and dissolved, men never learn to find themselves and, therefore, never learn how to love one another.

7. Solitude is so necessary both for society and for the individual that when society fails to provide sufficient solitude to develop the inner life of the persons who compose it, they rebel and seek false solitudes.

A false solitude is a point of vantage from which an individual, who has been denied the right to become a person, takes revenge on society by turning his individuality into a destructive weapon. True solitude is found in humility, which is infinitely rich. False solitude is the refuge of pride, and it is infinitely poor. The poverty of false solitude comes from an illusion which pretends, by adorning itself in things it can never possess, to distinguish one individual self from the mass of other men. True solitude is selfless. Therefore, it is rich in silence and charity and peace. It finds in itself seemingly inexhaustible resources of good to bestow on other people. False solitude is self-centered. And because it finds nothing in its own center, it seeks to draw all things into itself. But everything it touches becomes infected with its own nothingness, and falls apart. True solitude cleans the soul, lays it wide open to the four winds of generosity. False solitude locks the door against all men and pores over its own private accumulation of rubbish.

Both solitudes seek to distinguish the individual from the crowd. True solitude succeeds in this, false solitude fails. True solitude separates one man from the rest in order that he may freely develop the good that is his own, and then fulfill his true destiny by putting himself at the service of everyone else. False solitude separates a man from his brothers in such a way that he can no longer effectively give them anything or receive anything from them in his own spirit. It establishes him in a state of indigence, misery, blindness, torment, and despair. Maddened by his own insufficiency, the proud man shamelessly seizes upon satisfactions and possessions that are not due to him, that can never satisfy him, and that he will never really need. Because he has never learned to distinguish what is really his, he desperately seeks to possess what can never belong to him.

In reality the proud man has no respect for himself because he has never had an opportunity to find out if there is anything in him worthy of respect. Convinced that he is despicable, and desperately hoping to keep other men from finding it out, he seizes upon everything that belongs to them and hides himself behind it. The mere fact that a thing belongs to someone else makes it seem worthy of desire. But because he secretly hates everything that is his own, as soon as each new thing becomes his own it loses its value and becomes hateful to him. He must fill his solitude with more and more loot, more and more rapine, seizing things not because he wants them, but because he cannot stand the sight of what he has already obtained.

These, then, are the ones who isolate themselves above the mass of other men because they have never learned to love either themselves or other men. They hate others because they hate themselves, and their love of others is merely an expression of this solitary hatred.

The proud solitary is never more dangerous than when he appears to be social. Having no true solitude and, therefore, no spiritual energy of his own, he desperately needs other men. But he needs them in order to consume them, as if in consuming them he could fill the void in his own spirit and make himself the person he feels he ought to be.

When the Lord, in His justice, wills to manifest and punish the sins of a society that ignores the natural law, He allows it to fall into the hands of men like this. The proud solitary is the ideal dictator, turning the whole world from peace to war, carrying out the work of destruction, opening the mouths of ruin from city to city, that these may declare the emptiness and degradation of men without God.

The perfect expression of a society that has lost all sense of the value of personal solitude is a state forced to live as a refugee in its own ruins, a mob without roofs to cover it, a herd without a barn.

8. True solitude is the solitude of charity, which "seeketh not her own."* It is ashamed to have anything that is not due to it. It seeks poverty, and desires to give away all that it does not need. It seems to feel distaste for created things: but its distaste is not for them. It cannot hate them, for it cannot even hate itself. Because it loves them, it knows it cannot own them, since they belong to God. Charity desires that He alone should possess them and receive from them the glory which is His due.

Our solitude may be fundamentally true, but still imperfect. In that event, it is mixed with pride. It is a disturbing mixture of hatred with love. One of the secrets of spiritual perfection is to realize that we have this mixture in ourselves, and to be able to distinguish one from the other. For the temptation of those who seek perfection is to mistake hatred for love, and to place their perfection in the solitude which distinguishes itself from other men by hating them and which at the same time loves and hates the good things that are theirs.

The asceticism of the false solitary is always double-dealing. It pretends to love others, but it hates them. It pretends to hate created things, and it loves them. And by loving them in the wrong way, it only succeeds in hating them.

Therefore, as long as our solitude is imperfect it will be tainted with bitterness and disgust, because it will exhaust us in continual conflict. The disgust is unavoidable. The bitterness, which should not be, is, nevertheless, there. Both must be used for our purification. They must teach us to distinguish what is truly bitter from what is truly sweet, and not permit us to find a poisoned sweetness in self-hatred and a poisoned bitterness in the love of others.

The true solitary must recognize that he is obliged to love other men and even all things created by God: that this obligation is not a painful and unpleasant duty, and that it was never supposed to be bitter. He must accept the sweetness of love without com-

* "Caritas . . . non quaerit quae sua sunt" (I Corinthians 13:5).

plaint, and not hate himself because his love may be, at first, a little inordinate. He must suffer without bitterness in order to learn to love as he ought. He must not fear that love will destroy his solitude. Love is his solitude. . . .

DARING

BREAKING SURFACE ON THE SAHARA
Philippe Diolé

The author of "Breaking Surface on the Sahara," Philippe Diolé, is a Frenchman who has explored by aqualung under the waters of the Mediterranean and by camel among the sands of one of the world's greatest deserts. He has written about both ventures in books of lyrical prose which include The Undersea Adventure, 4000 Years Under the Sea, *and* The Gates of the Sea. *In* Sahara Adventure *he recounted discoveries of many unusual works of pictorial art in one of the least known parts of the Sahara, the South Fezzen region.*

Undersea exploration and Sahara exploration have, in the last analysis, a common denominator—the explorer himself. The force which drives man down into the trough of the sea is the same as that which impels him to the earth's vast reaches of emptiness. In the quest of self-discovery, the map's expanses of blue and of white have an equal value. Besides, they are very much alike. . . .

Water or sand, each is the same immutable kingdom; a realm of unbounded empty distances, where the intruder is no more than a passer-by; virgin depths of water, virgin lands, equally harsh and inhospitable, though not in the same way; wrought upon by light and by erosion.

The ocean floor and the desert have been victims of the same misconception: both were long believed to be flat and sandy. But their sands—in undulations of the same "ripple marks"—cover only a meager portion of their extent: in the Sahara hardly one fifth. It is not only stretches of sandy beaches that we find undersea and in Africa, but labyrinths of rock, peaks and cliffs, valleys, canyons, and caves. Sometimes, too, the crust of the earth, under the water or the sun which bears down upon it, turns green in spite of everything, in an oasis, in forests of seaweeds, in rivers of palms. And in the blackest "abysses" of the sea, as in the worst "infernos" of the desert, a miraculous flower will bloom in the rubble, marking, as with a golden nailhead, the stubborn presence of life.

The sea and the desert gnaw equally at the wrecks lost upon their surfaces: the stranded truck eaten away by rust, the ship aground on the sands, prone on its side. In the solitude of the sea, in the silence of the desert sand hill, there is the same anonymity, the same melancholy of things dying rather than dead, given over defenseless to the sands of the sea bottom, to the sands blown by the wind.

These are landscapes which resemble each other, under the pressing weight of the water and of the sky, not by their strangeness but by their ambiguity. We know that this is a similarity of aspect only, and we remind ourselves that, contrary to a widespread belief, the Sahara is not a sea that has dried up; there was no Saharan Sea in the Quaternary Period. These are the unexplored fringes of the world, on the margin of the earth "civilized" by man, and of reality turned to usefulness. They are alien to the highway, the plowed field, the hearth, the achievements of technology; they have been neither made over by usage nor rendered commonplace by habit. These are the Promised Lands of the mind and spirit, the only ones left upon our planet which can offer a certain ease and smoothness to the processes of thought.

"I am here because of a taste for luxury," was the remark often made to me by Commandant X, who had not left the Sahara for twenty years, even on home leave.

The men who roam the sea and the desert resemble each other too. Divers and camel drivers inhabit murmurous silences, forever carrying on an unspoken monologue, and delighting in a solitude that is almost dizzying. Spirit and body float in undisturbed equilibrium in the peace of the waters and in the peace of the Sahara, in the swaying of the camels' movement and in the cradling of the deep dive.

Literature has blurred the features of the men who have chosen the empty spaces of the planet for their domain, who seek the broad plains of solitude. All the clichés about "adventure," all the banalities about the "magic of the sands," or the "appeal of the desert," have thrown a veil of confusion over the truth.

The man who becomes a denizen of the Sahara is neither the one stereotype always straining every nerve toward feats of heroism, nor the other who bears within him the unhealed wound of a great love.

A sick heart finds no more effective cure in the desert than anywhere else; rather less, probably. The image of the man who is made a "Saharan" by duty, by resentment, or by despair is entirely false. To picture the desert as a convalescent home or a place to retire to—what a misconception this is! The desert enriches only those who are already rich. It strengthens only the strong. One must entrust to it the heart's abundance and the mind's vitality; for these it brings to fruition.

It does more. Like the sea, it reveals the depths of being within us. Through it, there is every chance of our arriving at a certain secret door within ourselves. From this threshold other inner landscapes appear before our eyes. When consciousness makes its way beyond this wall, it achieves the greatest of all transitions: the transplanting of the inner man.

It is here that the sea and the desert have an equal value, are one in their human significance. It is here that the spell of the Sahara and the spell of the ocean depths bring a richness and satisfaction to certain spirits that the charms of cities, the smiles of women, the sweetness of home, cannot bestow. Is this the arrogance of choosing a bleak and naked destiny? The vanity of the hermit? I am not so sure of that. In these retreats into sparseness and solitude, these voluntary divestments of all that is extraneous, the same psychological alchemy is at work. There is always the question of a spiritual gain. The stake is the appropriation of the world by irrational means: a stake à la Rimbaud.

I have found again in the desert—or rather, I have brought to perfection there—the magic process by which, in the water, a diver is able to loose the ordinary bonds of time and space and bring life into consonance with an obscure inner poem: to by-pass habit, language, memory. . . . It is precisely the " 'I' is an other" of Rimbaud. To satisfy the "other" is an effort that lasts all our lives.

This unauthorized guest finds his enjoyment when his host is wholly absorbed in the present. That moment may be encountered at any of a number of crossroads: it may come in dream, poetry, intoxication, the nullification of gravity, solitude, silence, or mystical experience. There must be a kind of shifting in existence, which temporarily conceals its unreasonableness and holds the individual in suspense above time and space, attentive only to what goes on within himself.

Our psychology has not gone very far, obviously, since it has not yet plainly recognized this state of being, and given it a name.

We speak, to be sure, of "twilight states." But there is a disparaging emphasis in this use of the word "twilight," a smell of anesthetics. What I am thinking of is not that! On the contrary, this is a matter of exceptional clarity. Consciousness expands under another light.

The term we are looking for might perhaps be found in Proust. He has characterized as "instants of eternity," or "of perpetual adoration," those moments when man succeeds in "fixing the time which nothing fixes."

Yet it is less a question of "fixing the time" than of passing to its frontier or beyond it.

"I have gathered the smallest atoms of time into evermore-substantial textures," wrote Mallarmé. To give substance to that thin thread of water or sand that runs between our fingers—that is our sole problem. It is this which inspires the mystics, as it inspires the poets. "The contemplation of time is the key to human life," says Simone Weil.

It may be thought that this is going a long way in search of justification for enjoyment of the Sahara and its links with underseas "tourism." Yet, however mundane these aquatic or terrestrial promenades may be, their one merit in my eyes is that they do sometimes offer those "instants of eternity" which fix man in the present moment and put him outside the context of time.

Whether one walks, rides a camel, flies, or dives deep into the sea, it is for the sole purpose of crossing a frontier beyond which man ceases to feel himself the master, sure of his techniques, upheld by his inheritance, backed by the crowd. The more powerless he is, the more his spirit permeates his being. The horizon of the world and the horizon of thought coincide within him. Then the water, the rocks and the sand become vital nourishment, and perhaps a poem.

The sea and the desert are countries of lowly material attributes, where mind and spirit find luxury.

ON THE STRENUOUS MOOD

William James

William James (1842-1910), son of the Swedenborgian theologian, Henry James, and brother of the novelist Henry James, was for many years at Harvard in the department of psychology and philosophy where in addition to the many works growing out of his theory of pragmatism he wrote extensively in a field between philosophy and religion, including the books The Will to Believe, The Varieties of Religious Experience and The Meaning of Truth. The following is an extract from The Will to Believe and is taken from the essay "The Moral Philosopher and Moral Life."

The deepest difference, practically, in the moral life of man is the difference between the easy-going and the strenuous mood. When in the easy-going mood, the shrinking from present ill is our ruling consideration. The strenuous mood, on the contrary, makes us quite indifferent to present ill, if only the great ideal be attained. The capacity for the strenuous mood probably lies slumbering in every man, but it has more difficulty in some than in others in waking up. It needs the wilder passions to arouse it, the big fears, loves, and indignations; or else the deeply penetrating appeal of some one of the higher fidelities, like justice, truth, or freedom. Strong belief is a necessity of its vision; and a world where all the mountains are brought down and all the valleys are exalted is no congenial place for its habitation. This is why in a solitary thinker this mood might slumber on forever without waking. His various ideals, known to him to be mere preferences of his own, are too nearly of the same denominational value: He can play fast or loose with them at will. This too is why, in a merely human world without a God, the appeal to our moral energy falls short of its maximal stimulating power. Life, to be sure, is even in such a world a genuinely ethical symphony; but it is played in the compass of a couple of poor octaves, and the infinite scale of values fails to open up. Many of us, indeed—like Sir James Stephen in those eloquent "Essays by a Barrister"—would openly laugh at the very idea of the strenuous mood being awakened in us by those claims of remote posterity which constitute the last appeal of the religion of humanity. We do not love these men of the future keenly enough; and we love them perhaps the less the more we hear of their evolutionized perfection, their high average longevity and education, their freedom from war and crime, their relative immunity from pain and zymotic disease, and all their other negative superiorities. This is all too finite, we say; we see too well the vacuum beyond. It lacks the note of infinitude and mystery, and may all be dealt with in the don't-care mood. No need of agonizing ourselves or making others agonize for these good creatures just at present.

When, however, we believe that a God is there, and that he is one of the claimants, the infinite perspective opens out. The scale of the symphony is incalculably prolonged. The more imperative ideals now begin to speak with an altogether new objectivity and significance, and to utter the penetrating, shattering, tragically challenging note of appeal. They ring out like the call of Victor Hugo's alpine eagle, "*qui parle au precipice et que le gouffre entend,*" and the strenuous mood awakens at the sound. It saith among the trumpets, ha, ha! It smelleth the battle afar off, the thunder of the captains and the shouting. Its blood is up; and cruelty to the lesser claims, so far from being a deterrent element, does but add to the stern joy with which it leaps to answer to the greater. All through history, in the periodical conflicts of puritanism with the don't-care temper, we see the antagonism of the strenuous and genial moods, and the contrast between the ethics of infinite and mysterious obligation from on high, and those of prudence and the satisfaction of merely finite need.

The capacity of the strenuous mood lies so deep down among our natural human possibilities that even if there were no metaphysical or traditional grounds for believing in a God, men would postulate one simply as a pretext for living hard, and getting out of the game of existence its keenest possibilities of zest. Our attitude towards concrete evils is entirely different in a world where we believe there are none but finite demanders, from what it is in one where we joyously face tragedy for an infinite demander's sake. Every sort of energy and endurance, of courage and capacity of handling life's evils, is set free in those who have religious faith. For this reason the strenuous type of characters will on the battle-field of human history always outwear the easy-going type, and religion will drive irreligion to the wall.

It would seem, too—and this is my final conclusion—that the stable and systematic moral universe for which the ethical philosopher asks is fully possible only in a world where there is a divine thinker with all-enveloping demands. If such a thinker existed, his way of subordinating the demands to one another would be the finally valid casuistic scale; his claims would be the most appealing; his ideal universe would be the most inclusive realizable whole. If he now exist, then actualized in his thought already must be that ethical philosophy which we seek as the pattern which our own must evermore approach. In the interests of our own ideal of systematically unified moral truth, therefore, we, as would-be philosophers, must postulate a divine thinker, and pray for the victory of the religious cause. Meanwhile, exactly what the thought of the infinite thinker may be is hidden from us even were we sure of his existence; so that our postulation of him after all serves only to let loose in us the strenuous mood. But this is what it does in all men, even those who have no interest in philosophy. The ethical philosopher, therefore, whenever he ventures to say which course of action is the best, is on no essentially different level from the common man. "See, I have set before thee this day life and good, and death and evil; therefore, choose life that thou and thy seed may live"—when this challenge comes to us, it is simply our total character and personal genius that are on trial; and if we invoke any so-called philosophy, our choice and use of that also are but revelations of our personal aptitude or incapacity for moral life. From this unsparing practical ordeal no professor's lectures and no array of books can save us. The solving word, for the learned and the unlearned man alike, lies in the last resort in the dumb willingnesses and unwillingnesses of their interior characters, and nowhere else. It is not in heaven, neither is it beyond the sea; but the word is very nigh unto thee, in thy mouth and in thy heart, that thou mayest do it.

AN UNDERGROUND EPISODE
Edmund Ware

This story appeared in the magazine Story in the middle of the depression, the work of a young writer, Edmund Ware Smith.

Three figures leaned against the slanting rain—Alamo Laska, Nick Christopher, and the boy who had run away from home. They rested on their long-handled shovels and, as they gazed into the crater which by their brawn they had hollowed in the earth, the blue clay oozed back again, slowly devouring the fruits of their toil.

Laska, the nomad, thought of the wild geese winging southward to warm bayous. Nick's heart, under the bone and muscle of his great chest, swelled with sweet thoughts of his wife and child who lived in a foreign city across an ocean. The boy felt the sting of rain against his cheeks and dreamed of his mother who seemed lovely and far away.

It was Sunday. The regular deep-trench gang lounged in their warm boardinghouse and drank dago red, while out on the job the three men toiled alone. They breathed heavily, and the gray steam crawled upon their backs, for it was cold.

"Look at 'er filling in," growled Laska, "faster than a man could dig."

"Mud's get inna pipe," said Nick. "The Inspector make us tear him out if she fill any more."

Backed close to the edge of the crater stood a giant trench-digging machine. In the dusk it appeared as a crouched and shadowy animal—silent, gloomy, capable. But a broken piston had crippled its engines and they were swathed in tarpaulin.

A long gray mound stretched away from the crater opposite the machine. Buried thirty feet below the mound was the new-laid sewer pipe. From the bottom of the pit at the machine, the pipe ran a hundred yards horizontally under the surface, opening in a manhole. This hundred yards of new-laid pipe was the reason for the three men digging in the rain. They had dug eleven hours trying to uncover the open end of the pipe in order to seal it against the mud. But rain and ooze and storm had bested them. The bank had caved, and the mud had crawled into the mouth of the pipe, obstructing it.

"It's getting dark fast," said Laska, "an' we're licked."

"We can't do nothing more," said the boy.

Nick Christopher scraped the mud from his shovel. He looked up into the whirlpools of the sky. "In a year I go old country. I see my wife. I see my kid."

"Nick," said Laska, "go over to the shanty and get a couple of lanterns and telephone Stender. Tell him if he don't want the Inspector on our tail to get out here quick with a gang."

Nick stuck his shovel in the mud and moved away across the plain toward the shanty.

The cold had crept into the boy. It frightened him, and in the darkness his eyes sought Laska's face. "How could we clean out the pipe, even when the gang got down to it?"

"Maybe we could flush her out with a fire hose," said Laska.

"There's no water plug within a mile."

Laska said nothing. The boy waited for him to reply, but he didn't. Picking up his damp shirt, the boy pulled it on over his head. He did not tuck in the tails, and they flapped in the wind, slapping against him. He looked like a gaunt, serious bird, striving to leave the ground. He was bare-headed, and his yellow hair was matted and stringy with dampness. His face was thin, a little sunken, and fine drops of moisture clung to the fuzz on his cheeks. His lips were blue with cold. He was seventeen.

Laska stared into the pit. It was too dark to see bottom, but something in the black hole fascinated him. "If we could get a rope through the pipe we could drag sandbags through into the manhole. That would clean her out in good shape."

"How could we get a rope through?"

"I dunno. Stender'll know." Laska walked over to the digging machine and leaned against its towering side. The rain had turned to sleet. "It's cold," he said.

The boy followed Laska, and went close to him for warmth and friendship. "How *could* we get a rope through?"

Laska's shoulders lifted slowly. "You'll see. You'll see when Stender gets here. Say, it's freezing."

After a long time of waiting, a yellow light flamed into being in the shanty, and they heard the muffled scraping of boots on the board floor. The shanty door opened. A rectangle of light stood out sharply.

Swart figures crossed and re-crossed the lighted area, pouring out into the storm.

"Ho!" called Laska.

"Ho!" came the answer, galloping to them in the wind.

They heard the rasping of caked mud on dungarees, the clank of shovels, the voice of Stender, the foreman. Lanterns swung like yellow pendulums. Long-legged shadows reached and receded.

The diggers gathered about the rim of the pit, staring. Stender's face showed in the lantern light. His lips were wrinkled, as if constantly prepared for blasphemy. He was a tall, cursing conqueror. Orders shot from his throat, and noisily the men descended into the pit and began to dig. They drew huge, gasping breaths like mired beasts fighting for life.

The boy watched, his eyes bulging in the dark. Hitherto he had thought very briefly of sewers, regarding them as unlovely things. But Laska and Nick and Stender gave them splendor and importance. The deep-trench men were admirable monsters. They knew the clay, the feel and pattern of it, for it had long been heavy in their minds and muscles. They were big in three dimensions and their eyes were black and barbarous. When they ate it was with rough and tumble relish, and as their bellies fattened, they spoke tolerantly of enemies. They played lustily with a view to satiation. They worked stupendously. They were diggers in clay, transformed by lantern light into a race of giants.

Through the rain came Stender, his black slicker crackling. "They're down," he said. "Angelo just struck the pipe."

Laska grunted.

Stender blew his nose with his fingers, walked away and climbed down into the hole. They lost sight of him as he dropped over the rim. The sound of digging had ceased and two or three men on the surface rested on their shovels, the light from below gleaming in their flat faces. Laska and the boy knew that Stender was examining the pipe. They heard him swearing at what he had found.

After a moment he clambered up over the rim and held up a lantern. His cuddy, gripped firmly between his teeth, was upside down to keep out the wet.

"Someone's got to go through the pipe," he said, raising his voice. "There's fifty bucks for the man that'll go through the pipe into the manhole with a line tied to his foot. Fifty bucks!"

There was a moment of quiet. The men thought of the fifty dollars, and furtively measured themselves against the deed at hand. It seemed to the boy that he was the only one who feared the task. He did not think of the fifty dollars, but thought only of the fear. Three hundred feet through a rathole, eighteen inches in diameter. Three hundred feet of muck, of wet black dark, and no turning back. But, if he did not volunteer, they would know that he was afraid. The boy stepped from behind Laska and said uncertainly: "I'll go, Stender," and he wished he might snatch back the words; for, looking about him, he saw that not a man among those present could have wedged his shoulders into the mouth of an eighteen-inch pipe. He was the only volunteer. They had known he would be the only one.

Stender came striding over holding the lantern above his head. He peered into the boy's face. "Take off your clothes," he said.

"Take off my clothes?"

"That's what I said."

"You might get a buckle caught in a joint," said Laska. "See?"

The boy saw only that he had been trapped very cunningly. At home he could have been openly fearful, for at home everything about him was known. There, quite simply, he could have said: "I won't do it. I'm frightened. I'll be killed." But here the diggers in clay were lancing him with looks. And Laska was bringing a ball of line, one end of which would be fastened to his ankle.

"Just go in a sweater," said Laska. "A sweater an' boots over your woolens. We'll be waiting for you at the manhole."

He wanted so desperately to dive off into the night that he felt his legs bracing for a spring, and a tight feeling in his throat. Then, mechanically, he began to take off his clothes. Nick had gone clumping off to the shanty and shortly he returned with a pair of hip boots. "Here, kid. I get 'em warm for you inna shanty."

He thrust his feet into the boots, and Laska knelt and tied the heavy line to his ankle. "Too tight?"

"No. It's all right, I guess."

"Well—come on."

They walked past Stender who was pacing up and down among the men. They slid down into the crater, deepened now by the diggers. They stood by the partly covered mouth of the pipe. They were thirty feet below the surface of the ground.

Laska reached down and tugged at the knot he had tied in the line, then he peered into the mouth of the tube. He peered cautiously, as if he thought it might be inhabited. The boy's glance wandered up the wet sides of the pit. Over the rim a circle of bland yellow faces peered at him. Sleet tinkled against lanterns, spattered down and stung his flesh.

"Go ahead in," said Laska.

"Just keep thinking of the manhole, where you'll come out," said Laska.

The boy's throat constricted. He seemed to be bursting with a pressure from inside. He got down on his belly in the slush-ice and mud. It penetrated slowly to his skin and spread over him. He put his head inside the mouth of the pipe, drew back in horror. Some gibbering words flew from his lips. His voice sounded preposterously loud. Laska's voice was already shopworn with distance. "You can make it! Go ahead."

He lay on his left side, and, reaching out with his left arm, caught a joint and drew himself in. The mud oozed up around him, finding its way upon him, welling up against the left side of his face. He pressed his right cheek against the ceiling of the pipe to keep the muck from covering his mouth and nose. Laska's voice was far and muffled. Laska was in another world—a sane world of night, of storm, and the mellow glow of lanterns.

"Are you makin' it all right, kid?"

The boy cried out, his ears ringing with his cry. It re-echoed from the sides of the pipe. The sides hemmed him, pinned him, closed him in on every side with their paralyzing circumference.

There is no darkness like the darkness underground that miners know. It borrows something from night, from tombs, from places used by bats. Such fluid black can terrify a flame, and suffocate and drench a mind with madness. There is a fierce desire to struggle, to beat one's hands against the prison. The boy longed to lift his pitiful human strength against the walls. He longed to claw at his eyes in the mad certainty that more than darkness curtained them.

He had moved but a few feet on his journey when panic swept him. Ahead of him the mud had built into a stolid wave. Putting forth his left hand, he felt a scant two inches between the wave's crest and the ceiling of the pipe. There was nothing to do but go back. If he moved ahead, it meant death by suffocation. He tried to back away, but caught his toe in a joint of the pipe. He was entombed! In an hour he would be a body. The cold and dampness would kill him before they could dig down to him. Nick and Laska would pull him from the muck, and Laska would say: "Huh, his clock's stopped."

He thrashed with delirious strength against his prison. He felt the skin tearing from the backs of his hands as he flailed the rough walls. And some gods must have snickered, for above the walls of the pipe were thirty feet of unyielding clay, eight thousand miles of earth below. A strength, a weight, a night, each a thousand times his most revolting dream, leaned upon the boy, depressing, crushing, stamping him out. The ground gave no cry of battle. It did no bleeding, suffered no pain, uttered no groans. It flattened him silently. It swallowed him in its foul despotism. It dropped its merciless weight upon his mind. It was so inhuman, so horribly incognizant of the God men swore had made it.

In the midst of his frenzy, when he had beaten his face against the walls until it bled, he heard a ringing voice he knew was real, springing from human sympathy. It was Laska, calling: "Are you all right, kid?"

In that instant the boy loved Laska as he loved his life. Laska's voice sheered the weight from him, scattered the darkness, brought him new balance and a hope to live.

"Fine!" he answered in a cracking yell. He yelled again, loving the sound of his voice, and thinking how foolish yelling was in such a place.

With his left hand he groped ahead and found that the wave of mud had settled, levelled off by its own weight. He drew his body together, pressing it against the pipe. He straightened, moved ahead six inches. His fingers found a loop of oakum dangling from a joint, and he pulled himself on, his left arm forward, his right arm behind over his hip, like a swimmer's.

He had vanquished panic, and he looked ahead to victory. Each joint brought him twenty inches nearer his goal. Each twenty inches was a plateau which enabled him to vision a new plateau— the next joint. The joints were like small deceitful rests upon a march.

He had been more than an hour on the way. He did not know how far he had gone, a third, perhaps even a half of the distance. He forgot the present, forgot fear, wet, cold, blackness; he lost himself in dreaming of the world of men outside the prison. It was as if he were a small superb island in hell.

He did not know how long he had been counting the joints, but he found himself whispering good numbers: "Fifty-one, fifty-two, fifty-three . . ." Each joint, when he thought of it, appeared to take up a vast time of squirming in the muck, and the line dragged heavily behind his foot.

Suddenly, staring into the darkness so that it seemed to bring a pain to his eyes, he saw a pallid ray. He closed his eyes, opened them, and looked again. The ray was real, and he uttered a whimper of relief. He knew that the ray must come from Stender's lantern. He pictured Stender and a group of the diggers huddled in the manhole, waiting for him. The men and the manhole grew magnificent in his mind, and he thought of them worshipfully.

"Seventy-six, seventy-seven, seventy-eight . . ."

The ray grew slowly, like a worthwhile thing. It took an oval shape, and the oval grew fat, like an egg, then round. It was a straight line to the manhole, and the mud had thinned.

Through the pipe, into the boy's ears, a voice rumbled like half-hearted thunder. It was Stender's voice: "How you makin' it?"

"Oh, just fine!" His cry came pricking back into his ears like a shower of needles.

There followed a long span of numbness. The cold and wet had dulled his senses, so that whenever the rough ceiling of the pipe ripped his face, he did not feel it; so that struggling in the muck became an almost pleasant and normal thing, since all elements of fear and pain and imagination had been removed. Warmth and dryness became alien to him. He was a creature native to darkness, foreign to light.

The round yellow disc before him gave him his only sense of living. It was a sunlit landfall, luring him on. He would close his eyes and count five joints, then open them quickly, cheering himself at the perceptible stages of progress.

Then, abruptly, it seemed, he was close to the manhole. He could hear men moving. He could see the outline of Stender's head as Stender peered into the mouth of the pipe. Men kneeled, pushing each other's heads to one side, in order to watch him squirm toward them. They began to talk excitedly. He could hear them breathing, see details—and Stender and Laska reached in. They got their hands upon him. They hauled him to them, as if he were something they wanted to inspect scientifically. He felt as if they thought he was a rarity, a thing of great oddness. The light dazzled him. It began to move around and around, and to dissolve into many lights, some of which danced locally on a bottle. He heard Stender's voice: "Well, he made it all right. What do you know?"

"Here, kid," said Laska, holding the bottle to his mouth. "Drink all of this that you can hold."

He could not stand up. He believed calmly that his flesh and bones were constructed of putty. He could hear no vestige of the song of victory he had dreamed of hearing. He looked stupidly at his hands, which bled painlessly. He could not feel his arms and legs at all. He was a vast sensation of lantern light and the steam of human beings breathing in a damp place.

Faces peered at him. The faces were curious, and surprised. He felt a clouded, uncomprehending resentment against them. Stender held him up on one side, Laska on the other. They looked at each other across him. Suddenly Laska stooped and gathered him effortlessly into his arms.

"You'll get covered with mud," mumbled the boy.

"Damn if he didn't make it all right," said Stender. "Save us tearing out the pipe."

"Hell with the pipe," said Laska.

The boy's wet head fell against Laska's chest. He felt the rise and fall of Laska's muscles, and knew that Laska was climbing with him up the iron steps inside the manhole. Night wind smote him. He buried his head deeper against Laska. Laska's body became a mountain of warmth. He felt a heavy sighing peace, like a soldier who has been comfortably wounded and knows that war for him is over.

THE FIFTY-FIRST DRAGON

Heywood Broun

A crusader against oppression and injustice, a humorist, newspaper columnist, founder of the American Newspaper Guild, husband for many years of a feminist who founded the Lucy Stone League, and (at the end of his life) married to a stage dancer and singer of Spanish descent, Heywood Broun has been likened (by his friend the late Christopher Morley) to "a kind of mediaeval figure, a strolling friar." A man of large physical frame, "like an amiable bear," he was much in public life during the period he wrote for the old World and the Nation, and lectured on drama at Columbia University and the Rand School in New York. He joined the Socialist party and once ran on that party's ticket for Congress. Reared an Episcopalian and for many years a free thinker, he was received into the Roman Catholic Church a few months before he died, December 18, 1939, in Stamford, Conn., of pneumonia shortly after his 55th birthday.

Of all the pupils at the Knight School, Gawaine le Coeur-Hardy was among the least promising. He was tall and sturdy, but his instructors soon discovered that he lacked spirit. He would hide in the woods when the jousting class was called, although his companions and members of the faculty sought to appeal to his better nature by shouting to him to come out and break his neck like a man. Even when they told him that the lances were padded, the horses no more than ponies and the field unusually soft for late autumn, Gawaine refused to grow enthusiastic. The Headmaster and the Assistant Professor of Pleasaunce were discussing the case one spring afternoon and the Assistant Professor could see no remedy but expulsion.

"No," said the Headmaster, as he looked out at the purple hills which ringed the school, "I think I'll train him to slay dragons."

"He might be killed," objected the Assistant Professor.

"So he might," replied the Headmaster brightly, but he added, more soberly, "We must consider the greater good. We are responsible for the formation of this lad's character."

"Are the dragons particularly bad this year?" interrupted the Assistant Professor. This was characteristic. He always seemed restive when the head of the school began to talk ethics and the ideals of the institution.

"I've never known them worse," replied the Headmaster. "Up in the hills to the south last week they killed a number of peasants, two cows and a prize pig. And if this dry spell holds there's no telling when they may start a forest fire simply by breathing around indiscriminately."

"Would any refund on the tuition fee be necessary in case of an accident to young Coeur-Hardy?"

"No," the principal answered, judicially, "that's all covered in the contract. But as a matter of fact he won't be killed. Before I send him up in the hills I'm going to give him a magic word."

"That's a good idea," said the Professor. "Sometimes they work wonders."

From that day on Gawaine specialized in dragons. His course included both theory and practice. In the morning there were long lectures on the history, anatomy, manners, and customs of dragons. Gawaine did not distinguish himself in these studies. He had a marvelously versatile gift for forgetting things. In the afternoon he showed to better advantage, for then he would go down to the South Meadow and practice with a battle-ax. In this exercise he was truly impressive, for he had enormous strength as well as speed and grace. He even developed a deceptive display of ferocity. Old alumni say that it was a thrilling sight to see Gawaine charging across the field toward the dummy paper dragon which had been set up for his practice. As he ran he would brandish his ax and shout "A murrain on thee!" or some other vivid bit of campus slang. It never took him more than one stroke to behead the dummy dragon.

Gradually his task was made more difficult. Paper gave way to *papier-mâché* and finally to wood, but even the toughest of these dummy dragons had no terrors for Gawaine. One sweep of the ax always did the business. There were those who said that when the practice was protracted until dusk and the dragons threw long, fantastic shadows across the meadow Gawaine did not charge so impetuously nor shout so loudly. It is possible there was malice in this charge. At any rate, the Headmaster decided by the end of June that it was time for the test. Only the night before a dragon had come close to the school grounds and had eaten some of the lettuce from the garden. The faculty decided that Gawaine was ready. They gave him a diploma and a new battle-ax and the Headmaster summoned him to a private conference.

"Sit down," said the Headmaster. "Have a cigarette."

Gawaine hesitated.

"Oh, I know it's against the rules," said the Headmaster. "But after all, you have received your preliminary degree. You are no longer a boy. You are a man. Tomorrow you will go out into the world, the great world of achievement."

Gawaine took a cigarette. The Headmaster offered him a match, but he produced one of his own and began to puff away with a dexterity which quite amazed the principal.

"Here you have learned the theories of life," continued the Headmaster, resuming the thread of his discourse, "but after all, life is not a matter of theories. Life is a matter of facts. It calls on the young and the old alike to face these facts, even though they are hard and sometimes unpleasant. Your problem, for example, is to slay dragons."

"They say that those dragons down in the south wood are five hundred feet long," ventured Gawaine, timorously.

"Stuff and nonsense!" said the Headmaster. "The curate saw one last week from the top of Arthur's Hill. The dragon was sunning himself down in the valley. The curate didn't have an opportunity to look at him very long because he felt it was his duty to hurry back to make a report to me. He said the monster, or shall I say, the big lizard?—wasn't an inch over two hundred feet. But the size has nothing at all to do with it. You'll find the big ones even easier than the little ones. They're far slower on their feet and less aggressive, I'm told. Besides, before you go I'm going to equip you in such fashion that you need have no fear of all the dragons in the world."

"I'd like an enchanted cap," said Gawaine.

"What's that?" answered the Headmaster, testily.

"A cap to make me disappear," explained Gawaine.

The Headmaster laughed indulgently. "You mustn't believe all those old wives' stories," he said. "There isn't any such thing. A cap to make you disappear, indeed! What would you do with it? You haven't even appeared yet. Why, my boy, you could walk from here to London, and nobody would so much as look at you. You're nobody. You couldn't be more invisible than that."

Gawaine seemed dangerously close to a relapse into his old habit of whimpering. The Headmaster reassured him: "Don't worry; I'll give you something much better than an enchanted cap. I'm going to give you a magic word. All you have to do is to repeat this magic charm once and no dragon can possibly harm a hair of your head. You can cut off his head at your leisure."

He took a heavy book from the shelf behind his desk and began to run through it. "Sometimes," he said, "the charm is a whole phrase or even a sentence. I might, for instance, give you 'To make the'—No, that might not do. I think a single word would be best for dragons."

"A short word," suggested Gawaine.

"It can't be too short or it wouldn't be potent. There isn't so much hurry as all that. Here's a splendid magic word: 'Rumplesnitz.' Do you think you can learn that?"

Gawaine tried and in an hour or so he seemed to have the word well in hand. Again and again he interrupted the lesson to inquire, "And if I say 'Rumplesnitz' the dragon can't possibly hurt me?" And always the Headmaster replied, "If you only say 'Rumplesnitz,' you are perfectly safe."

Toward morning Gawaine seemed resigned to his career. At day-break the Headmaster saw him to the edge of the forest and pointed him to the direction in which he should proceed. About a mile away to the southwest a cloud of steam hovered over an open meadow in the woods and the Headmaster assured Gawaine that under the steam he would find a dragon. Gawaine went forward slowly. He wondered whether it would be best to approach the dragon on the run as he did in his practice in the South Meadow or to walk slowly toward him, shouting "Rumplesnitz" all the way.

The problem was decided for him. No sooner had he come to the fringe of the meadow than the dragon spied him and began to charge. It was a large dragon and yet it seemed decidedly aggressive in spite of the Headmaster's statement to the contrary. As the dragon charged it released huge clouds of hissing steam through its nostrils. It was almost as if a gigantic teapot had gone mad. The dragon came forward so fast and Gawaine was so frightened that he had time to say "Rumplesnitz" only once. As he said it, he swung his battle-ax and off popped the head of the dragon. Gawaine had to admit that it was even easier to kill a real dragon than a wooden one if only you said, "Rumplesnitz."

Gawaine brought the ears home and a small section of the tail. His schoolmates and the faculty made much of him, but the Head-master wisely kept him from being spoiled by insisting that he go on with his work. Every clear day Gawaine rose at dawn and went out to kill dragons. The Headmaster kept him at home when it rained, because he said the woods were damp and unhealthy at such times and that he didn't want the boy to run needless risks. Few good days passed in which Gawaine failed to get a dragon. On one particularly fortunate day he killed three, a husband and wife and a visiting relative. Gradually he developed a technique. Pupils who sometimes watched him from the hilltops a long way off said that he often allowed the dragon to come within a few feet before he said *"Rumplesnitz."* He came to say it with a mocking sneer. Occasionally he did stunts. Once when an excursion party from London was watching him he went into action with his right hand tied behind his back. The dragon's head came off just as easily.

As Gawaine's record of killings mounted higher the Headmaster found it impossible to keep him completely in hand. He fell into the habit of stealing out at night and engaging in long drinking bouts at the village tavern. It was after such a debauch that he rose a little before dawn one fine August morning and started out after his fiftieth dragon. His head was heavy and his mind sluggish. He was heavy in other respects as well, for he had adopted the somewhat vulgar practice of wearing his medals, ribbons, and all, when he went out dragon hunting. The decorations began on his chest and ran all the way down to his abdomen. They must have weighed at least eight pounds.

Gawaine found a dragon in the same meadow where he had killed the first one. It was a fair-sized dragon, but evidently an old one. Its face was wrinkled and Gawaine thought he had never seen so hideous a countenance. Much to the lad's disgust, the monster refused to charge and Gawaine was obliged to walk toward him. He whistled as he went. The dragon regarded him hopelessly but craftily. Of course it had heard of Gawaine. Even when the lad raised his battle-ax the dragon made no move. It knew that there was no salvation in the quickest thrust of the head, for it had been informed that this hunter was protected by an enchantment. It merely waited, hoping something would turn up. Gawaine raised the battle-ax and suddenly lowered it again. He had grown very pale and he trembled violently. The dragon suspected a trick. "What's the matter?" it asked, with false solicitude.

"I've forgotten the magic word," stammered Gawaine.

"What a pity," said the dragon. "So that was the secret. It doesn't seem quite sporting to me, all this magic stuff, you know. Not cricket, as we used to say when I was a little dragon; but after all, that's a matter of opinion."

Gawaine was so helpless with terror that the dragon's confidence rose immeasurably and it could not resist the temptation to show off a bit.

"Could I possibly be of any assistance?" it asked. "What's the first letter of the magic word?"

"It begins with an 'R,' " said Gawaine weakly.

"Let's see," mused the dragon, "that doesn't tell us much, does it? What sort of a word is this? Is it an epithet, do you think?"

Gawaine could do no more than nod.

"Why, of course," exclaimed the dragon, "reactionary Republican."

Gawaine shook his head.

"Well, then," said the dragon, "we'd better get down to business. Will you surrender?"

With the suggestion of a compromise Gawaine mustered up enough courage to speak.

"What will you do if I surrender?" he asked.

"Why, I'll eat you," said the dragon.

"And if I don't surrender?"

"I'll eat you just the same."

"Then it doesn't make any difference, does it?" moaned Gawaine.

"It does to me," said the dragon with a smile. "I'd rather you didn't surrender. You'd taste much better if you didn't."

The dragon waited for a long time for Gawaine to ask, "Why?" but the boy was too frightened to speak. At last the dragon had to give the explanation without his cue line. "You see," he said, "if you don't surrender you'll taste better because you'll die game."

This was an old and ancient trick of the dragon's. By means of some such quip he was accustomed to paralyze his victims with laughter and then to destroy them. Gawaine was sufficiently paralyzed as it was, but laughter had no part in his helplessness. With the last word of the joke the dragon drew back his head and struck. In that second there flashed into the mind of Gawaine the magic word "*Rumplesnitz*," but there was no time to say it. There was time only to strike and, without a word, Gawaine met the onrush of the dragon with a full swing. He put all his back and shoulders into it. The impact was terrific and the head of the dragon flew away almost a hundred yards and landed in a thicket.

Gawaine did not remain frightened very long after the death of the dragon. His mood was one of wonder. He was enormously puzzled. He cut off the ears of the monster almost in a trance. Again and again he thought to himself, "I didn't say 'Rumplesnitz'!" He was sure of that and yet there was no question that he had killed the dragon. In fact, he had never killed one so utterly. Never before had he driven a head for anything like the same distance. Twenty-five yards was perhaps his best previous record. All the way back to the Knight School he kept rumbling about in his mind seeking an explanation for what had occurred. He went to the Headmaster immediately and after closing the door told him what had happened. "I didn't say 'Rumplesnitz,'" he explained with great earnestness.

The Headmaster laughed. "I'm glad you've found out," he said. "It makes you ever so much more of a hero. Don't you see that? Now you know that it was you who killed all these dragons and not that foolish little word 'Rumplesnitz.'"

Gawaine frowned. "Then it wasn't a magic word after all?" he asked.

"Of course not," said the Headmaster, "you ought to be too old for such foolishness. There isn't any such thing as a magic word."

"But you told me it was magic," protested Gawaine. "You said it was magic and now you say it isn't."

"It wasn't magic in a literal sense," answered the Headmaster, "but it was much more wonderful than that. The word gave you confidence. It took away your fears. If I hadn't told you that you might have been killed the very first time. It was your battle-ax did the trick."

Gawaine surprised the Headmaster by his attitude. He was obviously distressed by the explanation. He interrupted a long philosophic and ethical discourse by the Headmaster with, "If I hadn't of hit 'em all mighty hard and fast any one of 'em might have crushed me like a, like a—" He fumbled for a word.

"Eggshell," suggested the Headmaster.

"Like a eggshell," assented Gawaine, and he said it many times. All through the evening meal people who sat near him heard him muttering, "Like a eggshell, like a eggshell."

The next day was clear, but Gawaine did not get up at dawn. Indeed, it was almost noon when the Headmaster found him cowering in bed, with the clothes pulled over his head. The principal called the Assistant Professor of Pleasaunce, and together they dragged the boy toward the forest.

"He'll be all right as soon as he gets a couple more dragons under his belt," explained the Headmaster.

The Assistant Professor of Pleasaunce agreed. "It would be a shame to stop such a fine run," he said. "Why, counting that one yesterday, he's killed fifty dragons."

They pushed the boy into a thicket above which hung a meager cloud of steam. It was obviously quite a small dragon. But Gawaine did not come back that night or the next. In fact, he never came back. Some weeks afterward brave spirits from the school explored the thicket, but they could find nothing to remind them of Gawaine except the metal parts of his medals. Even the ribbons had been devoured.

The Headmaster and the Assistant Professor of Pleasaunce agreed that it would be just as well not to tell the school how Gawaine had achieved his record and still less how he came to die. They held that it might have a bad effect on school spirit. Accordingly, Gawaine has lived in the memory of the school as its greatest hero. No visitor succeeds in leaving the building today without seeing a great shield which hangs on the wall of the dining hall. Fifty pairs of dragons' ears are mounted upon the shield and underneath in gilt letters is "Gawaine le Coeur-Hardy," followed by the simple inscription, "He killed fifty dragons." The record has never been equaled.

RAFT OF DESPAIR

Ensio Tiira

Adrift, alone, in the middle of the Indian Ocean, on a four-foot-square metal and canvas raft, his once hardy Foreign Legionnaire's body reduced by suffering and starvation to a scant fifty pounds, his companion dead and the man's body finally jettisoned and consumed by the sharks which still hung about the raft slashing at its sides, Ensio Tiira recounts here the events on the thirty-first and thirty-second days of an almost incredible ordeal at sea.

Weeks earlier, while the transport Skaubryn was outward bound from Algeria to Indo-China with troops of the French Foreign Legion, Tiira and his Swedish friend Ericsson slipped overboard at 3 o'clock in the morning of February 23, 1953, as the troopship entered the Straits of Malacca, their intention being to escape further hardships in the Legion with which both, as volunteers, had become thoroughly disillusioned.

Since the ship would be passing within a few miles of Sumatra, they planned the escape for that hour, believing that a few hours paddling would take them across a calm sea to freedom. Unable, however, to reach shore, their tiny craft was carried out into the Indian Ocean, and what followed was starvation, delirium, battles with sharks and the death of Ericsson (on the seventeenth day), and whether, in spite of his will to live, Tiira would long survive, as occasional ships failed to sight him, seemed hardly likely.

If I have ever been certain of anything in my life it was that on March 25, 1953, my thirty-first day at sea, I was about to die. Sometimes I thought that I had died. The thread between life and death had now become so slender, the transition from one state to another almost a matter of degree.

I lay on my stomach in the sun, waiting for death, expecting it at any moment. The pain had gone from my body, or, if it hadn't gone, it was all one pain and I couldn't tell where it was that I hurt.

The day began well with rain early in the morning. It started to fall before daybreak and went on for more than an hour, heavy and drenching, forcing me into action. Not knowing why I did it I worked my way painfully into a half-lying, half-sitting position on one of the lifejackets. I fumbled to bring out the plastic bag and the water-bottle. I cradled the bag on my stomach, making a sort of funnel with it that led down into the bottle.

Sometimes I slept while I was gathering the water and sometimes the bottle fell over and all I had collected spilled out over my legs and went down into the raft. But somehow I got half a bottle. My fingers were so weak I couldn't put the stopper back in the bottle. They shook and couldn't find the opening. I took it quietly and rested and tried again, holding the top of the bag between my knees and using both hands until I got the stopper in the hole and turned it tight.

When I had finished I wondered why I bothered. I was utterly without hope. I had no will to do these things that helped to keep me alive a little longer. I didn't want to live. I remembered the prayers I had said for Ericsson when he went out of the raft to the sharks and now I wanted to say them for myself. I couldn't speak them but my lips moved and formed the shape of the words:

> "The Lord bless thee and keep thee,
> The Lord make His face to shine upon thee . . ."

These were my better moments. During one I thought I should try to scratch the names on the side of the raft. But there was no power left in my arms and legs, nor any in my heart, that could move me to this labor. Though I was often unconscious I moved constantly in the raft, turning from side to side, rolling and struggling. When I came to my senses for a few fleeting minutes I would see that I had moved again, sometimes perilously towards the edge. Lapsing into unconsciousness, I felt drawn all the time from the raft, and once more awoke to find my feet in the water.

In a moment of terrifying reality I saw more sharks than I had seen all the time on the raft. A long procession of them came past the raft. Again I thought they were porpoises until they came close and I saw them for what they were, a parade, a very convocation of the brutes. Coming for me. It didn't matter. Nothing mattered.

The sharks went on their way and the skeleton on the raft drifted back into delirium. During the dreadful heat of this thirty-first day I don't remember having any water. I am sure I didn't. In the evening when a cool breeze brought me back to life I found the bottle still rolled in the lifejacket. The stopper was in hard and I would never have had the strength to unfasten it and close it up again. I took a little water now but it had no effect on my throat if it ever got that far. I felt my lips wet with the water and took a long time getting the stopper back into the bottle. There was little relief in the water now.

I'd lost all sense of a second person being in the raft. The guardian angel who kept me company after Ericsson's death left the raft with my own loss of hope.

Though the cool of the evening brought a little strength back to me I still could not sit up. I fixed my bed for the night, pushing the paddles together with the lifejackets over them. The torch batteries had expired at last and I smiled with a foolish pride that I'd lasted the longer.

The night was a repetition of the day, some real sleep and a good deal of delirium. I believed I was dead and that I had been rescued and that I was having a great dinner. Again I was leaving the raft and awoke to find myself draped half over the edge.

The thirty-second day blends into the thirty-first. I don't know where one ended and the other began. I have no recollection of the sunrise or anything that happened until the morning was well advanced. There was nothing by which I could measure the passing of time.

Life returned and the day began when despair changed into hope and I came slowly out of the gloom into reality. The change was spiritual, but the body responded. My nerves produced a final effort, my muscles worked and my mind coordinated. It was about mid-afternoon, very hot, no wind. A fair swell sluggishly moved the raft on the sea. I lay on my right side, completely conscious now, staring out across the water with only half-seeing eyes, when I saw a ship. It was a tanker going west, about three miles off. I forced myself on to my elbows and took the shirt lying by my side and waved. The paddle was beyond my capacity. I couldn't lift it. But I must get higher. Up on the lifejackets and they would be able to see me better. I pushed one paddle against the side of the raft and inched forward until I was sitting on it. I waved more successfully now, but there was little strength in my back and repeatedly my head fell forward and my back slumped after it. To straighten my back and get my head up took another great effort, but I managed it and waved until the ship had gone down and there was nothing left to wave to.

Before despair could settle in me I saw another ship, another tanker of about 8000 tons. This one was going east and was not more than a mile away. It was on the far side of the raft and to signal to it I had to turn about. I found my body heavier than the shirt. Much heavier. First I got one leg around, then the other, and with it my body. I seemed to have no backbone and several times I fell forward and had to heave up with all my strength, pulling on the ropes for additional support.

The ship came very close. Though my eyes were weak and I couldn't focus properly, the seconds of proper vision were rewarding. There were people on deck and I waited for someone to see me, for the ship to signal and turn towards me. But like the many others that had gone before it, this one also sailed on its way. I was too weak to wave for more than a few seconds at a time. My arm wouldn't stay upright and the longer I sat up the more tired and uncontrollable my back became.

This second ship had not disappeared, however, before another came on the scene. This, like the second, was going east, though farther off. Two, perhaps three, miles. I had no hope of attracting attention aboard this ship. If I'd missed out on the ship that came so close to me it was unlikely that I could hope to make myself seen aboard one three times the distance off.

But I wasn't disappointed. Three ships in an hour. How could I be disappointed? The ships had been on both sides of me and I felt that I was back in the sea lane. If there were three ships, there would be more.

Now I wanted to live. If I could last another day I still had a chance. I was determined to stay alive. I willed myself to live. For two days I'd expected death, welcomed death. A lot of the time I was more dead than alive. I was dying and I wanted to die.

Everything had changed now. Another day, if only I could live just one more day. I hadn't touched the water-bottle all day but now the exertion and the hope filled me with thirst and I got the bottle from the lifejacket. I held the water in my mouth and tried to swallow it, but my throat was bound up. The muscles had ceased to work. I got a little water down and I thought of babies and how they had to learn to drink and to swallow. When I got away—if I got away—I would have to learn all over again.

In the twilight of the thirty-second day, a fourth ship appeared. It was on the far horizon as the sun went down and by the time it came opposite the raft my shirt-waving was a pitiful, hopeless effort. But I waved, nevertheless. With the dark the ships would not see me and this one was my last hope. The swell which had been running in the morning was still fairly heavy and I rested when the raft was in the deep with my head and shoulders bent forward. But when the raft came briefly to the top of the swell I forced myself upright again, as high as I could, and waved and waved.

The ship was close. Perhaps just over a mile away. It was too dark already and I cursed that the torch had given out. This was flashlight time and I had no means of signalling. One S O S, I was convinced, would have brought a boat to my side.

I flicked the torch again with fumbling fingers but there was no life in it. In the exasperation of despair I hit it against the side of the raft. No glimmer of light came. But the lights of the ship went on to the east.

Now there was no point in looking for ships. If I saw them they wouldn't see me. I had no hope of attracting their attention. Just at the time when I needed to use every minute of every hour left to me in this world I had half of my day and all my chances snatched away from me.

I pulled at the lifejackets and paddles to make myself a bed. I was frightened to lose control of my much-improved senses. I was living on my spirit, and sleep, I was afraid, might lead me to death. I desperately wanted to live. I wanted to wake up alive the next morning more than I have ever wanted anything in my life before. "I must stay alive, I must stay alive," I repeated over and over to myself. And to stay alive I had also to stay awake.

I didn't wrap my head in the shirt this night because I didn't want to do anything that would help me to sleep. If water splashed over the raft and woke me by falling on my head, well and good. If the moon was too bright in my eyes, so much the better. I dreaded the early hours of the morning most. Those were the hours when the night was darkest and the spirit lowest. I wanted to get through the crisis hours. I was on the sea lane and when the sun came up there would be ships. I had to stay awake until sunrise if I wanted to live for another day.

The moon was very bright. The evening of our escape had been a night like this. The brightness might help to keep me awake. I looked at the stars and for mental exercise tried to place the planets. I wanted to keep my mind active and this was the only way. But the more I looked the more difficult it was to keep my eyes open. The stars twinkled and merged and disappeared. I fought against the darkness when my eyes closed. I forced them open by will-power and saw the stars again. But my eyes could not stay open and, hating myself for my weakness and afraid that I wouldn't live to see the sunrise, I fell asleep.

Sleep . . . and now the great noise of a ship going fast

through the water came to me. It cut into my troubled dreams and registered in my subconscious mind. My body didn't react even when I awoke. The night was full of sound. Suddenly all the importance of the noise hit me.

I moved as I hadn't moved in days. Not twenty yards from me, going east, was the bow of a ship. A light. If only I had a light I could make myself seen. I tried to shout but it was a tiny sound, no voice to carry even the few yards across the water to the ship. What I shouted was, "Hello, ship," in English. But no one could have heard me.

I saw some men on deck, but whether they were looking at me or far out across the sea I couldn't say. I took the white shirt and waved it, but who would see a shirt even on a moonlit night like this?

The black sides of the ship slid along beside me; high above my head were lights and the sound of shouting voices. It was right on top of me. Instead of saving me the ship was going to run me down. I cursed myself for sleeping. I screamed a great shout to tell them and no sound came out. Even to me my shout was sound-less. How could I expect the ship to hear?

It missed me and I grabbed for a paddle, slipping and clawing over the ropes until I reached it. It couldn't go without seeing me. With my two hands I lifted the paddle and banged with all my might on the floats, mouthing shouts at the ship. As I brought the paddle down I heard the ringing sound on the metal. The ship had to hear it, too.

I banged again and again and, exhausted, went down with my head in my shaking hands. As I sat there I heard a man's voice, very loud. There was no form in his words, just the sound of a human voice. The most wonderful sound in the world. At once I heard a bell, the engine-room bell, and I took the paddle again and brought it banging down on the floats. My shouting voice was silent but the noise of the paddle on the floats was loud and I was sure it would be heard on the ship.

The ship went away. I willed it to return and it got farther and farther away. I've never felt so futile. I had no light to flash. No voice to call. My mouth made the right movements but no sound reached me. "Please, please, come back," to the ship. Lying on the ropes, I watched it leave me. There was no more I could do.

At least on the ship they had thought there was something on the water. Out from its deck came a light which fell on the sea about a hundred yards from my raft. It lit up a great patch of water and the light went in and out, in and out.

But the ship went slowly back into the darkness. I couldn't get it back. If only I had the torch—just the flicker of a light and it wouldn't go away. Someone had been curious but his curiosity had died. I would die, too. There'd been no answer to the voice and no answer to their light. I had no voice and no light. But surely someone would have heard the noise as I banged on the floats.

I sat, not daring to hope, and was surprised a long time later to see the lights coming nearer again. There was no mistaking it. This time the ship came in a large circle and I knew it looked for me. I didn't try to shout. I waited for the right moment when I could start banging again.

When the lights were very close I lifted the paddle and let it fall on the metal sides of the raft to guide them to me. And suddenly it was all right. They found me. A great beam of light came straight on my face and I sank down on my knees to save my eyes from the glare, and knew it was all over.

The good light stayed on me and suddenly I was ashamed of my appearance, tattered and torn, straw-like hair sticking up all over my head, bristling, matted beard, a barefooted derelict.

But I still wasn't prepared for the voice that came from the ship as someone saw me, caught in the beam of light.

"It's a Russian," I thought I heard the voice say.

Perhaps it was the color of my hair or perhaps the wildness of my appearance that made me look like a Russian. Maybe it wasn't "Russian," but that's how it sounded to me. My lips formed the words: "I'm not a Russian," and nothing came out. It didn't matter.

For five minutes the light was on me and then the ship turned again. She was too far away to pick me up. But I knew she wouldn't leave me now. This ship was going to save me.

As it turned and the beam left my face I looked up again and saw the ship and the lights and movement along the decks. The whole ship was alive. Lights from cigarettes were all along the rails and the sound of men's voices—a pleasant sound to a man who hadn't heard another voice for so long. Not even his own.

I felt sure they would throw me a rope now and waited anxiously, trying to catch the words that came to me over the sea. I wished they didn't have to go away. I didn't want to be alone again. If they lost me this time they would give up. They couldn't be expected to search all night.

Out into the dark the ship went again. It made another great circle and a flare went out on the water a long way from me. The ship went away and with it the lights. I was exhausted and wanted to lie down and to sleep, to be away from the anxiety and doubts.

They were trying hard and there must be something I could do to help. I was so helpless, so useless. They might lose me even now if I fell asleep. And I wanted to sleep so badly. If I slept they would never find me. Keep my eyes open. My eyes were all I had. I had no voice to call, no light to shine. What else? I racked my slow mind and saw the shirt and tied it to a paddle. It was the biggest effort of my life. I'd achieved something miraculous. I'd saved my own life. So long as I could keep the shirt upright on the paddle I would live.

Hold it up. Hold it up straight. Don't let the paddle wobble. But the paddle was a drunken man, falling to the raft and wavering all the time in my unsteady hands. Still, it was most important to keep the paddle in the air. Even as my eyes dropped, when I had to lie right down, I forced myself to keep the paddle up. I fell into sleep or unconsciousness and woke to find the paddle beside me, its tattered white shirt lifeless on the ropes. Angry, I stuck it into the ropes and it stood quite well and easily without my help. Trying to hold on I fainted and fell into darkness. I stopped existing and left it to the ship and to the paddle, standing crookedly in its place, to save me.

I couldn't have been out for long. Now there were two ships, one close by with lots of lights, the other away over the water. My paddle still stood, but the shirt had fallen down and I let it stay there.

My boots. I must get my boots on; this was important. I put them on as the ship came closer. My feet were so thin and the boots felt enormous. Struggling with the laces, being very clever about tying them to keep them on my wasted ankles.

There was a lot to do and I did nothing well. My feet were falling out of the boots. I felt for the paddle and put the shirt back on it. I was full of a great effort, a frenzy of painfully slow activity. I'd fallen down on what I should have done. I must hang on hard to consciousness. Try to do something, try to keep alive until they get me. I clutched with my hands and legs to the paddle with its shirt waving and let it drop again and took up the paddle and rowed, or tried to row, into the light that couldn't find me.

I did things in spasms. In the middle of something I would go out and find myself lying on my back, my feet in the water. I picked up the paddle again, lifted my body from the ropes and banged and the ship came very slowly, its bow pointed straight at the raft. There were many voices, so many men against the rails.

A rope came down over the raft, over my body and I caught it in the air as the end fell into the water. I was happy to be doing things well. I nearly forgot the plastic bag and the bottle. My precious bottle. I needed the bottle. There was still some water in it. I put the bottle with the bag against my stomach and put the rope around them, around my waist. I knew it would hold.

They would want a signal. I lifted my hands and made a circle in the air and people shouted while the ship slid by, all its long side. Then the stern came nearer. And now I was in the air. The raft fell behind me and I was in the water up to my waist. The thought of sharks came to me then, only once, and I didn't care any more.

It was as well for my peace of mind in this moment of rescue that I didn't see what the officers and men waiting above could see. For the water was boiling with sharks and the rope that pulled me high and free against the steel hull of the ship moved only just in time. As I swung out of the water the men above saw the upheaval of an attack that came too late, the white belly and the fin of the shark that had missed its prey.

I knew nothing now until hands had me by the shoulders. There were faces all around me. Indian faces and white faces and the faces were tender and kind. Hands put me on a blanket and hands gave me water.

"Thank you," said my mouth, and they took away the water. Only a mouthful.

"More, please, oh, please."

They cut away my clothes and my flesh came, too, in long strange pieces. Tenderly the hands stripped my shirt and wrapped me in a blanket.

Lying on my back I looked up and saw an officer, standing high on another deck. He was looking at his watch. They told me later it was twenty-past three in the morning of March 27, thirty-two days almost to the minute since Fred Ericsson and I jumped off the *Skaubryn* and into the sea.

MAN IN A SKYROCKET

William Bridgeman and Jacqueline Hazard

William Bridgeman, an ex-Navy pilot who, after nine thousand flying hours fighting Japanese in the Central Pacific and later ferrying planes across the ocean to others, was entrusted after the second World War with breaking-in the experimental Skyrocket, a swept-wing turbojet and rocket-engine plane built by Douglas for the Navy in cooperation with the National Advisory Commission for Aeronautics.

Costing $12,000,000 and engaging the best efforts of one hundred and fifty designers, engineers and draftsmen for three years before it reached its first flight in 1949, the Skyrocket attained speeds necessitating long conditioning in pressure clothing and learning how to breathe at heights and speeds never hitherto attempted by man. On one test trip the windshield frosted over and Bridgeman nearly lost his life; on others the buffeting the plane took as it approached and passed the sound barrier proved experiences unlike anything in traditional aeronautics.

The flier's notes (in The Lonely Sky) here give his experiences on two final record-setting flights, one in which an attempt was made to push the Mach speed number up to Mach 2, or twice the speed of sound, and the last flight to reach an altitude higher than the plane had ever previously attained.

Along the road the Joshua trees, angular-trunked with branch-arms held up like the warnings of scarecrows in a field, stood in irregular lines back into the gray sand. The irritation I had first felt when Carder singled me out to fly the new program was gone. In its place was a feeling of pride that I should be entrusted with the assignment.

Still this was something unknown. They were trying for speeds and heights nobody had ever attempted. Here there would be no one to tell you what to expect. I would be alone. And I thought of excuses to turn it down.

During the war I had picked up a book in Honolulu by a French pilot, Antoine de Saint-Exupéry, and I remembered the words: "There is no liberty except the liberty of someone making his way towards something." No matter what arguments I set up against the advisability of these new flights, I knew I would accept them. This was the kind of freedom the French flyer talked about that subconsciously I had sought all along, and here before me was a big chunk of it. All I had to do was take it. Here was the choice: going toward something, freedom—or security and stagnation. One or the other, the two were incompatible; there was no compromise. Find out, move, reach out. If I turned down this "freedom" I knew that later the knowledge that I had would never leave me alone.

Mach 2: Twice the Speed of Sound

There she was, a celebrity now, the crew, members of a midnight cult, priming her for the big flight in their cumbersome, hooded uniforms.

I was at the height of conditioning as I approached the fueling scene, half out of the pressure suit, followed by the specialist Stum. I was determined to get everything out of her this time, to get it over with. There was nothing to fear. The roll had been conquered and no structural damage had resulted from it. She sat snug in the belly of the mother ship, gleaming iridescent white with her new skin of lacquer. Today was the culmination of three years' work.

The fueling was completed. The engineers came up one by one to offer some last-minute word, the equivalent of "Good luck." "See you after the flight" . . . "We'll discuss it afterward"—optimistic references to the future. Stum finished fussing with the helmet and thumped the top of it with his hand. The 29 fired up her engines, taxied out, and we were airborne.

I am no longer embarrassed by my need for the Dixie cup. It has become an established part of the flight. When it drops out, Everest, in his chase plane, familiar with the sight, calls, "Dixie cup away."

Thirty-five thousand feet. I acknowledge Jansen's salute. Twenty minutes later my hands are gripping the wheel.

"Two . . . one." The shaft of light, a sensation I am accustomed to meeting. Today the pullout is smooth, without any loss of rocket-seconds. How practiced I have become! How easily I control the power pouring from the four tubes. The tension I have felt waiting in the bomber has left me and the action of performing the job well acts as an exaggerated salve. Even the constant adjustment in the climb is an effortless series of practiced movements. How well she responds to my hand.

At the top I will push her over sharply and let her go. I am really going to put it to her . . . with the added acceleration at the pushover, she should do it.

Piercing up through the minus-80-degree sheer air, I hit 64,000 feet in a matter of seconds—the top of the hill. Now! She eats up 3000 feet while my hand moves the wheel. Over the top, right down into it. No gradual rocket-second devouring arc, but over the top like a roller coaster. Straight down in front of me I push the wheel and the limitless blue brilliancy ahead slides away and out of the silver windows the curve of the horizon moves up in its place.

And quietly she begins to "roll." The thing that had me on the edge of my parachute three long flights ago I take as a matter of course. And now, .25 G, just the other side of zero G where you beat gravity, where a pencil on the cockpit floor will float in midair. I glue the white needle to the figure .25 on the accelerometer. Let's see what you can do with *this*, baby! She accelerates into the hypersonic zone at one third of a mile a second.

The roll! I can't ignore it. It sets in more firmly as she plunges deeper into the pushover. *Well, let it, damn it. We're going this trip. She can take it.* Without changing the condition she protests against, I grip the wheel. Nothing is going to jar her loose from the .25 holding steady on the accelerometer. There is nothing she can show me that is going to stop me. Hunched over the wheel, I hang on.

Harder she rolls, harder and faster. The flat horizon line flips wildly through the squinting slit windows. I fight the crazy gyration with the ailerons. They are no weapons. They are feathers in a wind storm. Still, they are the only weapons I have. The flipping is so fast that I cannot get in phase against it with the ailerons. She has turned on me! I am making it worse with the ailerons and panic floods up into my chest and throat. I am almost sick with it as I fight a force so great now that my frantic flailings against it are pathetically puny.

There has got to be a way to bring order out of this. I release my hands from the aileron control and try to get in phase with the roll that snaps me violently back and forth in its teeth, flipping me over on my side level with the horizon, then instantly back in the other direction. A dog beating a cat against the ground. I do not fight it now, but wait to allow the crazy accelerated, windshield-wiper-like, flipping of the Rocket to neutralize so I can jump in and hold my strength against it. *Now.* I missed it. *I'll get it this time. I'll get it now.*

The action has a meager effect on the force that has grabbed us, but it is positive. It is a glimmer of control and I am somewhat retrieved from total despair. The wheel is a ridiculous toy against the thing that has hold of the ship. *Why don't they give me something to fight with, for God's sake?* A toy in my hands to fight the whole goddamned sky that has turned on me. One hundred and eighty pounds against a new world full of enraged energy. The frail weapons of my arms ache with the futile exertion put upon them.

I turn my back on the ridiculously matched contest long enough to glance at the Machmeter. It is building fast: 1.79, 1.80, 1.81, 1.82, 1.83, 1.84, 1.85.

That is the answer! That is the reason. No-man's-land. She's going. It is a justification.

I am aware of the face-plate that separates my eyes from the panel before me. Coatings of steam from my breath rapidly appear and disappear on the glass and the terrible sound of my lungs gasping and heaving air in and out vibrates like wind in a barrel through my ears. Despite all the activity I am aware of the terrible, animal-frightened sound.

Into this isolated, hopelessly vulnerable world that is myself and the Skyrocket comes another kind of faraway unreality—the voice of Al Carder, high and thin, crackling through my helmet.

"Has he started to descend yet, Chuck?" From his position on the floor 13 miles down, the project coordinator has been able to follow my white vapor trail in the climb. Then the Skyrocket reaches air that is too thin to condense.

I am swallowed up by the sky. It is an easy matter to get lost in the sky.

Yeager's voice, lost from me somewhere out there, "No. He was still climbing when his vapor trail disappeared and he left me."

"Any idea of his position, Chuck?"

"Last time I saw him he was fading away over Barstow."

It is like hearing voices of people standing over you when you are half-conscious. You are unable to answer. I would like to say something memorably glib, but I cannot.

My hands and face are wet with perspiration. Rivulets of stinging sweat drop into my eyes. How curious that a man can sweat in minus-80-degree-below-zero temperature.

If a horse is throwing you, you can let yourself be thrown. You can get away from the beast. But not this thing. I am part of it. Until she wears out the tantrum, I have no alternative but to go where she takes me.

Still doggedly I hold the needle on .25 G. The horizon of gyrating, half-blue, half-brown, is gone now and in its place is solid brown earth in a half-circle spin, spinning half around and respinning back again. A corkscrew at Mach 1.87 down toward the ground. Beyond the thickening fog of my face-plate there is no sky. It is all flat, hard earth that I head for.

I am losing the battle. To hang on longer is stupidity. A decision must be made. Cut off her energy! That will surely stop this horror. Behind me I feel for the switch that will turn off the 6000 pounds of thrust. I click it forward.

She shudders and decelerates into the wall, but the wild ride continues as if no change had been made. It doesn't alter her furious action. It is with terrible surprise I realize that the loss of power has no effect upon her condition.

The lake is 40 miles behind me and getting further and further away as the Skyrocket carries me far from my only port. To enter a turn back to the lake is impossible. I cannot force her into a bank. She won't leave her path! And now over my eyes the frost on my face-plate has thickened into a heavy white curtain and I can no longer see the gyrating, whirling bottom below me.

My cramped cockpit world has moved into my helmet. All that exists now is the white frost on the face-plate, the violent thrashing of the plane, and the feel of the wheel under my fingers. In the silent ship the terrible, convulsive breathing is my only companion.

A blind man in an out-of-control Rocket plunging, through low-pressure areas that can burst my body like a balloon, toward the ground at a speed twice as fast as a bullet in flight.

Altitude. It is the only road left to me, the only way I can go now. It is the margin, the delayer. In altitude there is some security. Time to think. With all the strength I am able to summon I pull back on the wheel and inflict a radical directional change on the downward-screaming ship. Bent upward into the big, safe sky by the tremendous force of the tight pull-up, I am sucked down into the pressure suit and my lower jaw is grabbed wide open like a man screaming for his life, and I know that I am moving away from the awful brown that I was headed into. It's soft blue before me now.

And now like a black night diluted slowly by the incipient watercolor dawn, the gyrating falls away. I feel it fade away. It has stopped. All of the violence and horror is gone. The Rocket has changed back into a silent, gentle, featherlike missile, whooshing straight up in a steep climb.

She is controllable but I am blind. The windshield wiper! I remember with a flood of thankful discovery the windshield wiper that had been installed after the last flight at Al Carder's insistence. Thank God for Carder and the ridiculous little rubber lever that I move manually to clear away the frost.

Without power and bent into the steep climb, she will start shuddering into the first warnings of stall. The indicated air speed is the dial that commands my regained sight. It is sinking fast. *Fly her now, Bridgeman; she's all yours again.* Once more I am a pilot. I drop the nose a bit to pick up speed. Now I roll her over, drop the long nose, pulling positive G, and pull her on through. The Skyrocket is turned back in the direction of home. My ship again.

The chase pilots have lost me. Right now I am incapable of worrying about getting the rest of the way home. At this moment I am overwhelmed with relief that the Skyrocket is once more something I can understand and she is heading in the right direction.

The last few minutes have left my body still in a state of emergency despite the abrupt cessation of the nightmare. My legs and arms shake uncontrollably.

Sometime during the pushover I re-enter the altitude where my vapor trail forms again. Carder has seen it. From the ground it appears like an erratic corkscrew furrowed by my wild path. The jumble over the radio starts as Carder sees it with alarm.

"Chuck, can you see the vapor trail again? Can you get over there?"

Weakly I hear the sound of help coming and I wonder absently how I am going to explain this one to Carder. And why did I hang on so tenaciously to that .25 G? As I sit here trembling, guiding the empty Rocket sapped as dry of energy as I am, I remember the moments just passed.

Holy God! Not once did I think of the escape lever. Is it possible that I would have let her take me right into a 40-foot hole in the ground?

"Yeah, Al, I can see it. I'll be on him in a couple of minutes."

"That's a crazy-looking trail he's dragging. How does he look, Chuck?"

Chuck is coming. The now-obedient Skyrocket decelerates out of the supersonic zone down through the tender .9, emitting her usual shudder. The once-awesome shudder makes me smile weakly.

"Hold on. I haven't found him yet." The warm, competent, Southern softness of Yeager's steady voice is soothing as the first inhalation of fine sourmash whisky. "Now I've got him. He's pretty far away but he seems to be all in one piece."

"Bill," Carder calls to me now, "how are you doing?"

There it is! I can see the lake bed far below me and ahead. Just a few more minutes. "Shut up, will you?"

Beside me Chuck Yeager's silver F-86 slides in close and cozy.

"Hi, hotshot." A friend to see me home. I lift my hand to him. He is silent as he follows my glide path down. He knows. It is all I can do to follow the precise maneuverings necessary to get the still-hot little ship onto the lake bed. Even without power she'll land nearly a third again as fast as the F-86.

After a respectable length of time Chuck says, "I thought you were going to Arizona for a while there, Buddy."

With a great deal of effort I am able to answer. "I thought so too."

Fifteen Miles Above the Earth

There was no horseplay this morning, no labored wisecrack. My associates were vaguely ill at ease when they greeted me. I suppose it was because I was more preoccupied than usual. The crew picked up the mood. They waited for me to open any conversation and they were more attentive than usual. Before I could ask for anything it was right there. I was grateful for the silence. Horseplay takes time and effort; it breaks the chain of thought. There had been other mornings when I had restrained myself from cutting a well-meant joke with, "Shut up." It was sometimes awkward and taxing to be obliged to make the effort of a retort.

The hoses had been withdrawn from the Skyrocket and the last lacing had been adjusted on the "corset." Everything was in order.

George received his okay to take off and the big bomber began to jog along the runway.

This flight will be discovery. I will know a thing I have never known before. Mixed with the clinical thoughts of how to handle the ship and the familiar counterpoint of the fear syndrome, today there is expectancy. Adventure. Before, the flights have been carefully controlled. Today I am going to let her go as far as she will. It is up to her.

Time! It will begin in ten seconds. A new road. The chase plane at this end checks in and stands by. Silence connects me now to the three chase planes, the men who wait on the ground, the mechanics in the hangar—clustered around loud-speakers as if for the last game of the World Series—the control tower, and Jansen who holds the pickle in his hand ready to count off the ten remaining seconds of security that I have snug in the womb of the mother ship. Now!

"Four . . . three . . . two . . . one," I hold the cold wheel in my bare hands and lean forward, "*Drop!*"

Four buttons down. One, two, three, four, and four gigantic blow-torches rumble into life. Mathematical at the beginning. A formula of numbers. Breathe air on the count of 1001, blow it out at 1005. Around the corner, feel it, at G. Going up. The numbers on the dials, .85 on the Machmeter. Hold it! Everest's voice in the F-86 counting, "One is good, two is good, three is . . . good." The report from the chase plane fades into distance. It is faraway and barely audible now, . . . "He's got all four!"

The needle on the indicated air speed falls off as the number .85 holds on the Machmeter. Change the numbers on the dials now. The needles slide up and down and around—.85 becomes Mach 1, she bumps into the quiet area and the high-drag rise of the shock waves. The larger altimeter hand winds up to 42,000, 43,000, reeling off the altitude. No pushover. Straight up. All the way, bending back a little more, a little more. The only world I am aware of is the world of dial eyes in front of me. The perpendicular light on the newly installed angle-of-attack instrument creeps up steadily as I move the stabilizer trim switch. *Zut . . . zut. Zut . . . zut*, pointing her nose higher, a little bit higher.

I follow the plan of the aerodynamicists in the Testing Division at Santa Monica. It looks like it is going to work after all. Five dials. A constant check as they all speak at once. Indicated air speed, Mach needle, angle-of-attack light, the rocket-seconds that remain, and the reeling off of the altimeter hand. Reeling off 57,000, 58,000, it rapidly reels back every 1000 feet I climb through.

In the thin air, actually, she does not want to fly but miraculously she does; she is held by a fantastic power that takes over. A ball atop a slim stick, she maintains an uncanny balance in the unresisting, weak air. She is going up at such speed that in reality she is close to stall. We are buoyed on a pivot that keeps us in balance. Although I am acutely aware of this circumstance, I am not alarmed by it. I am reluctant to believe she will not continue to fly.

Fifty-nine thousand, 60,000, reeling off 61,000. I have left the world. There is only the ship to identify myself with, her vibrations are my own, I feel them as intensely as those of my body. Here is a kind of unreality mixed with reality that I cannot explain to myself. I have an awareness that I have never experienced before, but it does not seem to project beyond this moment. Every cell, fluid, muscle of my body, is acutely awake. Perception is enormously exaggerated—black is blacker, white is whiter. Silence is more acute. It is the tender edge of the unknowable. And with this adrenalin-inflicted state floats the feeling of detachment.

It is an incompatible set of emotions I experience. Fear seems to be independent, a ghost sitting on my shoulder. And although it is most surely there, I am anesthetized to its warnings. I am without anxiety. I am powerless to anticipate what will happen the next moment. Time is now. Nothing but this experience is significant now. The rocket pressures are meaningless, the world of figures and equations that a second or two ago held such urgency have no reality in the face of *this* reality. I have the unshakable feeling that no matter what the instruments read, it will have no effect on the power that is making this ship fly. An independent, supernatural kind of power she has. She is alive with her own unknowable and unmovable power. I have complete faith, a faith that wraps me like a warm blanket now, that she will not be interrupted in this free-dom.

Sixty-two thousand, 63,000 feet reeling off, reeling off the climb. The left wing is dropping! I respond automatically with no alarm, a robot racking in aileron against the dipping wing. I watch the eyes in front of me. The instruments stand out brighter— 64,000 feet on the altimeter, reeling away . . . the Mach number . . . the rocket-seconds left to spend. Gently the wayward wing eases down again. Aileron full throw against it. No response this time. No effect. The wing keeps on going down. I kick the rudder against it but, of course, the rudder is locked. Seventy thousand feet. Check the Mach number: 1.4. I know I must bring her nose down. I am reluctant to reduce the altitude but I must; she will surely roll otherwise. Now slowly the aileron control comes back and I can once more return the ship to the nose-high altitude. Zut, zut, the pole-nose moves up. Seventy-five thousand feet. Again the wing dips. I ease the pole down once more and bring the wing level. It is a matter of easing her along the steep path tenderly. Give a little and grab a little. Seventy-six thousand feet registers on the dial and the rockets sputter off.

From hours of rehearsal my hand automatically hits the stabilizer switch for the pushover. It is with elation I feel the great force that shoves her over the top at .5 G. Even without the rockets she still has enough power to climb higher. Next time I will convert this en-ergy to more altitude. In the arc she picks up a couple of thousand feet. The altimeter stops its steady reeling and swings sickly around 80,000 feet. The altitude is too extreme for the instrument to func-tion.

Eighty thousand feet. It is intensely bright outside; the contrast of the dark shadows of the cockpit is extreme and strange. It is so dark lower in the cockpit that I cannot read the instruments sunk low on the panel. The dials on top, in the light, are vividly appar-ent. There seems to be no reflection; it is all black or white, appar-ent or nonapparent. No half-tones. It is a pure, immaculate world here.

She levels off silently. I roll to the right and there it is. Out of the tiny window slits there is the earth, wiped clean of civilization, a vast relief map with papier-mâché mountains and mirrored lakes and seas. The desert is not the same desert I have seen for two years; it is a pale brown hole bordered by dwarf mountains that run into other dwarf mountain chains that plait into other chains down to the Gulf of California and the Republic of Mexico. The coastline is sharply drawn with little vacant bays and inlets, a lacy edge to the big brown pieces of earth that dissolve into grays and the glimmer of lake puddles cupped in mountaintops and back to brown, gray, and finally the enormous black-blue of the Pacific. A globe-world in a planetarium, the earth curves to the south.

It is as if I am the only living thing connected to this totally strange, uninhabited planet 15 miles below me. The plane that carries me and I are one and alone.

There is a world down there and it must be revisited. There is the turn back to the place where the field is a pinpoint on the globe under me. The only way back from the springboard I am on has to be from memory, automatic. This, now, is the payoff for my preflight conditioning, for the drills, for the memorizing of steps back. Without this conditioning I am sure at this moment that I would not be able to return quickly enough from the euphoric state that holds me.

Following the steps mechanically, I am able to enter the turn. I am on my descent and slowly I return to what I knew before. Again I hear myself laboring for oxygen inside the helmet, and the world under me comes gradually into focus as something identifiable with life. At 15,000 it is comfortingly familiar. I take the faceplate out of the helmet and breathe air again, deeply, and I am back, fully returned to time and dimension and the brief span that is allowed me.

DOING

FATHER ANDREA
Pearl Buck

Pearl Buck, novelist, winner of the Nobel Prize for Literature, was born in West Virginia but was taken to China when a child by her parents who were both missionaries. At seventeen she was taken to Europe and later to America where she completed her education and went back to China where she married Dr. John Lossing Buck, an agricultural missionary. Her first book to obtain wide popular acceptance was The Good Earth in 1931. She is now married to Richard Walsh, her publisher, and lives in Perkasia, Pa., with her two daughters and four adopted children. In 1941 she founded the East and West Association for mutual understanding between Asia and the West, and in 1949 founded Welcome House for the care and adoption of American-born children who have Asian ancestry. She is one of two women among the fifty members of the American Academy of Arts and Letters.

" 'Father Andrea' was one of the first stories which I ever wrote," she says. "Living far inland in China and traveling still farther to places where few white people went, I often came across a lonely priest, serving his flock by day and at night studying the stars for his comfort. I used to wonder why so often they turned to the stars— I suppose because living in a world of poor and troubled people they needed to be reassured of the existence of God. Father Andrea was one of those priests and I saw him die and that is what the story is about."

Father Andrea lived all day for the hours at night when he might study the stars. The days in his parish in the Chinese city were long and crowded, filled with people and voices crying and complaining and demanding, and the nights were short and radiant with the silent, peaceful stars, shining like torches out of the dark purple sky. He could never get enough of them. The hours with his telescope went so quickly that many times he remembered to sleep only when the dawn came up out of the east with such ruddy splendor that the stars faded. But he did not need sleep. He could return to the day refreshed and braced by those hours of study and observation of the golden stars, when the voices that clamored after him all day were asleep for a brief while. "Bless sleep!" he would say to himself, chuckling as he climbed the steps to the tiny observatory he had built on top of the schoolhouse.

He was a small, stout, smiling man, whose exterior revealed nothing of his soft, mystic soul. If one saw only his apple cheeks and dark beard and red, smiling mouth, one would say that he was a lover of visible life. One needed to see his eyes to discover that he was a lover of things unseen. His lips went on smiling even when a leper came twisting and beseeching about his feet, or a wretched slave-girl ran in, cowering and crying, through the gates of the mission. But his eyes, deep set and dark, were often full of tears.

During the day he lifted up the lepers with his hands and washed them and fed them and soothed them and smeared oil upon their wounds. He stood between the slave-girl and her angry, cursing mistress, smiling, waiting, talking in that quiet, ceaseless, murmuring way he had. The woman's angry voice rose above it like a storm above a brook, but sooner or later his gentle, insistent speech won, and she would sit sulking, in answer to his invitation, in the seat of honor at the right of the square table in his little guest-hall, and sip the tea he had asked the servant to bring. And then, with his small, dark, tragic eyes grave above his smiling mouth, he would talk on, praising, suggesting, regretting, hinting gently of the necessity of better things, until in the end the slave went away with the mistress. He would never help people to break away from what held them fast. His great concern always was to help them bear more easily the inevitable yoke that life had placed upon each of them. That was the one thing he was sure of —that there was no getting away from the oppression that life itself brought.

Talking in the morning to the boys in his school, he said one day more earnestly than he had ever before said anything:

"My sons, I will tell you a thing. You think, when you are children, that you will break away from the bondage of your parents and that when you go to school you will be free of them. In school you dream of manhood, when there will be no more teachers for you to obey. But you can never be free! When your immortal souls took on flesh, they became even as the Son of Man was—bound. No man is free—we are not free of one another—we can never be free of God.

"The thing is, not to cry futilely after freedom, but to discover cheerfully how to bear the burden of bondage upon us. Even the stars in heaven are not free. They too must obey the paths of order in law, lest by their wantonness they wreck the universe. You have seen the shooting stars in the sky in summer. They seem beautiful in freedom, a burst of light and splendor against the clouds. But their end is destruction and darkness. It is the stars marching steadily on in their appointed ways which endure to the end."

The little blue-coated Chinese boys stared at him, wondering at the passion in his quiet voice and at the unwonted somberness of his round, smiling face. They did not understand him at all.

All day long he trotted hither and thither about his duty, beginning at dawn by saying mass for a few faithful old women who came decently garbed in their cotton coats and trousers, with black kerchiefs folded about their heads. It troubled him sometimes that they did not grasp much of what he said; his Chinese had never been perfect and it was spoken with a soft Italian elision that could never seize the gutturals firmly. But at last, seeing their patient faces as they fixed their eyes on the Virgin and her Son, he decided that it did not matter what he said so long as they looked at the sacred picture and struggled to think of its meaning.

Before noon he tried to teach a little in the boys' school, but it was a harried business, because at any moment he would be called without to settle some affair of the poor.

"Father, I sold this man tenpence of rice last night and trusted him until this morning for the money, and now, having eaten the rice, he tells me he has nothing."

Two men in coolie trousers, their backs bare and blackened with the sun, stood before him, one angry, one defiant.

"Now, then, was not my stomach empty? Am I to starve when you have food? The revolutionists are coming, and, when they come, all men like you who have rice must give to us who have not, and no talk of money, either!"

The two glared at each other as angry cocks will glare before attacking, and Father Andrea put a hand on each man's arm. His hands told the story begun by his eyes, small, brown, perfectly shaped hands that were broken and wrinkled with the washings and scrubbings he gave them. It was one of the agonies of his life that he could not subdue his flesh to the point of touching dark, unwashed bodies without some shrinking of his spirit. It was an obsession with him to wash his hands again and again, so that they were always scented faintly with carbolic soap. One of his private penances was to go without washing his hands, making himself endure the shuddering when he put them upon a child's head, crusted with the scald of disease. He had schooled himself to touch everything that made him recoil and, seeing his freely moving, kindly, expressive hands, no one dreamed of the inner withdrawal.

So now, one of his hands warm and persuasive upon the arm of each man, he said to the defiant one: "My friend, I know nothing of the revolutionists. But this I do know. My garden needs weeding today, and, if you will weed it, I will gladly pay you wages and, out of the wages, I who know your good heart am sure you will not withhold the tenpence to your neighbor. He is a poor man with children, and you have eaten his rice. It is written, 'If any would not work, neither should he eat.' It is one of the laws of life, which even the revolution cannot rightly change."

Instantly the tension on the two faces faded away, and the two men laughed and showed their white teeth, and Father Andrea laughed, wrinkling his round, rosy face, and went back to his boys. At the end of the day he paid the man double wages. "Take it," he said when the man made a feint of refusal. "Some day I will ask you to work for me again, and on that day I may not have the money by me."

In the afternoon, after his dish of rice and beans and macaroni, he put on his flat black hat and went out and visited the people and drank tea with them and ate the hard-boiled eggs the housewives would cook for him, although his soul loathed them, and listened, smiling, to all that was said. He knew no rich people. These scorned him as a Catholic priest and a foreigner, and he would not have forced his presence upon them even if he could. He went into the low, thatched houses of the poor and into the mat sheds of beggars, and he gave them his money as fast as it came into his hands. Of the great storm gathering without, the storm of the revolution, these people knew nothing, and no more did Father Andrea know. He had read no newspapers for years, and he had no idea of anything that was happening beyond this round of days and splendid nights.

Once a week he allowed himself to remember his own country. On the evening of the seventh day he washed himself and trimmed his dark beard and put a little scent upon his hands, and then he went up into the tiny observatory and sat in an old easy chair he had there. On the other nights he sat upon a stool by the table and took out his pens and papers and his measuring instruments and in his small, accurate handwriting he made notes which he sent to his Superior in Siccawei. Through all these years of evenings he had gradually become one of the chief of a group of astronomers in the Far East, although he did not know it. To him his study of the heavens was the relaxation and exhilaration of a brain formed for meticulous observation and keen, hard thinking.

But on this seventh day he took no paper and pens. He sat down and opened the windows and fixed his eyes upon the stars and allowed his thoughts to take him back to Italy, his country, to which he had not returned for twenty-seven years and which he would never behold again. He had been a young man when he left, scarcely thirty, but even after all these years he remembered with passionate sharpness the agony of that parting. Even yet he could see the bay, rounding into a circle smaller and smaller as the ship drew out from the land. Every week he thought gravely and with a sense of guilt that above his sense of mission still was the memory of that parting, and that sharper than the parting of his body from his motherland, from his home and parents and his sister and his brother, was the parting of his spirit from his beloved, his Vitellia, who had loved his brother more than him.

He had done penance all these years for this sin, that he had come into the Church, not for devotion to God and Mary, but because Vitellia did not love him. Not that she or anyone else knew it. His brother was tall and handsome and grave, with beautiful, languishing brown eyes, and Vitellia was tall and pale and exquisite as an olive-tree in new leafage, her colors all soft and subdued and mistlike. She was head and shoulders above the little rosy man he always was. No one thought of him seriously. He was always laughing and joking and merry, his small, deep-set, black eyes crackling with humor.

Even after his brother's marriage he did not stop his joking. But he waited to see whether or not his brother was good to Vitellia. There was nothing to complain of there. His brother was a good man, although a little dull inside his beauty of body, and, when he found himself married and soon with a child coming, he settled down into his father's wine business and they were very happy. No, there was nothing to complain of there.

Then it was that Andrea became frightened at the power of his passion. He saw that nothing would keep him from revealing himself except entire submission to his fate. That took a year of fever and agony, and it was not complete until he saw that for him there was no renunciation wholly efficacious except priesthood in some far country. Then he fled to the fathers in his village.

His family had laughed at him—everyone laughed at him—and Vitellia had nearly ruined him by clinging to his hand and saying in that voice of hers that was more to him than music, "But brother mine, my Andrea, who will play with my children and be always in my house?" He had shaken his head, smiling and speechless, and she had looked at him in surprise and seen that his eyes were full of tears. "Must you, if you mind so much, Andrea?" And he had nodded.

Ah, well, it was all done, long, long ago. For many years he had not allowed himself to think of her because she was another man's wife, and he had come to the stars night after night and prayed passionately for peace. It seemed to him that he could never do penance enough for loving Vitellia more than anyone else always to the very end. That made him deny himself fiercely and force himself to every distasteful touch and duty. Once, when his flesh had burned after her, he had gone wildly out into the streets and had brought in a beggar from the winter's night, a poor, shivering wretch, and had laid him in his bed and covered him with his blankets and had stretched himself out beside the creature all night long, his teeth clenched and his stomach sick. But in the morning he whispered triumphantly to his body, "Now will you be quiet and cease troubling me!" All this explained the smiling tragedy in his eyes and his constant preaching of bearing one's yoke.

When one day a black-bordered letter came, the first letter in many years, he opened it, and within was the news of Vitellia's death. Then it seemed that peace of a sort came upon him, and after a while he allowed himself this relaxation on the evening of seventh days and even at last permitted himself to think a little of her. Now that she was dead, he could imagine her up yonder, moving in that free, light way she had, among the stars. She was no one's wife now—she belonged to no one. She was a part of heaven, and he could think of her as of a star and be without sin.

He began to preach less vehemently and more patiently about bearing the yoke. When one of his schoolboys ran away to join the revolutionists, he went out with a sigh and sought him and talked with him gently, begging him to come back to his weeping mother.

"The good God puts us into life with a duty to perform," he said tenderly, smiling a little, with his arm about the boy's shoulders.

But the boy shook himself free and moved away. "In the revolution there is no God and there is no duty," he said imperiously. "We are all free, and we preach a gospel of freedom for everyone."

"Ah?" said Father Andrea softly.

For the first time a premonition fell upon him. He had up to this time paid no attention to the talk of revolution. His paths had not led him a mile from the congested quarter where he lived. It occurred to him that now he must look into such talk, especially if his boys were going off like this. He began to speak then of other things, but the boy was wary and obviously eager to have him gone. There were other lads about and an officer or two. The boy's answers grew shorter and shorter. He cast angry looks at his fellows. At last Father Andrea said kindly: "I see that you have other things on your mind. I will leave you now. Do not forget the prayers that you have been taught, my child."

He put his hand on the lad's head for an instant and turned away, but, before he left the barracks, a hoot of laughter arose, and he heard the lads shouting to their comrade, "Running-dog of a foreigner, are you?"

He had no idea what this meant, and he thought once of going back. He stopped to listen. Someone cried out, laughing like a whip's cut, "Ah, a Christian!" Then he heard the boy's voice raised angrily, half-sobbing: "I hate the priest—I know nothing of his religion. I am a revolutionist! Does anyone dare to question me?"

Father Andrea stood stricken. What words were these to come from his lad's mouth, his lad who had been in his school ever since he was five years old? He trembled a little, and a thought shot into his mind like a pang. "So did Peter deny his Lord!" And he went back into the little mission that was his home and shut himself up in his room and wept bitterly.

After that it seemed to him that he had been standing on the edge of a whirlpool and had not known it. He had said that he must investigate this revolution and see that his boys were not carried away. But there was no need of investigation. Knowledge and experience came pouring over him, and he was caught in a maze of difficulties.

There was so much he had not known. He had never heard of political differences between East and West. He had come only as one who wished to bury himself in his mission to a land where there was not his true Church. In this one spot in an immense crowded city he had lived day after day for twenty-seven years, and his small, black-robed figure had become as much a part of the street as an ancient temple or bridge. Children, as long as they could remember, were accustomed to the sight of him, trudging along in all weathers, his pockets bulging ridiculously with peanuts for them. No one thought of him. Women washing at the well looked up as he came by, knew that it must be an hour after noon and sighed to think of the hours before sunset. Men nodded at him carelessly from the counters of the little shops open to the streets and accepted with good humor his tracts and pictures of the Virgin.

Now this was changed. He was no longer Father Andrea, a harmless, aging priest. He became instead a foreigner.

One day a child refused to take the peanuts he held out to it. "My mother says they may be poisoned," the child said, looking up at Father Andrea with wide eyes.

"Poisoned?" said Father Andrea vaguely and in great surprise.

The next day he returned with his pockets as heavy as when he started, and after that he took no more peanuts. Once a woman spat after him as he passed the well. Then men shook their heads coldly when he smiled and proffered his tracts. He was completely bewildered.

At last one night his native assistant came to him. He was a good old man with a straggling, scanty white beard, honest and a little stupid, so that he never quite got his Aves right. Father Andrea had wondered sometimes if he should not find someone more able, but he could never bring himself to tell the old man that he was not perfect. Now he said to Father Andrea, "My Father, do not go out until this madness is past."

"What madness?" asked Father Andrea.

"This talk about foreigners and revolutions. The people are listening to these young men in long black gowns who come from the South, and they say that the foreigners are killing the people and stealing their hearts with new religions."

"New religions?" said Father Andrea mildly. "There is nothing new about mine. I have been here preaching and teaching for more than a quarter of a century."

"Even so, sir, you are a foreigner," replied the old man apologetically.

"Well," said Father Andrea at last, "this astonishes me very much!"

But he listened to the old man after the next day; for, when he stepped from the gate into the street, a great stone flung at him flew against his breast and broke into two pieces the ebony cross that hung there, and, when he put up his hand, aghast, another stone flew against him and cut his hand badly. He turned white and went into the mission house and shut the door and fell upon his knees and looked at the broken cross. For a long time he could say nothing, but at last words came to his lips and he prayed an old prayer. "Father, forgive them; for they know not what they do."

After that he stayed in the compound. Within a few days no one came any more, and he locked the door of the empty schoolroom sadly. It was as if he were in the quiet center of a storm. From outside the lonely compound where he and his old assistant pottered about the garden, strange sounds rose up in confusion from the streets. He locked the gate, opening it only once a day in the evening for the old man to creep out and buy a little food. At last one day the old man came back with his basket empty.

"They will not let me buy food for you," he said piteously. "To save your life I must pretend to leave you, and I must pretend to hate you. But every night I will throw food over the western corner of the garden. And every evening at the hour I will repeat the Ave. Our God must look after you beyond this."

Thereafter Father Andrea was quite alone. He spent a great deal of time in the observatory, and he allowed himself to think and remember every evening now. The days were long and solitary, and he missed even the lepers. There was no more need to wash his hands except of the clean garden earth that clung to them after he had been working among the vegetables. And, outside, the noise rose and mounted until he fancied that he was on some small island in the midst of a raging sea and that one day the waves would break over him even there.

He withdrew into his thoughts more and more, and he built little dreams of Italy and of the grape garden where he had played as a boy. He could smell the hot sun on the ripe grapes—incomparable fragrance! Sitting in the old easy chair night after night, he began to reconstruct from the beginning his life. It was May, and the stars were brilliant in a purple sky. But he no longer touched his note-books and pens. He had become indifferent to anything of the stars except their sheer unearthly beauty Thank God for stars and sky everywhere! These Chinese skies in May were like the skies of Italy in summer, the stars hanging heavy and golden in the dark sky. Once on a night like this in Italy he had leaned from his window and gone suddenly mad with the beauty of the stars, and he had run blindly out of the house to Vitellia. His heart was beating like a great drum, shaking his body with every throb, and he had cried that he must tell her that he loved her. When he had got to his brother's house, his brother had opened the door and said kindly: "We were just about to sleep, Andrea. Is there anything we can do for you?"

Behind his brother he saw Vitellia, shadowy in the room, her face pale and indistinct as a flower in the twilight. She came forward and rested her hand lightly upon her husband's arm and leaned her head upon his shoulder. She was quite content. Passion went out of him.

"No, thank you," he stammered. "I thought—I did not know it

was so late—I thought I might come in and talk a little while, perhaps."

"Yes, another day," said his brother gravely. And Vitellia had called, "Good night, brother Andrea!" And the door shut, and he was alone.

That was the night he had stayed in the garden the whole night through, and at dawn he had said at last that he would give himself to the poor, since Vitellia did not need him—the poor of a far country.

Ah, all that passion and pain and the youth he had had to wear down by sheer indomitable will to suffer! He would still never be free of it—never, so long as he lived, quite free. He wondered if there among the stars Vitellia knew—there where surely everything was known. He hoped so. That would mean that he need not tell her of all the pain. She would understand as she had never understood on earth, and they could start in at once on the new heavenly relationship.

He sighed and went down into the garden then, and there at the western end he found a small bundle of cold rice and meat wrapped in a lotus leaf and he ate it and then said his Aves, his fingers hovering over the broken cross on his breast.

From outside the wall, in the street, there came the sound of steady, marching feet, thousands upon thousands of feet. He listened awhile, wondering, and then, with a sigh, he went up again to his observatory and sat down, and, looking off into the clear spaces of heaven, he slept lightly.

In the morning he awoke with a start of premonition, as if he had been aroused suddenly by a noise. He could not for an instant collect himself. The stars were weak in the gray light of the dawn, and the roof of the church was dark and wet with dew. From without there came a sound of mad confusion, and shooting and shouts rent the air. He listened. There were several shots in quick succession. He sat up, trying to think what this could be. Was this what had waked him? There was no more marching. A huge blaze lighted up the distant eastern sky. Something was burning—that was the rich quarter of the city, where the streets were hung with the scarlet and yellow banners of the big grain-shops and silk-shops and sing-song houses. But it might be only the sun rising? No, there was no such splendor of sunrise out of this gray sky.

He dragged himself from the chair and went downstairs heavily, with vague alarm. He had not slept restfully, and his mind felt fogged. As he reached the foot of the steps and stood upon the grass, there came a terrific pounding at the gate, and he moved quickly to open it, rubbing his head a little to collect his thoughts. This was the noise he had heard in his sleep! He fumbled at the great wooden bar and withdrew it at last and opened the gate and stared out in amazement. Hundreds of men stood there in a mass—soldiers in gray uniform. Their faces were ferocious as he had not dreamed human faces could be, and he shrank from them as he had never shrunk from his lepers. They leveled their guns at him then with a tigerish shout. He was not afraid, only completely amazed.

"But what do you want, my friends?" he asked in surprise.

A young man, scarcely older than his schoolboy who had run away, stepped forward and tore the rosary from about his neck. The fragment of broken cross, all that was left of the cross he had worn for so many years, fell to the ground.

"We have come to rid the world of imperialists and capitalists!" the young man shouted.

"Imperialists and capitalists?" said Father Andrea, wondering. They were words he had never heard. It had been many years since he had read anything except the ancient Church fathers and his books of astronomy. He did not have the faintest idea what the lad meant.

But the boy cocked his gun and pointed it at Father Andrea. "We are the revolutionists!" he cried. His voice was rough and harsh as if he had been shouting for many hours, and his smooth, youthful face was blotched and red as if with drinking. "We come to set everyone free!"

"Set everyone free?" said Father Andrea slowly, smiling a little. He stooped to pick up his cross from the dust.

But before his hand could touch that cross, the boy's finger moved spasmodically upon the trigger and there was a sharp report, and Father Andrea fell upon the ground, dead.

THE JOURNAL OF A WRITER
WITH A HOLE IN ONE SOCK

John Cheever

John Cheever, native of Quincy, Mass., is the author of two collections of distinguished short stories and a recent novel The Wapshot Chronicles. *He is a winner of the National Institute of Arts and Letters Award in Literature.*

I am a writer. My agent tells me that this is an unpopular truth and that I should keep it under my hat. For years I have attributed my perceptions, sentiments, and conjectures to imaginary elevator men, lost children, nuns, hardened gamblers, tarts, and others, but this morning, when the monotonous rain seems to be falling straight from the gray skies of my childhood, I will make them the skies of my childhood for once. I have no taste for disguise, and while I can see that a writer sometimes has the status of a stagehand, I think that these concealments and imposturings can be exaggerated. A young woman writer, let's say, traveling between Salt Lake and Los Angeles, falls in love with another traveler. When the time comes for her to write her story she will disguise herself as a middle-aged spark-plug salesman going to his mother's funeral. Who is deceived? We see how clumsily she has stuffed her long hair up under a felt hat. She has not been able to conceal her sensitive features or the fact that she doesn't know one end of a spark plug from the other. I think she has wasted her powers of description and her time. I have been a soldier, a boatman, and a clerk, and I have thought along the lines of these occupations when they were mine. Now I am a writer and it is apparent in my mail, in my habits of thought, in the tennis sneakers I am wearing on this cold autumn day—even in the hole in my sock.

I am writing this in the suburb of X in the county of Y in what was once the tool shop or Petit Trianon of a millionaire. This good man began life as a machinist and, after his retirement, had a tool or machine shop built on one corner of his estate where he could amuse himself with lathes. The lathes were sold after his death and the place was turned into a guesthouse, which we rent from the chatelaine. The drains are often clogged, the heating plant is infirm, and the roof leaks, and because of these considerations we pay a modest rent. We have the pleasures of fine lawns and great trees and are established inexpensively in the bosom of a wealthy community with excellent public schools. In the bosom, I say, but this isn't so. I don't pay taxes, belong to the country club, or ride the commuting trains. I am, perforce, an outsider. I write stories that imply a considerable familiarity with the social axis of the place, but between you and me I haven't been inside the country club more than a dozen times.

These living arrangements are common enough. My friend P, the historical novelist, lives in a chauffeur's apartment in Greenwich. The poet K lives in a gatehouse in Mount Kisco. I must know a dozen people of aesthetic persuasions who live in stables and gardeners' cottages. There may be a hint of patronage in these arrangements, and there would be nothing wrong with that. The thought of a patron has often crossed my mind and I am not ashamed to say that I once tried to cultivate such a relationship. This was with a very rich man named Russell Berryman whom I met in the Army. It is unlikely that I would have met such a rich man anywhere else. We were companions in the Army, where Russell appeared to be retiring and poor. Then some time after the war, when I was living with my family in Manhattan, Russell telephoned and asked me to have lunch with him.

His office was in Rockefeller Center, listed as the Russell Berryman Foundation. In the brightly lighted outer office there were three or four men waiting. They all carried brief-cases and seemed anxious about the crease in their trousers and the knots in their ties, but they all lacked the heartiness of salesmanship. The receptionist took me into a further office where my friend was waiting. We had not met then for over a year and I was very pleased to see him. While we walked up Fifth Avenue he explained his position in life. His grandfather had left him a large sum of money. "I feel a responsibility to Grandfather," he said, "and I've organized the trust in his memory. I'm the only contributor. I've set a small trust aside for myself and my wife, and I intend to administer the rest of the income in a way that will assist education, the creative arts, all the things that Grandfather would have been interested in if he had had the time." He said that he had read some stories of mine and wanted my opinion on the advisability of helping writers.

This was the first time that I had ever been face to face with such largess and I piously gave him the names of two friends who needed help. I was thinking principally of my own case but I kept quiet about this. After luncheon I telephoned the friends whose names I had given to Russell. This was a mistake: He never got in touch with them. Walking back to his office after lunch, I asked him what grants the foundation had made and discovered that, although he had been in operation for a year, he had not yet parted with a nickel.

I saw a lot of Russell that fall and winter—ostensibly to discuss the general problem of philanthropy, with a good many broad hints at my own problems. I wanted to write a long book that no one was willing to finance, and there were times when Russell and I seemed made for one another. He was rich. Richness influenced every part of his life. It was a kind of richness that I have never seen outside the City of New York. Returning to Manhattan sometimes after a long absence, I am reminded of the Berrymans by the women in blond furs on Park Avenue, the dogs, and the doormen. In the meantime I had met Mrs. Berryman and had dinner at their apartment several times. I had given Russell an outline of my book and he had assured me that he meant to help. One afternoon in October or November, Lucia called and told me to hurry over to their place. "Russell has got to see you," she said. I walked across town to their apartment a little before dark.

My keenest recollections of New York have to do with my children. Moving as I do from neighborhood to neighborhood and knowing and liking many people in the city, there is almost no street in Manhattan I can walk on today without being met by the statuary of my past. I remember going to work, going to parties, going to visit friends in trouble, going to the drugstore to buy medicine, but none of this is as clear or as deep as the recollections I have of walking with my children.

On Sundays our destination was either the river or the zoo, and on weekdays when the children were good enough to be rewarded they would be taken to a Japanese store on Fifty-ninth Street to spend their change. This was always late in the day and often in the winter. Most offices were shut or closing, and the crowds on the sidewalk were mostly going east and going home. The Nedick's stand on the corner was brightly lighted and so were all the other stores—the watch-repair place, the Italian grocer, the cheap furniture store and the butcher, and all these lights generated in the cold the vitality of a human festival. Business at the Japanese store was never very brisk and the place had a clean smell like a laundry. The boxes in which a coin vanishes magically, the rubber spiders and water flowers that the children bought were linked to my earliest memories of childhood, and the vitality of the double line of lighted store fronts seemed linked to some even earlier memory. I walked past the Japanese store and through this festival to the Berrymans' that night.

They lived then on Park Avenue. Upstairs a butler let me in. He read the Bloomingdale label in my hat and coat before he hung them up. Some interior decorator had put a sumptuous and impersonal fix on the place. Lucia Berryman and her sister Mrs. Giacomo were in the living room where a fire was burning. Mrs. Giacomo was a dark-haired woman whose husband was on the police force.

She came to visit her sister once a month and took away Lucia's discarded finery. They had settled on this by the time I arrived. Mrs. Giacomo was sitting beside a pile of hat and suit boxes.

God knows how old Lucia Berryman was. Her hair was curled and burnished to the color of light mink. She had small hands, small feet, a pretty figure, and a harsh voice. Her temperament was gentle and prosaic. Most of her friends seemed to come from the theater and she had several times—cheerfully—offered to act as a procuress for me. She spoke of sexual passion in the same prosaic terms she used for hygiene. Hygiene often entered her conversation, but the bulk of it dealt with clothes and we won't go into that here. She had been poor; she was rich. She could be shrewish in defining her new position and once, when we had gone to the Plaza for dinner, she gave the captain hell for seating us at a table where the cloth had been darned.

"Russell has got to see you," she told me on that particular afternoon. "He's in there with his analyst but he'll be out in a little while. If you want to hear him you can," she said. She went to the library door and listened at the crack. "He's talking about food," she said. "That's mostly what he talks about. Dr. Parminter keeps asking him to try and remember things but all he can remember is things he ate." Then she tripped back across the room, sat on the arm of my chair, and kissed me. "You look so cute in a blue shirt, sweetie," she said. Everybody was sweetie, everybody was nifty, everybody was a cute kid. Even Jules Brulatour and Hope Hampton were cute kids; even Peggy Hopkins Joyce.

"Well I guess I'd better go," Mrs. Giacomo said. She put her hands on the arms of her chair and started to get up but this was as far as she got. She lived with the patrolman and her four children somewhere in Brooklyn and the thought of her trip or her destination seemed to attack her resolve. But she got to her feet when she heard some movement behind the library door. "I guess I'd better get a move on before he comes out and finds me with the loot," she whispered. She gathered up her boxes and Lucia walked her out to the elevator. I asked the butler to get me a drink, which he did. The library door opened and I could hear Dr. Parminter saying good-by to Russell. He crossed the living room as Lucia returned. "We're making progress, we're making progress," he said mournfully. He nodded sadly in my direction and went out the door. "He's such a cute kid," Lucia said. "I guess you can go and see Russell now."

Although Russell was not in business, he liked the atmosphere of an interview. He sat at a large desk in his library and gestured to a chair on the other side of the desk. "I've read your outline," he said. "I was thinking about you last night and I've come to a decision. You're a writer and I think some of the things you've written have been quite interesting and yet you're not successful. Very few people know your name. I was wondering why you seem to be such a failure and it came to me that you're never seen anywhere. You never go to good restaurants, you never go to opening nights at the theater, you never go to places where you'll be seen. I think you ought to go out more, I think you ought to be seen. I know that you don't go to expensive restaurants because you can't afford them and I'd like to help you. I'll arrange, if you're interested, to open charge accounts."

I suppose that I was sore because he hadn't mentioned the brilliance of my outline. I didn't admire, until later, how succinctly he had brought out the differences in our point of view. I thanked him—morosely, I suppose—but what good was a charge account at Le Pavillon for a man with a hole in his sock? He asked me to stay for a drink but I said it was late and we went together into the living room. "You can't go until you've seen Boris," Lucia said.

"Who's Boris?"

"He's my Russian friend," she said. "Wait a minute."

She came back into the room wearing what I guess was a sable coat. "Isn't he beautiful?" she asked. "Isn't he the most beautiful thing you ever saw? I picked every skin by hand and I've had my name put on every one of them. He's been photographed in *Harper's Bazaar* and *Vogue*, and Revillon wanted to put him in their window but I wouldn't let them. Oh Boris, Boris! When I put on Boris and walk down Fifth Avenue I'm just about the happiest woman in the world. He just makes me feel so good. I mean I feel young and pretty and rich and dated up solid for weeks and just everything. He makes me feel so good."

He did, too; you could see that. Her happiness was infectious and even my wounded feelings seemed to improve. Naturally I didn't see as much of the Berrymans after this clarification in our relationship but I still continued to see them now and then. I met Lucia one early evening in February, coming out of the St. Regis Hotel. It was a cold night and the excitement that the city seems to me to generate each winter season was at its height. The crowds on the street were richly dressed, excited, and happy, and there is nothing much in the neighborhood of the St. Regis that doesn't bear directly on pleasure. The cold was as exhilarating and the stars as bright as on any skating pond of my youth. We embraced and Lucia gave me a prosaic kiss and said sadly, "I've lost Boris." She took both of my hands in hers and looked sidewise into the gay crowd. "We went down to Miami ten days ago and I took him with me. I shouldn't of. It was terribly hot. The first night we went out to a night club to see this show. It was a waste of time. I've asked myself a hundred times why I ever went to that night club. The air-conditioning machinery was broken down and everybody was perspiring. I didn't enjoy a minute of it. When we got back we found that someone had broken into our rooms. They stole Boris. He was insured, of course, but what good does that do me? They'll never be another coat like him." I asked her to have a drink with me but she didn't have the time and so we kissed good-by—the unhappy princess and the writer with a hole in one sock.

The occupational hazards of writing, like those of night work and travel, have a profound effect on the emotional life. My first marriage suffered as much from literary ambitions as anything else. My wife was named Mary Lou, and she was a beauty—an authenticated beauty who had worked as a photographer's model. Her mother was a power in the millinery and gift-shop aristocracy of upper Madison Avenue and they both spoke in the deep Georgia accents of Their Plantation. This was a real Plantation and not a fantasy as you might suspect. I had been there. It stood for a way of life that they had every reason to remember vividly. Mary Lou was a high-spirited girl with the go-to-hell airs of the middle 1930's and many poignant and loving traits. When we had been married for about six months we reached a decision. I was wasting my time at a job. I wanted to be a writer. Why shouldn't I be a writer? She would find a job and support me while I finished the play I had been writing on weekends. I could repay the money when the play was produced. I could see that there were some hazards in this arrangement, but it seemed to me that in the progress of every love affair, blooming like the rose, there are hazards and that it is only intelligent to cope with them. All that Mary Lou wanted to express was her faith in my giftedness and in the giftedness of men in general. I gave up my job and she went to work.

I was happy to get along with the play, for to make a clear and sober record of what I experience and imagine is as strong in me as the need in some men to collect bits of old string or practice chip shots. Mary Lou put her wages in a joint checking account and we escaped any bad feeling about money. It seemed to make her happy to express her faith in me by taking a job: "Monkey's writing a play," she said proudly to everyone who might be interested and to many who were not.

My habits, I noticed, were undergoing a gradual reform. I had begun to do the shopping and wash the vegetables, and when I answered the doorbell (wearing an apron) and tried to put off the Fuller Brush man or a young woman with a soap sample, I had a painful feeling of dislocation. But the play went quickly, and when the second act was finished a producer took an option and paid me some money. I shouted out the news to Mary Lou when she came home from work but she wasn't excited. It didn't occur to me at the time that she took some pleasure in supporting me.

The news that I was writing a play excited in some people a sense of pity and responsibility. Soon after I had finished the second act an old friend telephoned and said that at long last he had found me a job. He asked me to lunch so that he could describe the benefits of the job he had found. He had pulled a lot of wires to get the job, and my refusal and particularly my reasons for it irritated him intensely. I could see his face form itself in an unhappy and perhaps final look of separation as if he could see me, while I drank my gin, slipping into that world inhabited by those queer men and women who are determined to forge an artistic career: those middle-aged messenger boys who are writing an epic poem about the death of innocence; those short-order cooks who are painting the fall of Rome; those lonely secretaries who slave all weekend over their reminiscences and short stories—that host of attic and cellar dwellers who are always "tied up" with some ephemeral project, always "too busy" to take the good jobs offered them by business friends; who handle their responsibilities toward the practical world poorly, scornfully, or not at all, and who seem— like drunkards on the downgrade—not to recognize their salvation and to perceive some destiny that has no bearing on their happiness or well-being. While we were eating lunch a man approached our table and my friend leaned toward me before he introduced us and said: "Don't tell him you're writing a play."

I was, though, and I was very happy, for the play let me feel that I was interpreting a passage in human relationships that had been chaotic and that this act of interpretation for myself and the other principles could only have constructive results. But Mary Lou was tired when she got home that night. She asked if I was going to work. I said that I wanted to. She asked if I minded if she went out to dinner.

"With a man from the office?"

"Yes."

"What kind of a man?"

"I don't know," she said.

"I'll cook dinner," I said.

"All right," she said. "I'll take a bath."

But when I put on the apron and started traveling between the stove, the sink, and the icebox, my mood changed and I began to put on the forms, one after another, of every despicable male that has ever crossed my path. I don't like to cook. Everything that I cook tastes burned and unfresh. Mary Lou still seemed tired when she came to the table and I did not have enough cheer or love to lighten that apartment. Since I had begun working on a play my musical tastes had improved, and after dinner I played the first Rasomouvsky Quartet on the phonograph. When I called Mary Lou's attention to the beauty of the second movement I found that she was asleep.

After this Mary Lou began to buy clothes for me, although I neither wanted nor needed clothes. But neither of us seemed to understand the career of solicitude and independence that she had embarked on. Then she took a lover. The consequences of this were violent and sordid and I won't go into them here. I never saw her lover or even learned his name. Our marriage would have lasted, I think, if I had done my work and she had done hers, if I had brought home the bacon and she had peeled the potatoes. I don't see why office hours should tyrannize our most intimate relationships, but the truth of the matter is that it didn't do us any good to have her come home from a hard day's work and find me bent over the typewriter. And there was one more thing. "You have your play," Mary Lou said to me during one of our quarrels. "I don't have anything but you have your play." She always spoke as if the play were a wife and three children, a steady income, and a place in the sun.

The play was finished and cast in June, and I killed a lot of time hanging around the theater when rehearsals began. The director and I didn't see eye to eye, but the production costs were estimated at $150,000, and with a hole in one sock my aesthetic position was precarious. My expenses were paid for a week in Philadelphia where the play opened. I also went to the opening in New York.

The royalties from Philadelphia wouldn't have justified anything like a celebration, but I had to be careful not to open a vein of

petulance and eat my supper in the Automat on opening night. I
ate in a place in the Village called the Rochambeau and walked to
the theater when the time came. It was a very windy night in the
autumn—the kind of night that is exciting in New York even
though you keep getting soot in your eyes. The play opened at the
Fulton and when I turned the corner there was a string of taxis,
and around the maw of the theater bloomed one of those lovely
yellow caves of light. The play was terrible, and I watched the
second and third acts from the back of the balcony. At the end I
went backstage because this was my privilege, but there was no one
there but the producer's assistant and a young actress who was
buying the curtains off the set. The lights in the lobby and on the
marquee were put out so swiftly that I had to struggle with my
coatsleeves in the dark. There I stood in an empty street where
whole sheets of the *Daily News* with their light freight of may-
hem and scandal ballooned around the middle air between the
dark buildings like the souls of our unborn children. I never went
back to the apartment or anywhere else with Mary Lou.

I divorced her and got married again. We had two children and
I was still living in Manhattan with my second wife when I was
approached through a series of intermediaries and asked if I would
write the biography of a banker's father. I will call the banker Mr.
Guilfoyle. He was a successful investment banker who had succeeded in avoiding publicity. His picture had never appeared in
the newspaper, etc. He had recently changed his tack and had begun to live publicly. He was angling, someone said, for an ambas-
sadorial post. He lived in a Hudson River castle north of Peekskill
and I went there to be interviewed.

He was a bullet-headed man of around sixty, I should say, with
bulbous features and charming eyes. He seemed to exhale a whole-
some atmosphere of requited ambition. His mind was virile and
elegant, but I think he had no imagination. The marbles in his
garden all came from Carrara and San Vincenzo, but the statues
were mostly of little children with pets. I don't mean this to seem
critical or bizarre but only as a measure of his lack of depth in this

one direction. In his belvedere there was a monumental represen-
tation of a marble child with three kittens and a ball of twine.

"I want you to write a biography of my father," he said. "As it
happens, I don't know anything about my father. I never saw
him and I don't know who he was, but a man in my position
needs some background and that's what I'm paying you to give
me."

I could see where bastardy—and this was what I guessed he was
suffering from—might stand in the way of his getting an ambas-
sadorship, and I said that I would try. I was to be given a room in
the castle and I could go down to New York on weekends. We
had a second interview and I outlined my ideas for him. The father
I would manufacture would be a Yankee minister—wiry, blue-eyed,
pious—raised in Newburyport and educated for the clergy in Boston. He would accept a call in China and his son would be born
in the mission compound at Nanking. His son would be educated in the United States but the Reverend and his wife would
remain in the Orient and be massacred by the Communists.

I hadn't finished my outline before Mr. Guilfoyle turned to me
eagerly as if there was some reality to this imaginary parent. We
were in his study in the castle, and when I spoke of the fictitious
old man he seemed to experience some emotional relief. He left
the castle the next day and I began my work. The Reverend's boyhood in Newburyport was easy to imagine, and when they came to
enter him in divinity school I found in the Peekskill library many
books of biography and reminiscence dealing with the ministry. It
was easy enough to piece together a background and imagine
events to fill it. The missionary compound was even more richly
documented and his years in China were the easiest to write. In a
secondhand bookstore in New York one afternoon I found an old
photograph of a handsome man with a clerical collar riding in a
rickshaw, and I bought this for a frontispiece.

The book was nearly done by spring, and I was pleased to think
of ending my life there, pleased with the money I had in the bank,
pleased with having completed something I had begun, and

pleased with a sense of accomplishment that was more than this, for the one thing that the Guilfoyle castle lacked was the ghost or at least the memory of a substantial male parent. The lack was in the air of the house and gardens, for while they were real enough, and while the intelligence that had made the money to buy them was real enough, they seemed to possess no secure place in time, as if Mr. Guilfoyle might be defeated in his exertions by the fact of bastardy. But if it is a corollary of our complex lives that we must be made by wise and loving people to the music of fountains, it is a flimsy one. Copies of *The Yankee Minister* could be put on the guest-room table so that people, asking themselves where Mr. Guilfoyle's wealth and acumen originated, could content themselves with the image of a Yankee minister. "He's the son of a poor missionary," people could say behind his back. It would be better than nothing. "He was born in China. . . ." It seemed to me that the legend would add some beauty to Mr. Guilfoyle's house and gardens and improve his reality.

This was in the spring, as I say, and I was taking a walk one night after dinner. Way past the flower gardens and the greenhouse were a vegetable garden and a second greenhouse that was no longer used. I had never been there. There was a cottage or shed at the end of this greenhouse, and I saw smoke rising from the chimney that evening. I wondered if the gardeners were using the old greenhouse for vegetable sets and I went down to see. They were using it, but not for growing. It was a storeroom or dump for scraps of chicken wire, house plants, lumber, and dried herbs.

I had turned to go when I heard someone calling after me, "What's your hurry, Sonny Jim, what's your hurry?" I saw an old man standing in the door to the cottage or shed that was attached to the greenhouse. He was bent. His coat-sweater was buttoned crookedly, and his trousers weren't buttoned at all. His cigarette was brown with spit. "Don't be afraid of me, don't be afraid of old Popsy," he called, kindly, I suppose, but the blue of his eyes was so faded that I felt uneasy. "Come in, Sonny Jim," he called, "come in and drink a little Kentucky courage with an old man." Stooped and duck-footed, he paddled into the cottage at the end

of the greenhouse and I followed him into a small room fur-
nished with broken and dirty chairs and tables. In the city sometimes, looking for ice or firewood or coal or a lost child, you will
go down some steep areaway stairs into an old man's lair pasted
with pictures of girls. It was like this. The smell was terrible. It was
not the staleness of the air itself that was oppressive; it was the
stink of an eclipsed sensual life, that point in senescence where
everything—the girls and the blue sky—that had been a glad summons is turned into a burden. He poured some whiskey into two
glasses and I sat down on a box.

"You work up at the big house, Sonny Jim?" he asked.

"Yes."

"He's a hard taskmaster."

"I haven't anything to complain about."

"Well you're the only one. They tell me he's a regular Pharaoh."

"Happy days," I said.

"Happy days, Sonny Jim."

"Do you work for him?" I asked.

"Oh, the stories I could tell you."

"What stories?"

"Stories about his miserliness. Even when he wants to be
charitable he don't have it in him. Last year, for business reasons,
of course, he invited a bunch of poor kids out here for the day.
They come out in busses. There's more than a hundred of them.
Well, they have their little picnic and they play their little games,
and when it comes time for them to go home they're all made to
line up by the main gate and have their ragged little figures be
frisked by a couple of Pinkerton men to make sure they'd none of
them stolen one of his dirty butter knives or maybe picked a faded
rose. The poor little kids!" The old man's eyes filled with tears.

"Do you work for him?" I asked.

"Work for him, Sonny Jim? I'm his father."

"How's that?"

"You want to know the naked truth? Oh I'll tell you. He tried
to kill me, Sonny Jim. He's a parricide. It was three years ago. October 17. I was living up to the big house then and I spend the

evening down in Peekskill drinking a little with some old cronies. I come home at about midnight but I have this terrible thirst and my own bottle's empty so I go to that big cabinet in the alcove off the library where he keeps his stuff. It's a world-famous antique, this old cabinet, but I'm his only, only father, and on Judgment Day, Sonny Jim, which will weigh heavier in God's scales—a stick of furniture or the bones of a kindly old man? Well this cabinet is locked so I pick up one of them ornamental knives and smash in the door. I've got the doors broken and am drinking my drink when he appears in his silken night robe and all. He's angry, Sonny Jim, he's sick with anger when he sees me and he takes this knife and drives it into my old shoulder. The pain!" The old man began to cry again. "They took five stitches there and my life hung by a thread. After that I moved down here. Parricide!"

I got out of there as soon as I could, and walked back toward the castle past the monument of the little girl and her kittens. For my purposes there was no point in looking any deeper into the ugly picture that the old man had presented—and into what was true and false about it—but the morality of my fictitious and reverend Yankee seemed open to question. It was a palliative—I had seen that in Guilfoyle's face when I told him that his father had been a dedicated clergyman. One of the uses of fiction is palliative, but you can say the same sometimes about bourbon whiskey and love. The soft curtain of light in which the evening star had just then appeared was, I knew, an illusion of gas and dust, and although the moon at my back was uninhabitable and scarified with calcium, its lights and craters excited in me only cheerful feelings of tenderness and love. It was perhaps because the Reverend Guilfoyle was nearly finished—he would be massacred by the Communists in a day or so—that the question of his morality, presented on a spring evening, did not seem grave after all. And when the book was published with its phony frontispiece it was reviewed cordially and sold a few hundred copies. I saw old Mr. Guilfoyle at the opening day of the spring meeting at Jamaica. He was buying fifty-dollar win tickets and drinking Jack Daniels, and with a cold wind tearing at the clubhouse hydrangeas—those shipboard plants—and the band playing "Mavourneen, Mavourneen," where could he have been happier?

Now it is five o'clock. I know as much because my wife has just called to me and asked me to fix the drain in the kitchen. She would not have asked me sooner. The sky has cleared, and the last of the sun comes in at my window. The air smells of the fragrance and the rankness in the garden and the darker odors of the woods and the river near here, and my children are holding races on the grass.

In the face of this lightness and calmness my deep training in calumny—that armful of knives, pikestaves, umbrellas, baseball bats, and rifles that I carry over from French realism—seems to slide to the floor. The sound of these voices—my wife's and the children's —thrills me with a feeling of love that is mysterious and deep, and the beauty of the late afternoon appears with an extraordinary intactness—a lack of reflection—as, when we are walking on a beach, we are moved to pick up a worn shell gleaming with calcium and admire its form. So the afternoon, the hour, seems like a seashell. Presently it will seem like something else—a nave or a dungeon, and then—there are some dark clouds in the west—like something else again.

But hearing my wife and watching the children on the grass, I think that I have never written anything like this, about anything like this peace, and then I put the cover on the typewriter and I think that I will do this tomorrow; I will do something like this tomorrow.

BARREN TO THE STARS

Hallie Burnett

Hallie Burnett, whose family roots (Dutch, English, and French Huguenot) go back to seventeenth and early eighteenth century America, was born in St. Louis, Missouri, of parents transplanted from Louisiana and Vermont. Since her 16th year she has lived and travelled extensively in this country and Europe, although for the last fifteen years or so she has been most at home in the area around New York City. With Whit Burnett, her husband, she was an editor of Story magazine for eleven years, and, since the birth of their two children John Southgate and Ann Beekman in 1943 and 1946, has published many short stories and three novels.

The Reverend Mr. Trask looked small and old as he stood beside Bishop Matthews in the vestibule of the tiny Episcopal church. The wide white sleeves under the Bishop's cassock fell back in ecclesiastical grace from his lace cuffs and large, well-cared-for hands, and a look of power was upon him. Mr. Trask had none of this; in his worn black frock he seemed withdrawn and tired, and it was as if the years of his calling had taken much from him.

It was the first Sunday after Easter and the two clerics could look back now toward the nave and watch Mr. Trask's parishioners flow into the aisle like little tributaries emptying into a main and troubled stream, where they were propelled onward by the force of the Bishop's attraction. "Good to see you again—fine—fine—" Bishop Matthews murmured greetings in such a way that they passed out into the April sunshine smiling, pleased with themselves, and knowing they were honored by his visit. Mr. Trask could not avoid the thought that once they had approached *him* with the same air of expectancy, but he had lacked the grace to fold his hands over theirs as the Bishop did with such assurance, nor had he ever possessed the deep and booming voice to stir them with. It was not unnatural that a man so young, with this manner, had been made a Bishop.

That was never my ambition, reflected Mr. Trask. I only desired to remain in one place and be needed there. It is regrettable that I have found so little to admire in these people I was cast among. I have been with them for many years, and I have learned not to like them, he thought coldly, dispassionately. I was not surprised when things turned out as they did. . . . Now that he was leaving he could remember his first day, knowing that it is the end of anything that gives shape to its beginning. He had been young then, and hopeful for their love; thinking, surely the church was an expression of a larger generosity, a need to share—which was love in its essence—that brought them together under one roof every Sunday, that bent them to their knees in prayer, and lifted their heads in song. . . . .

But he had seen them begin to nod their heads in drowsiness a moment after the services had begun; he had noticed how their knees bent in prayer with less urgency than when they climbed the steps to their offices, or their homes; and their heads were unlifted, and their voices tuneless when they sang, as if they had not known they were singing for the Lord. And, they would be glad to see him go.

Bowing soberly to his parishioners, he could see himself as he was now. With a painful honesty he admitted that he lacked completely this grace that was so apparent even in the turn of the young Bishop's head; that it was not only a physical lack but a mental one as well. He knew his beliefs were angular and sometimes harsh, but he had not the gift to mold them into something different.

And when he had found himself unable to meet the rising cost of living within his frugal salary, he had felt right (so seldom before had he thought of money) in asking for the small increase; he had asked as if he had the right to expect it. It was that which had given them the opportunity to say, Times are hard for us all. We will have to get a young man, unmarried, who can live on your salary. We can't hold you from some parish that will give you more . . .

Now they were making a great fuss, as if they did not want to see him go. The Bishop's talk this morning about their regrets was fine and eloquent. The Bishop as always was the image of tact, and affability—his own requests would be subtly phrased when he made them, or not at all.

Just as the bitterness began to flicker again, Mr. Trask saw old Mrs. Johnson approaching, and he was glad he had been told she was not present at the meeting that decided his fate. Now she moved slowly as she had in the past year, so that her natural dignity seemed to grow greater as her strength grew less. She was not one of those nervous ones, he reflected, who fight against weakness in the sight of all; rather, she was accepting the gradual defeat of her body with a grace as timeless as the slow pounding of waves upon a rock.

And he felt tender toward her as he recalled her indignation because he was leaving, but she had not insulted him by offering to change things then. He also knew the purse the congregation would give him tonight was four-fifths filled by her. If it had not been, he could not take it, and yet he must, as it was in this way he had to permit his "flock" to salve their consciences.

There was an element of real sincerity in Bishop Matthews' manner now, in the lifting of his hand.

"Mrs. Johnson," he said in his deep fine voice, "I have thought so often of our charming evening in your home last winter."

Mrs. Johnson nodded, with the pleasant formality that seemed to intimidate no one, not even her grandchildren. "We expect you with us today, Bishop Matthews. Mr. Trask has promised to bring you for luncheon."

And she went on as though with no impulse to linger as had the others.

This pleased Mr. Trask. He had been in an oddly unpredictable state of mind for the past week when strange things pleased him, and others could fill him with an almost Biblical rage. He did not recognize himself drawn thus into the stress of living; the outer layers of his being seemed wrapped in the many garments of his errors, and it was as if he could not remove them, as yet unmoistened by his tears. He had been angry; he had known bitterness; he had failed to reach his people, and he had nursed his vanity in this failure like an open wound. Still he permitted himself a fleeting touch of amusement because Mrs. Johnson had said so little to the Bishop!

Walking across the grass to the rectory after the service Bishop Matthews no longer talked; his quick and well-phrased words rested behind a thoughtful smile, which was his way of communicating with lesser people. But he did say,

"Reverend, it is a pity you find you must leave here when Mrs. Johnson is obviously so very fond of you."

Coldly, Mr. Trask walked beside him, his lean nervous face controlled by habit, and also at this moment by his own anger.

"I shall miss Mrs. Johnson," he said. "She has been kind, always."

He knew what the Bishop meant; it was the very reason he had not gone to see her more often, had, with her, kept at a distance he did not wish. He had suffered when he had to ask her help for other members of the congregation, because she was a very rich woman, and because of this he must pretend not to love her, for fear she might think he cared for this. This too, perhaps, was a part of his failure as a man and as a leader among them; and yet, deeply, he felt that she understood.

Genevieve met them at the door. He saw his wife again now as she must look to the Bishop—a square, Germanic looking woman with protruding teeth, and he hurried quickly into the house. It was not that he wanted to escape her—he had never been aware of this as a desire—but because he felt he did not please her now more than he did the others. Because she was another part of his life that he had fitted into without grace, without understanding, and without enough love; and which, foolishly, he did not want to leave. His marriage, as his years here in Leesville, had meant no lifting of a veil on beauty, upon the rewards of a deeper life, a finer consciousness; in both cases the original outline had been superior to the finished work.

"I was just saying," repeated the Bishop as if continuing a long conversation, "that Mrs. Johnson seems to have a real fondness for your husband, Mrs. Trask. It is a pity—perhaps—"

Genevieve of course could see what the Bishop was getting at, and Mr. Trask watched her apprehensively. He had not believed her own sparse way of meeting people was the best, but at least she had not toadied to the important ones either, she had been firm and righteous with all—even the children of the parishioners and he reflected wryly how she made them eat everything on their plates when the young people had dined at the rectory. "It is a pity there were not more like her," said Genevieve acidly, unexpectedly, and although it was this thought that had been in Mr. Trask's mind, he looked at her with distaste.

"There are many fine people here," he said, hurriedly, but Bishop Matthews did not appear to hear him, nor had he seemed to understand Genevieve.

"It is quite possible, Reverend," he went on, "that an adjustment could still be made. I understand Mrs. Johnson was not advised earlier—and that it is not easy at this time to spare a young man for this post, so many of them are doing God's work in other ways, helping in other pastures—"

"No adjustment is possible, I am afraid," said Mr. Trask, quickly, and, whereas the anger before had been like a small flame that suddenly licked forth from a nest of coals, now it was detached and blue.

At last the Bishop did understand, and he must have been puzzled how two people could stand before him with the same reactions, and yet seem so far apart in relation to each other, as if, absurdly, each somehow had wished for the other to be different.

Bishop Matthews went to his room to rest, and Mr. Trask started for his study. As he made his way up the worn stairs, he thought of his house and how it must seem to the Bishop. The Mission furniture had endured and would have endured until he himself was dust. And the meals Genevieve served the Bishop were well-cooked, well-balanced. "Oh, now, Philip," she would say before anyone—"but this is *good* for you." Perhaps if there had been some taste to the food, or to the house. Just taste, he thought, I don't even ask for beauty—perhaps with a little of that *I* might have been different.

In the study he thought in this way for a while, but there was a pattern here that sooner or later got such digressions under control. The groove of dogma was strong in this room, and his thoughts quite naturally were drawn to a more orderly plane, and thus, a controlled one. And he fell then to completing plans to move to the little village thirty miles away, which was to be the scene, as here he could admit almost disdainfully, of his final defeat among the living.

At luncheon Mr. Trask had a small triumph when Mrs. Johnson asked him to confer the blessing. It was such a small thing, and it did not really move him at all, but he could see the schemes start again in Bishop Matthews' head like a hive of bees set in motion by the wind. The Bishop even looked at him with a little nod, not resenting this, but as if to say, You see, you do have her interest. Genevieve looked at her plate, her lips compressed; he knew her impulse was to speak, and say it was proper that the Bishop ask grace, and before a member of the congregation younger than Mrs. Johnson she would have spoken.

So with a quite irreverent feeling of amusement Mr. Trask bent his head and began, "Oh, heavenly Father—"

When he had finished, he caught a twinkle in the eye of Mrs. Johnson, as if together they had shared a joke. And for the first time in his life Mr. Trask recognized the impulse to wink; he even tried to, unsuccessfully, looking down on his plate, but he fancied

Genevieve was leaning over, about to speak, and he quickly recovered himself.

This one small incident, however, had set off something within him so that he felt rather giddy, as if his depression had been suddenly lifted, too suddenly. That this was largely due to Mrs. Johnson he understood, and that it was fleeting, he knew also. But today somehow he did not bother as before to fear the ogre of privilege; he was enjoying things he had not even noticed before. From the moment he had come in, he had been surprised to find that he was looking at things with a new appreciation, even as a few hours ago he had been too poignantly aware of the ugliness in his own home. He let the golden lights on the silver candlesticks please him, disproportionately, he noticed the intricate floral design on the fine old bone china, and he held the wine for an instant on the back of his tongue, tasting it, as he had once been taught to do by a Catholic priest. And he did not once look at Genevieve, but frequently at Mrs. Johnson, lovely in gray, with a creamy lace collar, and he thought her eyes were the most gracious he had ever seen. He thought if she were a young woman, and he a different kind of a man, this was the feeling he would like to have had in love! And he knew all this was because tomorrow he would die, and recklessness is a privilege of the damned. And he knew also that one of the hard things he had to face was knowing he would not see Mrs. Johnson again.

Later she took them all for a drive into the hills, and he was startled to find that the buds were already green and the earth black and moist for growth and he felt regret that the pending event of his leaving had not permitted him the freedom of impulse to walk into the country and see these things. He felt slightly feverish about everything and exhilarated in a way he knew would not last, but which he clung to as long as he dared.

It was not until Bishop Matthews had been put on the train, and he and Genevieve were left at their own door that he also recalled something he had been aware of earlier: a feeling of excitement, of anticipation in Mrs. Johnson, as if she knew something that perhaps he did not know. And occasionally she had a look of being faintly puzzled also; but he thought he understood. She knew him, he felt, hopefully, and she was happy about the purse they were to give him as any generous person was about a gift: and she felt a sense of anticipation for the pleasure of it. As for being puzzled, why then how could she know yet if he could accept this, being as he was? She did not know he had forced himself to recognize that he must.

There was a knock on the study door, and he knew it was Genevieve. Sitting very still in his old leather chair, his eyes closed, his hands folded over his vest, he waited, in case she should look in; but after a moment he heard her go away.

And then a great tiredness came over him, and he did not move again for a long time.

He and Genevieve came out of the rectory just at dusk, and the tiny steeple of his church rose above them, and he thought that has been called a finger pointing to God. But it is perhaps in reality only an extremity erected by the architect to rise above the houses around—remote from them, it does not contain apples and potatoes like a cellar, it contains only a bell that arouses them from their slumbers on Sunday morning, their suppers on Sunday night. Otherwise, I do not think it has any significance for them. But he thought this mildly, for now that the time was near, he was moved only by a feeling of sadness. The anger had been broken somewhere between lunch and sleep. My youth is gone, he thought, my hopes, my fine sermons that were never so eloquent as I wished, but which I thought would sometimes, if only by the law of averages, reach my people. Perhaps I have never reached them, he thought, sadly; I doubt if I was ever able to speak the words they wanted to hear.

They separated, and he went into the little vestry and put on his frock, while Genevieve entered the church from the front and sat down in the same pew she had occupied for so long.

They were all there, and now in his sadness he thought he could detect, if not regret, at least embarrassment, on some faces. That there is also regret in embarrassment he acknowledged to himself, as he noticed the silence that hung over the church.

"Oh Lord, my God, in thee have I put my trust," he began the ritual to the bowed heads.

The responses were soft to his listening ears, and the singing also. And when the banker, Mr. Gow, got to his feet at the appointed time, and cleared his throat, it was almost as if there was a presence in the church that had not been there before.

"We—the people of this congregation, would like to make this little gift of appreciation to the Reverend Trask for his services during these years and to wish him and Mrs. Trask a lot of luck on their new undertaking."

The banker was flushed, and his words were spoken gruffly, because he knew no other way, but at least now he was wide awake, and even mildly moved, if only by the solemnity of his own mission.

The purse was brought to Mr. Trask by the banker's daughter, Nellie, whose small face was very serious. He felt tender toward her for a moment, so that he could accept the gift better than he had thought he would. Holding the little bag in his hand, with the lettering First National Bank of Leesville on one side, he felt the bills and the silver, just as it had been collected, and it burned in his hands, so that he wanted to thrust it aside; but at this moment he found he could draw on some resource of graciousness he had not known, or had forgotten, that he possessed.

"Mrs. Trask and I accept this offering with deep gratitude," he said, and if his voice sounded remote even in his own hearing, he knew he was saying the words they wanted him to say, and perhaps had not been quite sure he would. "Our years among you have been rich and rewarding ones, we have gone through much together, war, the loss of friends, anxiety for the future—and we have, I hope, shared the same faith."

He looked toward Mrs. Johnson sitting upright, majestic in her pew, and her look of attention was a reward. He said another word or two, and looked back at her. And as his eyes passed over the congregation for a moment he had a strange feeling of triumph. I have reached them at last, he thought, here, in this hour of my defeat, I am at last among them. He felt a strange stirring in his breast, and when he lifted his hands above them for the Benediction the feeling flooded through him, so that his voice did not sound remote any longer, but strangely moved and resonant.

Abruptly he drew back into himself as they filed out; the weakness he had shown now embarrassed him. And he had seen also that Mrs. Johnson had been the first to leave, going down the aisle alone, and it had reminded him more forcibly than ever of all that he was losing.

She does not want to say goodbye, he thought. I believe that is it. She is moved, and perhaps sorry I must go. And this came as a surprise to him, for he had not for many years considered the possibility that one should feel so personally toward him.

The church was cleared quickly after this, and when he saw Genevieve waiting he told her that she was to go home alone, he would be with her soon. She did not speak, only nodded, and he saw that she also could have wept if she had been less strong. *We have been too strong*, he thought, *we have not let them be easy in this House*. But it is too late now, you can not undo the error of having expected too much from anyone. He and Genevieve were, in a sense, alike; only he had asked for more, and Genevieve did not question what the Lord had given her, or rather failed to give her. There had been no children. She had not even questioned the Lord's decision in this.

And perhaps, if we had been parents, we would have made the same mistakes, he admitted, painfully, sitting alone in the front pew, facing the tiny baptismal font on the right of the altar. We would have kept too much to the letter, and it may be, they also would have felt we did not understand and would have rejected us.

Where had it all gone wrong?

He had been thirty-two when he came to Leesville, feeling not young then except in his hope for a place in this new parish. Before that he had been in Minnesota, where the winters were cold and the land barren for long months of the year, and, in his section, intellectually barren as well. The parish here had not been much larger but it was the East, where, he always believed, the mind could feast with the body. He had spread the spiritual food before his people, gladly drawing on all the resources of his intellect —but he had stopped there, when he found they were not reaching out for it, for he had not known how to make them eat. And so, he had gone back into himself again, forgetting his failure after a time, taking it for granted in the cold pleasure of his own interior nourishment. And his years between thirty-two and forty-five had passed, and he had just learned, as each man does for himself how fast in time these years go.

It was too late now to retrieve what he had lost. It was too late, his heart cried, to start again, and perhaps fail as before. The ties that bind one person to others must be started early, begun with a small invisible thread, adding others, so that in time they become visible, and a pattern is made—

He felt like a man who has been long crippled, and now must walk by faith alone. Or not walk; perhaps even this did not matter now.

His loneliness suddenly became so acute, and his sorrow so deep that he got up quickly, and a few moments later was outside, the church darkened, and the night still, around him. The street lamp burned brightly on the corner, and the living rooms of the houses around him were warm pink glows of comfort; but outside where he stood was black solitude and he felt lost in misery. The barrenness of the world, he thought; and remembered a bitter phrase from some closed book—"the barrenness of the world extends even to the stars."

He felt his hand cold against his clothes, and his legs were so tired and heavy that if his will power had not been strong, they would have failed him as he stumbled up the dark walk, away from the rectory.

He must have walked for hours, his mind searching, condemning himself, and even when the moon came up full and glowing, he did not find an answer. He did not tire, and he did not stop; but the heavy weight of his own failure kept pressing in like a suffocation, and he could not escape it. The moon is the Bishop, he thought once, trying to lighten his mood, and I am but one of the little stars whose light grows dim as his light grows brighter. The strong ones, like Venus, survive.

The moon is Faith, some soberer answer came from his brain. Perhaps the stars, then, are one's problems, to be lost in the glow—

He did not know where to turn after a while, and it was then he let his feet lead him, willing them not at all. They kept going, like the knees of his parishioners, he thought, in robot fashion. So the bitterness is still there, he admitted; if only I could expel that, it would be easier to find my way. But the two extremes, his failure and the failure of others, kept swinging pendulum-wise within the confines of his mind.

It was not until he saw the lights in Mrs. Johnson's house that he realized how late it was. Some warning came into his consciousness, then, and he thought, although he had not known he was aware of the passing time, *Why it is late for her to be still awake!* And then he saw the doctor's car at the curb, and the maid in a wrapper suddenly drawing aside the lace curtains, roughly, as though she were frightened, and peering out into the night. He thought, *She is ill!*

His legs now carried him to the front door, and the maid flung it wide for him.

"Oh Mr. Trask," she cried, and her homely face was distorted with crying. "She was took so bad—I just got him here, the doctor — He don't leave the room, he don't open the door. I don't know what it is— She called me, Mary, she says—I was in my bed and she says, Oh, Mary— And I phoned the doctor. Oh—" The girl began crying loudly now, so that Mr. Trask tried to comfort her. "Maybe she'll *die*—" she moaned.

"She has lived many useful years, Mary," he said, and pushed her aside, gently. "Try to be calm. I will go and see." But once on the stairs, his own calm left him, and he moved quickly, so that in an instant he was outside the bedroom door, listening. For a long moment he heard nothing, and then there was a sigh, a long, tired sound like the brushing of a hand in a pile of dead leaves; and it struck him poignantly as he recognized even in this the peculiar quality of personality that was Mrs. Johnson's. Softly he touched the door with his knuckles, and the doctor called sharply.

"Who's there?"

"It is I, Mr. Trask—"

When the door was opened, he looked quickly, apprehensively, to the bed, not knowing what he would see. He had never before feared impending death, but he knew what death could be, and he could not bear to see disintegration in her.

She did not fail him. Propped high on her big pillows and breathing sharply, her fine white hair hung in serene and lovely braids over the coverlet. Even her eyes smiled for him, although he saw at a glance they were veiled by a sedative. But one side of her mouth was paralyzed, and a fold of gray-white flesh hung sadly over her chin.

"So—glad," he understood her to say. "You—were fine—."

She could not go on, but her eyes continued to look at him with the same sense of sharing he had felt earlier. It was as if they were both going away now, and she was encouraging him to look for what she seemed sure to find.

The doctor spoke. "She wanted you," he said. "We called, but Mrs. Trask said you were out—Mrs. Johnson asked for you."

"For me?" Deeply moved, Mr. Trask looked at the face on the pillows. *Me?*

"You were—fine," she whispered. "Tonight—you made them feel—you had courage."

"I have no courage," he had to say, softly, sorrowingly. "And no gift to give it to others—"

She tried to nod her re-assurance, but she did not speak again, she could not. But what she had said! Did she know the power of what she had said now! Was it more than kindness, more than last hour prescience that had let her speak? Perhaps, he thought suddenly, I have reached them.

Mr. Trask dropped to his knees beside her, and taking her long warm hand in his he began to pray. "Our Father, who art in heaven, Hallowed be thy Name," and he felt the doctor tiptoe from the room. The door closed softly. When he had finished, he felt his own tears on her hand, undrying, and looked up, wondering if she felt them, the first he had shed. But Mrs. Johnson was not living now, although on her face was a look as though she had been listening to the end.

He got to his feet stiffly, as if he had been there a long time, and yet he was able to move with more ease, and the tiredness seemed less. And he thought, gratefully, I was here with her up to the very last. I was able to reach her!

Slowly, he left the room, giving it over once again to the doctor, and he thought, It will not be so hard to go, now that she is no longer here.

And he thought also, tenderly, hurrying home to Genevieve— she would be worried that he was gone so long—how this day had been so important, perhaps the most important in his life. He could go now to the smaller parish with hope, for even there quite possibly would be other Mrs. Johnsons. At least he knew now he had touched one person deeply, a beautiful and gracious one, and in time he might reach others, even as she said he had tonight.

And he thought quite humbly that it would be fine to try again, after all. He knew better how it was done, now.

SHIP OF PRISONERS

Sidney Stewart

Sidney Stewart, a native of Oklahoma, was a draftee in the United States Army, and his first active duty was in Manila. He was taken into the Army one month after his twenty-first birthday, while he was in medical school. He arrived in Manila six weeks before Pearl Harbor.

As the author of Give Us This Day (first published in France, then England and finally in America) he relates the ordeals of himself and his companions who were captured by the Japanese in the Philippines. A survivor of Bataan, he was a captive for more than three years, experiencing one form of torment, privation and suffering after another. (He was finally rescued and now lives in France, studying and writing.)

Taken off the islands by the Japanese, the group Stewart was with looked hopefully toward the mainland of the conquerors where there might be a few drops more water each day and a little more food. But hundreds had died on forced marches, through starvation, through disease and through despair, violence and insanity, and when they were herded into the hold of a small ship, crowded tighter than cattle had ever been crowded there, lying or standing in manure, the men were not hopeful. . . .

JANUARY, 1945

Often I looked up above and saw the toothy, hunchbacked Wata glaring with distorted eyes through his thick-lensed glasses. Standing at the open hatchway, he grinned down at us. When the rice was passed around I saw what he considered funny.

A colonel who had once commanded an entire regiment stood, his eyes glazed with hopelessness, clutching his little handful of rice against his naked chest and eating it with filthy fingers. He was trying desperately to keep the flies away from it and to put the grains into his mouth without getting flies at the same time.

There were scientists with us, scholars, rich men. Misery had made us all alike. We were no longer men, save in brief flashes. Merely hulks of human flesh which contained only a desire to eat and a desire for water and a hope and a prayer to live.

More men were dying every hour. We moved them forward and stacked them just beneath the hatch so that when Wata, or any of the other Japs, looked down into the hold he could see the yellow, emaciated dead. The Japs knew that this would happen to all of us unless we received more food.

One of the hardest things to bear, as each man was carried forward and added to the growing pile, was the look on Father Cummings' face.

"If only I could do something," he would say. "If I could give them the last rites, or be with every man as he died. Maybe he would hold on to his faith that last flickering moment before he departed. I don't care whether they're Protestant or Catholic. If I could just hold their hands and pray with them as they died. But there are so many. I can't be with them all."

I looked around. Here were four of us, three of different Protestant churches, and one who didn't care what church but still believed in God. Not one of us was Catholic, and yet we all felt close to Father Bill. Because we knew he possessed that one thing that would save us all—if anything could.

One morning a dying man near us called out to Father Cummings:

"Father, please, I am afraid." His voice came in a dry, rasping sound. "Please, pray for me."

Father Bill crawled over and knelt beside the man. The prayer came to me in a humming whisper I could not hear. But when he had finished, the panic-stricken man clutched the priest's arm with his long bony fingers. In the faint light I could see his flesh grow white under the desperate grasp of that hand. I thought maybe the man was crazy and started to move toward them in case Father Cummings needed help. But the wide pleading eyes held me back.

"Father, I've never been baptized." Tears rolled across his shrunken yellow face. "Please baptize me. I don't want to die without being baptized."

"But, son, I have no water." Father Cummings spoke as though to a frightened child. But I could see, as I knew he could, that the man would not live until the next ration of water was lowered into the hold. Father Cummings reached down and unlocked the man's grasp on his arm.

"I'll be back in a moment," he said.

"Don't leave me, Father." He was sobbing now.

Father Cummings crawled back to where we were waiting. But the look on our faces told him without asking. We had no water. Desperately he looked at the other men, but they merely shook their heads sadly. My mouth was dry like cotton and my throat cried for moisture, but I would gladly have given him water had I had any. Only one man kept his eyes averted suspiciously. In this struggle for survival I knew Father Cummings would not ask for what a man did not offer of his own accord. Finally he turned and crawled back to the dying man and knelt beside him.

I saw him run his tongue across his dry lips. Then he spat on two of his fingers and ran them over the man's forehead.

"I baptize thee in the Name of the Father, and of the Son, and of the Holy Ghost."

Then he took the man's hand and held it while peace returned to the frightened eyes.

The stench of the bodies in the hold became so great that it was spreading to the upper part of the ship. Finally the guards threw ropes down into the hold and commanded us to tie the bodies together. They called some of the men on deck and allowed the bodies to be hauled up. Then the bodies were splashed into the water with weights to pull them to the bottom of the sea.

Each day, as the ship moved farther north, it grew colder, and we could feel the chill seeping down into the hold. We huddled together, trying to keep each other warm with our bodies.

One afternoon, when I was helping to drag another body and stack it with the rest of the pile, I stopped and looked up. Above me, standing on the deck and looking down, was a Jap private with a gun in his hand. There was a quiet look on his face, an expression almost of sorrow. He shook his head.

"Keena doko, nehimo," he said gravely, and then in faltering English, for fear I had not understood him, "I am sorry. I wish I could help you."

I spoke to him in Japanese and asked him what day it was.

He looked back over his shoulder as though afraid someone would hear him.

"It's the third of January, 1945," he said quickly. "We're sailing into Takaow, Taiwan."

I knew Takaow was on the southern tip of Formosa.

"We're sailing into the harbor now," he said. "It's a big harbor. Maybe they'll take you off here. I don't know." He turned and walked away. I walked back to my small group of friends and told them the news.

"One of the guards just told me that we're pulling into Takaow on the southern tip of Formosa."

It seemed to cheer them that we were in Formosa. We had been told that there were prison camps there and that conditions weren't too bad. Maybe they would take us ashore.

We were getting ready to tie up somewhere, because I could feel the anchor running out. The boat stopped its engines and settled down. We sat there for the rest of the day hoping. Two days passed. On the evening of the third day I heard planes circling in the air above the ship, and the spitting of anti-aircraft.

"My God! Not American planes here too," I thought. I walked over to one of the Navy men with us.

"Do you think there'd be American planes here?" I asked.

"Why not?" he countered. Then almost regretfully, "But I guess they aren't Navy planes. They're most likely coming from China. Army stuff."

I walked back to my group and carried the news. I knew that we couldn't stand another bombing. Surely they would get us out. I couldn't understand why we were just sitting here in the hold of the ship. We sat through the night worrying.

Would they get us off before American planes could strike?

It was early the next morning, while the Japs were lowering the water into the hold, that they suddenly dropped the ropes and began screaming. We knew something was happening. All of a sudden I heard the planes diving in the air above us and the ship began shaking with the quick rattle of the anti-aircraft guns.

Quickly I grasped Rass' hand. Then I turned and looked at Father Cummings. There was a thunderous crashing above us. My stomach rushed to my throat as if I were falling through space. The ship leaped and bucked. Again there was the screaming roar of the diving planes. Like a trapped animal, I cowered against the floor.

"Oh, God, here they come again!" Hughes cried.

Then my brain was bursting. My eyes felt a blinding flash. Bombs crashed down upon us. I heard a shattering, pulpy sound and warm liquid drenched me. A volcanic flash split my eyes again. A thousand hammers pounded against my body, dashing my head against the steel floor. Pungent smoke burned my throat. Things were falling like rain around us. I lost consciousness. Then I was jerked back by a chain of explosions bursting at the back of my brain. Something slashed like a white-hot knife down my spine, ripping and crushing my legs and hips.

My head cleared, but there was a horrible pain in my back. Smoke was thick and burning. Flashes of fire were everywhere. It was an inferno, with a din and rattle of guns above. A cave-like blackness engulfed me and I lost consciousness again.

When I came to, the roar of the planes was dim and distant. I had a sense of extreme, excruciating pain in my back and then suddenly I realized the fighting was over. A heavy beam was lying across my hips and a piece of a hatch cover on my legs. The floor was covered with blood and there were pieces of arms and legs and a head lying beside me, the head of someone I did not recognize. I looked around for my friends. Weldon and Hughes also had beams lying across their legs. White smoke floated in the air and burned my lungs like fire. My head was throbbing and my ears rang, dulling the pitiful cries of the torn and bleeding men.

I knew my legs were crushed. I was afraid to touch them, afraid to run my hands down for fear that maybe they weren't even there at all. There was no feeling in them.

I got up my nerve and ran my hand underneath the beam on my hips. The bones seemed to move at the base of my hips and I knew they were broken and my legs crushed. There was no feeling in them. They were numb.

Now men were standing up and walking around dazed. Some men were walking with their arms blown off. It seemed that there were only a few alive.

"Sid! Sid! Are you all right?" I heard Rass call frantically.

"No, I think my legs are broken," I called back. "Maybe my back."

Then he was beside me. There was a bloody slash that ran across his cheek, but he was not seriously hurt. He walked over and looked down at Weldon and Hughes.

"I think they're both gone," he said. "They're both out."

Then he bent over Father Cummings. Rass began to massage his arms and his face. After a moment or two Father Cummings sat up and he was all right. He wasn't hurt. He had just been knocked out by one of the beams. He and Rass came over and lifted the steel girder that had fallen across part of me and then the broken hatch cover.

"Do you think you can stand?" Father Cummings asked me.

I reached down and pinched my legs and there was no feeling. I seemed paralyzed from the waist down, but there wasn't much pain. I looked up and I could see the look of concern on Rass' face. Father Cummings was looking at the mess around us, at the many bodies and the wounded men, and tears were in his eyes. He and Rass started to walk away.

"Don't leave me!" I pleaded. Rass turned around.

"Take it easy," he said. "We're just gonna try to get Hughes and Weldon out from under this mess."

Father Cummings bent close to feel Hughes' pulse.

"Well, he's still alive," he sighed.

Rass bent over Weldon, massaging his arms and slapping his face.

"Weldon's alive too," he announced.

I watched them open their eyes. They shook their heads dazedly. Rass was busy examining Hughes' legs. He hesitated a long moment before he told us.

"They're both broken and crushed."

Father Cummings and Rass knelt beside Weldon and I saw Father Cummings shake his head.

"Well, he had only one leg broken, but it's a bad break," he said. "Part of the bone is protruding through the flesh."

Rass came back over and knelt down beside me. He ran his hand across my forehead and through my hair.

"Stew, try not to be scared and afraid," he said gently. "We're going to try and help some of the other guys. Don't get frightened. We'll be back. Just hold on to your nerve."

I watched him and Father Cummings walk around among the men, helping some to their feet, lifting beams off the others, and moving out some of the dead. Rass took charge of the section. He got hold of one of the American doctors, and they began calling for all the men who had any clothing at all to take it off and rip it up for bandages. They took pieces of the wood that had blown into the hold and used them for splints.

I began to fear that the planes would come back again. I knew I was crying. I couldn't help crying. I didn't want to believe in God. I wanted only to live. If the planes came back and struck again, none of us would live.

"Hey, Stew! Hang on to yourself, fellow." It was Weldon's voice and I felt ashamed, because I knew his leg was broken and yet he was holding on. I lay there, forcing a calmness of spirit. Gradually, by pulling myself along with my arms, I worked myself over and lay there beside Weldon.

"I'm sorry," I said.

"Aw, forget it, Bud. I know how you feel."

Then he started talking softly to Hughes, about home, about his mother. I just lay there thinking about home. If I never made it, I hoped they'd know how I died.

As soon as he could, Rass brought the doctor over to look at us. I couldn't understand why there was no feeling in my legs and no pain. The doctor was naked, and where was his stethoscope? This is a fantastic dream, I thought hazily.

The doctor didn't say a word. He stood up and then he examined Hughes and Weldon. Finally he turned to Father Cummings.

"All three of them have broken legs," he said, "but this boy," and he pointed to me, "I think his back is broken. I don't think there is much I can do for them. I don't have anything." There was an almost apologetic tone in his voice. I couldn't help feeling afraid and I looked at Rass.

"Do you think the planes will come back?"

"How could I know?" he said wearily. Then his face went calm. "Just don't think about it. If they come, well, after all, you've made it this far."

Father Cummings knelt down beside me.

"You've made it this far, boys, all three of you. Now try and listen to me. Just keep your thoughts on the fact that if you have faith, you can make it even now. You mustn't let it whip you. You can make it."

I looked to see if he was sincere. I knew that he felt I could make it. I became determined.

The planes did not come back and all morning and late into the afternoon Rass and Father Cummings worked with the other wounded. Toward the middle of the afternoon the cries of pain, the weeping and the pleas for water were making a madhouse of the hold. Finally Rass and Father Cummings came back and sat down beside us. I could see from the look on Father Cummings' face how bad things were.

"How many are there killed?" I asked Rass.

He shook his head as though he didn't want to say. Then I asked him again.

"How many are there dead?"

"I counted two hundred and fifty dead," he said. "There might be three hundred, and nearly everybody's wounded, wounded badly. Many men are going to die if the Japs don't give us anything pretty soon."

Then, very low, I heard Father Cummings praying. Praying to the God he believed in and that he wanted us to have faith in. I wanted to pray, but I couldn't. As the day stretched on I found myself at times crying for water, like the other men.

"Shut up, Stew!" Rass said. "You're just wasting your energy and making yourself weaker. These other fools, if they would realize that and conserve their energy, they'd be better off. Crying for water isn't going to get you any."

The day passed and then night came and the next day, until three days were gone. We lay there, and no water was given us, and no food. By now the stench of the blood and the rotting bodies around us seemed more than I could bear. Finally, in the middle of the third afternoon, I saw Colonel Olsen, who had been in charge of our whole group of prisoners in Davao, standing in the middle of the hold staring up through the hatch.

Above him I saw Wata's diabolical eyes and face. I looked again at Colonel Olsen. He had had an arm blown away and there was a rag tied above the arm as a tourniquet. He stared at Wata a while before he spoke.

"I ask nothing for myself," he said. "But these men are dying. In the name of humanity, in the name of the gods that you believe in, can't you do something for them? They will die if you don't give them bandages and medicine and food and water."

Wata just stared, and finally his lips curled, showing his yellow teeth.

"They were your planes that bombed," he said in his crooked English. "They were your planes. We don't care if you die. They were your planes and they have killed our men too."

He turned and left. I heard an almost hysterical weeping. Some of our officers were giving up hope. Then I heard Father Cummings.

"Listen to me, men! You must listen to me."

The crying stopped and there was no more groaning. Then in his deep, clear resonant voice he began to pray. It was the Lord's Prayer. It floated like a benediction through the hold, caressing every one of us.

"Our Father Who art in Heaven, hallowed be Thy name. Thy kingdom come. Thy will be done on earth as it is in Heaven. . . ."

I felt that God listened, that God watched us and that God cared. The day passed into night and I slept until morning. When morning came I was more rested and felt better, but when I reached down and pinched my legs there was still no feeling in them. Weldon and Hughes seemed better too.

As though in answer to our prayers, the Japs lowered small bottles of iodine and mercurochrome into the hold and a few small rolls of pitifully inadequate bandages. Then they lowered buckets of water and that was more than an answer to a prayer. Rass brought the ration of water for Weldon and Hughes and myself.

We huddled together there, the four of us, making a ritual of it, drinking our little bit of water, and helping each other build anew his desire to fight. But I couldn't get used to the strange fact that there was no feeling in the lower part of my body.

"Does your leg hurt very much?" I asked Weldon. "Does it pain you very much?"

"Aw, not much, just a little bit when I move." He grinned and turned to Hughes.

"How about you, kid? How do you feel?"

Hughes smiled. "They hurt some, not very much, but they hurt some. They're mainly kinda numb, but they hurt too."

I looked around the hold at the men who were standing. I watched them walking about in their dazed, shell-shocked way, moving among the bodies. They were beginning to reorganize, however, to do what little they could to pile the dead in the middle of the hold. The stench of the rotting bodies was almost unbearable. The next day Wata said that those who were strong enough would have to move the bodies. They were going to take them out of the hold.

Slings were lowered slowly down and the dead were stacked on the little rafts that were held by the ropes. They stacked the corpses in groups of about twenty-five. I watched the emaciated yellow bodies being pulled out of the hold, and I watched the tremendous effort on the part of the men who were moving them. These men, the living, were almost as much a part of the dead as the bodies. None of them had eaten a decent meal in many months now. They went about their work in a dazed, helpless way, lifting the bodies of their best friends, moving and separating the wounded from those who were dead. Finally, when all had been pulled up and lowered over the side of the ship to barges, Wata told five men to come out, and then he called down and asked five more and five more, until fifteen of the strongest men had left the hold.

They were gone many hours. When they returned late in the evening they told us what they had done. They had taken the bodies ashore and stacked them on piles of wood, where they were burned. It must have made a tremendous fire, about four hundred bodies burning. None of the men who had been out wanted to talk. They sat around dazed, as though they had seen something of which they and all of us would soon be a part.

Our life in the hold did not change. We were down in the hold nearly two weeks and men died every day and were loaded up and carried out of the ship. Finally Mr. Wata again appeared at the hatch above us and yelled down that we would be moved to another ship. They were going to move us on to Japan. Then he ordered all who could walk to come up on the deck of the ship.

Weldon, Hughes and I lay there watching all of our friends move away from us. We watched them climbing up the ladders and out of the hold, and we could not help wondering what would happen to us. Would they take us with them? Or would they leave us, kill us, as they had often done with the wounded who were unable to take care of themselves?

Within a few minutes I heard the booms of the ship moving. Then I saw the slings being lowered down into the holds. Tied to the ropes were little raft-like affairs. With relief I saw that prisoners were riding on them. When they reached the floor of the hold they walked over and began picking up the wounded and laying them on the rafts.

"Hoist away!" they yelled when the raft was full.

Rass and Father Cummings came down. They moved toward us and Father Cummings went to one of the priests who was badly wounded and helped lift him over and laid him on the little raft. Then he and Rass picked me up very carefully, one on either side of me, and carried me over and laid me beside him. They did the same with Weldon and Hughes. When the raft was loaded I heard them yell:

"Hoist away!"

We were pulled up out of the hold into the sunlight. The boom went higher into the air and it swung out over the water and lowered again. We were unloaded on barges, while other barges were pulling away already loaded. There were pitifully few men left now, as compared to the vast number of us who had left Manila.

The launch began churning the water and chugging across the bay, pulling us toward the next boat. There were many sunken hulks of blasted ships protruding from the water. When I looked at the large boat ahead, I felt a cold breeze blowing across the water. This would be our third ship.

I dreaded this boat with all the cold darkness of uncertainty, not knowing then that in it hundreds were yet to die.

FORMOSA TO JAPAN: JANUARY-FEBRUARY, 1945

The new ship was smaller than any of the ships that we had been on before. But looking at the group around me, I could see that it didn't matter, because there weren't many of us left now.

I was placed on the deck of the ship and laid near the other wounded who were unable to walk. Already about fifteen of the men had died. Presently Father Cummings and Rass came over and knelt beside us.

Rass said to the three of us, "Now you guys, hold on and don't worry. Father Bill and I will stick by you. You won't have to worry because you can't get around. We'll make it till we get to Japan. Just depend on us."

I knew that if anybody could help me to make it, Rass would. I noticed that Weldon reached over and patted Hughes' arm. Hughes smiled for the first time in many hours.

When it came time to go down into the hold, Rass lifted me up in a fireman's carry on his back. He fell to his knees, he was so weak. Slowly, by grabbing one of the ropes, he pulled himself to his feet, then struggled down the ladder with me.

The hold of this ship was not as deep as the others had been. We were very close to the upper deck of the ship and the badly wounded were laid just beneath the hatch opening. Soon Rass and Father Cummings carried Weldon and Hughes down and laid them beside me. We shivered together there in the hold, staring at the gray winter sky.

"Well, dammit, I guess it ought to be cold," Weldon said. "Here it is January the fifteenth, and it gets cold in this part of the country. If they don't give us some clothes pretty soon we'll freeze to death before we even get to Japan."

It was late in the afternoon before the boat pulled out. I knew if this ship didn't make it within a few days many of us would not live. It was bitterly cold. There was still no water to drink. One of the Japs told Rass that the water tank on board the ship had broken and that they were hauling all of their water. Consequently they would be able to give us only a very little.

As the boat headed out toward the China Sea the Japs lowered buckets of rice down into the hold and took men on deck to help them. American prisoners were allowed to work on deck. They carried slop buckets up and down for us to urinate in and use for bowel movements.

Each day passed in about the same way. We were given a small handful of rice to eat and about four and sometimes five spoonfuls of water per man. Many of the wounded were delirious or demented. Their screams before they died tortured us all. Men were becoming selfish now because they had so little energy to give. The dying died unaided, without help or solace.

In the evening, as it grew dark in the hold, Father Cummings stood and prayed. He started with the Lord's Prayer, and then said a prayer for the day, and for those who had died, and those who were dying around us. It grew colder and colder, and some snow and sleet began to fall down in the open hatch. We felt ourselves freezing. Our teeth chattered all the time. We were emaciated, almost bloodless, and the cold was unbearable.

Finally we begged the Japs to allow the hatch to be covered and laid over with canvas. They agreed. It made a gloomy, yellowish, almost a ghoulish light. More men died each day.

Some of the dying imagined they were home, back in their childhood. Some talked as though they were playing with their children, chatting with their wives, hearing an old friend tell a joke. They laughed and chuckled. It was a mad noise. I think hell must be very like that.

Rass and Father Cummings worked harder with us every day. I could see their strength waning. But Rass moved me and propped me up, and sometimes sat with his back against mine so that I could sit up straighter. He did the same with Weldon and Hughes.

I held on to each day, losing consciousness every so often, but gripping myself, afraid that if I relaxed, I might die. I didn't want to die. I begged my friends around me not to relax, but to hold on. They, too, would make it.

The men who went up on deck said that we seemed to be sailing among little barren Chinese islands. Occasionally the ship had to stop, go back and tow some ship whose rudder or steering gear had broken. Precious time was passing and more men were dying.

The wind was bitter cold now and sleet and snow were falling into the hold again. The demented wandered around, trying to catch the snowflakes that fell through the tiny opening, and licking the floor where they fell. At last the men became too weak to carry up the *benjou* buckets of slop, which spilled over on the floor.

The hold became filthier and filthier. We began to be crawled over by tiny things we couldn't see in the dark, which bit and stung us.

Finally Rass, who had gone up on deck to empty one of the buckets, told me that in the light he saw that they were lice, little gray lice. They were in my hair and in my eyebrows. If I closed my eyes to sleep they crawled over my eyelids and all over me, biting. It was strange. After all I had heard about other wars, only now were we meeting lice.

I watched Weldon and Hughes getting weaker. One day the Japs failed to give us water. They said the water was getting low because the trip was taking much longer than they had expected. They would be able to give us a little water only every other day. Yet somehow, my strength returned. Though I could not walk, I grew stronger even than Rass or Father Cummings. I began to pull myself about the hold, trying to help Weldon and Hughes as best I could. Rass and Father Cummings were so weak that they fainted with exhaustion. I tried to take over and care for Weldon and Hughes. Infection had started in their legs and they were burning up with fever. Their cries and mutterings, begging for water, were tortured, animal whimperings.

The Jap guards came down into the hold and stood at the edge of the ladder. They asked if there were any prisoners who had gold wedding bands, or West Point rings, which they would like to trade for water. Few of us had these things, but occasionally a man parted with his wedding ring for a rusty tomato can full of water. Sometimes before he could drink it, men would go crazy and fight him. He had to protect with his life the water he had traded for.

Each evening sanity returned to the men when Father Cummings began to pray. By now, almost all the other priests had died.

"There were eighteen, no, nineteen of us when we left Manila," he recalled one evening. "Now . . ." He didn't finish.

Each night the solace and the comfort that we received from the prayers was more than anything that anyone else could do for us. He gave us strength and hope. One evening, as it was getting dark down in the hold, Father Cummings stood and said his prayer. We tried to bed ourselves down so that we could sleep. Rass lay down close beside me.

"I'm afraid that Weldon and Hughes won't make it another day," he whispered. "They've been out of their heads now, delirious, for the whole day. They're weak and their temperature is high." He sighed with resignation. "Hughes is burning up with fever and his lips are parched and dry. I'm afraid he can't make it any longer."

Rass fell back exhausted, almost unconscious. I could see in the dim light that Father Cummings was already asleep. In the shadows of the night a faint reflection of light was cast through the small opening into the hold. I reached over and touched Hughes' hand. It was very hot, and he was whimpering. Occasionally he cried out, "Oh, God, give me water. Give me water."

I reached across him for Weldon's hand and he too was crying, and then choking as he coughed. I ran my hand over his forehead and it was very hot. I had to do something. I had to get them water. If they had water it would bring their temperature down. It would save them. I had to do something for them.

What could I do? I began to crawl around, pulling myself by my arms. I dragged my helpless, foolish legs that had no movement in them, that were insensible to feeling, insensible even to pain. I pulled my body with my arms over to where many of the dead bodies had been stacked, hoping against all hope that maybe one of the dead had a ring on his hand that I could trade for water. But it was foolish. All of them were cold now, stone-cold and stiff. None of them had anything. If they had had any clothing at all, it had been stripped by the living.

I crawled back and lay down again beside Hughes. His whimpering went on. I had to do something.

I started pulling myself around among the wounded. I saw a man lying there. I couldn't see who he was in the faint light, but on his finger I saw the yellow gleam of metal. I reached over and touched him. He lay there groaning. I laid my ear close to his mouth. He was unconscious but groaning. I thought, oh, maybe he will die and I can have the ring. I waited and it seemed like hours, but still the man didn't die. The night was getting late. I wondered if I dared kill him. My friends needed the water.

He was going to die anyway. They needed the water now if they were to live. Weldon's face and Hughes' face and their tortured cries came to my mind. I must kill this man. I looked down and examined the ring on his swollen hand.

It was a West Point ring and I knew the Japs would give me water for that. I laid his hand down again and pulled myself up near his head. I started to close my fingers about his throat. It would take only a little pressure and the man would choke to death. It would be easy.

But I couldn't do it. Each time I touched his neck I heard the prayers of Father Cummings. I tried again, but I could not bring my hands to do it.

Suddenly I heard a shuddering gasp from the man. Then he no longer breathed. He no longer groaned. I laid my head down on his chest and listened. His heart was still. The man was dead.

Quickly I reached for his left hand and began to tug at the ring. But his hand was too swollen and bloated, and the ring wouldn't come off. I laid my head down on his chest and pulled the hand up where I could get better leverage. Frantic now, I tried hard. But it wouldn't come. I was desperate. I looked around for help. But I knew if someone else saw me, someone stronger, he would take the ring himself.

At last a plan came to me. I lay my head on his chest and, taking the hand, I began to use my teeth. I felt like a carrion ghoul, but I had to do it. Weldon and Hughes were my friends. If only I could get the ring, I could trade it for a cup of water and it would save their lives.

After a while the ring-finger came free. Slowly I worked the ring off the bloody stump. It came free in my hand. I did not know how long it had taken me to bite through the man's finger, but as I looked up I saw the light was becoming brighter in the hold. It was very early in the morning. As I looked around I saw the men still sleeping exhaustedly.

I pulled my body over, clutching the ring in my hand, beside Hughes and Weldon. They were still alive, whimpering, crying for water. I left them, and pulled myself forward to the front of the hold, near the bottom of the ladder. The sentry was standing above with his gun in his hand. I called up to him and raised my hand, waving the ring between two fingers.

"*Kempi, kempi. Haitai san. Mazu,*" I said in Japanese—"Water, water, please."

He stepped over and climbed down the ladder until he could see. He knelt beside me and picked up the ring in his hand. He examined it slowly, and then he looked down at me and handed the ring back.

"I bring water," he grunted.

He crawled back up the ladder and I waited, looking around furtively for fear someone would see, someone stronger. After an eternity the Jap appeared at the hatch and climbed down. He held an old rusty tomato can. He handed it to me and it was full of water. I wanted badly to taste it, just a taste. I handed the Jap the ring and he climbed back out of the hold.

I looked around carefully for fear someone would see me. Then I used my arms to pull myself, slowly inching my way back to where my friends were. The light of morning was coming down into the hold and the men were beginning to stir. Some were sitting up.

I tried to crawl faster, faster, for fear someone would see the water can. At long last I reached Weldon and Hughes and crawled up between them. I wondered whom to give the water to first and I felt Weldon's head. It was terribly hot. I set the can on the floor beside me and pulled myself around behind him, edging my shoulder under his back to lift him up. Gradually I propped him to a half-sitting position.

"Weldon! Listen to me," I said. "I'm going to give you water."

"Oh, water!" he cried out. "Please give me water."

I laid his head against my shoulder and held it there. Then I reached with the other hand for the can and lifted it gradually to his lips.

"Slowly now. Take it easy, pal," I said. "Take it easy. You're going to get some water."

As the water touched his parched lips he ran his tongue across them, tasting the cool liquid.

"Water!" he screamed, and thrashed his arms crazily, striking the can. It fell from my hands and rolled clattering across the floor, spilling the water.

Men yelled, "Water!" Men scrambled all around me, throwing themselves on the floor, licking with their tongues the water that had spilled there in the filth. I watched them and I knew the water was gone. Weldon was whimpering and crying for water and the water was gone, all gone. I could get him no more.

Slowly I laid his head back on the floor of the hold. I felt that all was lost. There was nothing I could do now. I was exhausted. I did not care if I lived or died. There was nothing I could do.

I laid my head down on Weldon's chest and began to cry. I felt the sobs working through my lungs, shaking my whole body. I wept until I lost consciousness through sheer exhaustion.

2

When I came to, Father Cummings was shaking me by the shoulders.

"Wake up, lad. The water issue is coming down and you'll want your water. These boys—won't need theirs."

I raised my head. Rass was holding Hughes in his arms. In the ghastly yellow light I could see the tears forming and rolling down across his cheeks. He looked over at me and nodded his head. I knew they were both dead because Weldon's body felt cold under my hands.

I knew they were both dead. And I couldn't cry. No tears would come.

Slowly Father Cummings and Rass pulled the bodies over where the others were and laid them there. When the water was passed around I didn't want mine. I couldn't think of water now. I didn't want anything. I could only follow Father Cummings and Rass with my eyes. They begged me to drink the water.

"You must drink your water. You've got five spoonfuls today."

I didn't want any. If only I had had the water last night maybe it would have saved their lives. Without thinking I said, "Give my water to Hughes."

Rass smiled and patted my hand. "Water won't help them now. They need nothing in this world."

"Take it easy, fella." Father Bill laid his hand on my head. "You're gonna be all right."

From that time on I looked forward every hour for night to come, when Father Cummings stood and said his prayer again. I lived only for that prayer of faith and hope. It was the only strength I had. His voice was like the voice of God to me. I knew that Rass felt the same, Rass, who was always so much more religious than I. He was now so weak that it was all he could do to stand. Yet I knew he lived too for that prayer in the evening.

Men were dying at the rate of twenty and thirty a day. Every morning their bodies were wrapped with rope and drawn up through the hold and dropped into the sea. Each day I watched the bodies going up into the sky through the open hatch. The rope swung out across the deck and I heard the sound of the bodies as they splashed into the sea.

I missed Weldon and Hughes very much. Lying together helpless as we were, we had still kept up each other's spirits. We had talked of home. I had remembered that when I was a little boy and sick with the flu, lying there in my bed, my mother had brought a bowl of hot potato soup with little egg noodles floating on top. How good it was. I had told them of that and it had helped a little. Almost happily Hughes had remembered the hot beef tea that his mother used to make. Now, with both Rass and Father Cummings busy every waking moment, I had no one to talk to.

One afternoon Father Cummings crawled over to pray for a dying boy and did not come back. Rass went to look for him. He found him unconscious through exhaustion, so white and still that when he brought him back and laid him near me, I was frightened.

I knew I could not hold on without him. I was afraid to ask Rass if he was dead. Not saying a word, Rass shook his head.

"No." He laid Father Cummings beside me. I sat up and began to rub his arms and his hands and his face. Rass helped, and soon life returned. His eyelids flickered slowly and he opened his kind gray eyes.

"I'll be all right, boys." He smiled wanly.

But he wasn't able to walk any more. Rass cared for the two of us now. Father Cummings had been passing blood many days with dysentery. He was so weak that he could not walk. His lips were parched and cracked and his hands moved convulsively up and down his throat. I knew that he couldn't make it much longer. I prayed silently to myself that I would die before he did, that I would not have to see him die.

But that evening, as it was growing dark down in the hold, and the faint light that came through the hatch was nearly gone, he begged me, "Can you lift your arm behind me? I can't stand, but my voice will carry. They will hear my prayer."

I pushed my shoulder in behind him and put my arms around him and held him up. Faltering, he began to speak.

"Men! Men, can you hear my voice?"

Slowly he began to pray. "Our Father Who art in Heaven, hallowed be Thy Name. . . ."

The cries of the men became still. I concentrated on the voice that soothed me and gave me strength and the will to live. Then I felt his body shiver and tremble in my arms. He gasped for air and there was a terrible pain written on his face. He gritted his teeth, sighed and went on.

"Thy will be done—on earth—as it is—in Heaven."

I felt him tremble again as if he wanted to cough. His hands fluttered and his eyelids almost closed. Then with superhuman effort he spoke again.

"Give Us This Day. . . ."

I felt his body go tense all over. He relaxed and his hand fell by his side. I waited, but his eyes looked straight ahead. The eyelids no longer flickered. I knew he was dead, but I continued to hold him, afraid even to move. Rass crawled beside me. He lifted Father Cummings' hand and felt for his pulse.

"Lay him down, Sid," he said evenly. "He's gone. Lay him down. He's gone now."

I cradled his head against my shoulder. I didn't want to lay him down. I couldn't bear to face the fact that he was gone.

"Go ahead, Sid. Lay him down. Lay him down, he's gone," Rass said firmly.

I moved from behind him and laid his head gently on the floor. Then I noticed that the hold was quiet. The men had gone off into their exhausted, hungry sleep. Rass reached across the body and gripped my arm.

"Sid, he died like he would have wanted to die, praying to the God that he believed in, to the God that gave him strength."

"Why did he have to die, Rass? Why did he have to leave us?"

"Don't think about the fact that he is gone. Try to think of his last words. The last thing he tried to give us."

Rass went on calmly, "You know his last words were, 'Give us this day.' We must try only to live until we can see the sun up in the morning, you and I, and we'll make it. Live only for one day, for just twenty-four more hours."

Without answering him I laid my head back on the floor. I lay there with my eyes open, just thinking. An hour or so later I heard Rass speak again.

"Do you want me to move the body?"

"No, Rass. Leave it here until the morning. Keep him here with us until the sun comes up in the morning."

All through the night I didn't sleep. I lay there with my eyes open, thinking of all the man had done for those he felt suffered more than he because they did not have his faith. He had tried to give it to them, this thing he called faith.

When I saw the first ray of dawn coming down into the hold I knew that we had lived for the new day. If God gave us this day, we would make it until the next morning. We could make it one day and that was as far as we could think ahead.

A CORPORATE ACTIVITY

C. E. M. Joad

An agnostic for most of his life, a Rationalist of the nineteenth-century variety, Cyril Edwin Mitchinson Joad, professor of philosophy at the University of London, died at his home in England at 61 in April, 1953. Shortly after the second World War he embraced Christian belief, holding it "less improbable" than any other theory of the universe. This selection is from his volume The Recovery of Belief.

. . . Religion is, for most of us, a corporate activity. Few of us have the strength of will to practice it alone. Alone we cannot collect ourselves for meditation or constrain ourselves to utter prayers that are more than perfunctory. I speak, of course, for myself; yet also, I suspect, for many like myself. It is only when we come together that we come near to God and we come together in corporate worship. The worship is prescribed by the ritual of a Church which is, in my own case, the Church of England. Indeed, for me, it must be so. Religion is not like a language, something that you acquire; it is bound up with the ancestral elements of your being. (It is for this reason, I suspect, that in so many of my generation it "comes out" late in life, when the things that are ancestral take increasing possession of the stage of one's personality, and the things that are acquired fall away.) The countryside of England and the life of its villages are also, for me, bound up with the ancestral elements of my being. My people have for generations been "on the land."

Prominent in the life of the English village has been the church. In the past—though scarcely at all today—those who earned their living on the land had an affection, an affection which deepened on occasion into reverence, for the village church. Hence, when I came . . . to consider again the whole question of religion, it was natural that the process of reconsideration and reflection should take place within the framework of the Anglican Church, and that my worship, when at last I began to worship, should find its appropriate setting in the parish church. Indeed, I formed the habit of intermittently attending the services of village churches long before I came to believe in the truth of what they taught. I would, I used to tell myself, go out of curiosity because I wanted to learn what still went on in them. Or—and this, perhaps, was a little nearer the truth—I was attracted by the beauty of the setting and by the beauty of the Liturgy. And both of these did, indeed, have their way with me, calming my spirit and preparing me, albeit unconsciously, for a change of heart, until at last they prevailed and, after the doubts and hesitations, I became the diffident and halting Christian that I now am.

I am grateful, more grateful than I can say, to the Church of England and more particularly to its country churches, and to the men who, in spite of every discouragement, persist in teaching there the Christian religion as the Church understands it. Without them, I should not, I think, have come to Christianity.

THE CHRISTIANS-TWICE-A-YEAR

James W. Hyde

James W. Hyde is the Rector of St. John's Episcopal Church, at Salisbury, Conn., a parish of some four hundred members in a village in the foothills of the Berkshires. The church, a characteristic Colonial of its period, was established in 1754 at Salisbury by missionaries under the auspices of the English Society for the Propagation of the Gospel in Foreign Parts. It is a few steps north of the post office, and across the roadway from the Village Store, the Package Store and the Town Hall.

Last Sunday, being Easter Day, none of us was particularly surprised that we had unusually large congregations in this church. Every Christian Church in America—perhaps the world—had unusually large congregations last Sunday. It is probable, too, that every Christian minister in America—perhaps the world—has paused during this week to ask himself a question something like this, "Why don't these people come to church every Sunday? Where am I missing contact with these people? Why doesn't the church seem as demanding every week as it does on Easter Day?"

Now, the fact is that in this church last Sunday we had a total attendance which represented almost exactly the whole number of baptized members of the parish. We also had, within an error of two or three, exactly the number of communions as we have confirmed members. In other words, on that one Sunday the members

244 JAMES W. HYDE

of the parish were living up to the commitments which they made at their baptisms and confirmation.

Some of the old hands in the congregation will, of course, say, "But, we had a great many visitors." Well, yes we had, but not as many as you may think for almost all of the people present were known to me, and the visitors no more than made up for members I knew to be sick or out of town. The increase was not visitors but regular members of this church who just don't come often enough for you and me to even expect them to be present. These are the people who I am most concerned about and whom I wish I could get you, who are regular and faithful attendants, to be concerned about also.

If we are ever to command the loyalty of the half-hearted Christians who attend only at Easter and Christmas, however, we must be quite definite in our own minds what it is that we are offering them in asking them to come to church. Is it a suggestion or a conviction? Is it advisable or an imperative? Is it an idea or a fact ——a story or an experience——a legend or history——an escape or reality?

There can be no doubt which it was for those men and women who, in the first century of our era, carried the Christian message to the Roman Empire. It was not the good life of the Lord, His words, His deeds or even His miracles, they proclaimed. It was the simple fact that, "This Jesus, whom evil men slew, God hath raised up and made both Lord and Christ whereof we all are witnesses." They were less concerned about Jesus, His life, His teachings, His ministry, than they were about the mighty act of God which took place in and through Him. It is difficult for us to understand how little they were concerned about Jesus and how much they were concerned about God. I shock myself in expressing the almost blasphemous opinion that the early Christians were only slightly concerned about Jesus, but it is the fact that they were concerned about Him only in so far as He was the One in whom God revealed Himself—through whom God acted in the world.

St. Paul puts it this way: "The God to whom I address the inner worship of my heart, while I preach the gospel of his Son is my witness . . ." (Romans 12:9 Knox trans.) You see, God comes first and is the primary concern. Jesus, His Son, is preached as the fullest revelation, the most certain path to God.

It was this that gave those first Christian missionaries their irresistible power in a world which hated them and all they stood for. They were talking about another mighty act of God. The Jews knew all about many of God's acts—how He had created the world, how He punished men by a great flood, how He had re-peopled the land out of the loins of Noah, how He had made a covenant with Abraham, how He had rescued the Chosen People from bondage in Egypt and how He had renewed His covenant with Moses when He gave them the Law. All this was familiar and now God had acted again in the mightiest act of all by raising up, "This Jesus whom evil men had crucified and making Him both Lord and Christ."

This was no mere suggestion that Christianity was a good thing. It was the deepest conviction of their hearts and minds. It was a convincing experience to which they must witness before the whole world. . . .

The other day an older man in this parish said to me of one of the younger men about town, "You know, he is old enough now to begin to realize that he needs some spiritual foundation for his life. He ought to be taking an active part in the church." That remark sounds to me like the beginning of a long discussion which might or might not convince the younger man. The discussion would range widely through the advisability of church member-ship, the idea of God, the importance of stories and myths in our Western culture. It might go into the somewhat questionable realm of how to be a more successful business man through prayer. The one thing I am positive that the older man would never say to the younger is, "This Jesus hath God raised up and made both Lord and Christ, whereof we all are witnesses."

We just don't think of Christianity in those terms today. The fact of God's act, the historical reality of the Christian experience, the imperative demand of God, the conviction of truth is lack-ing in us, and for this very reason our religion far from being about to conquer an empire, as it did the Roman world, may well be about to be conquered by one.

We try to commend our faith to others, to the outright skeptic and the half-hearted Christian, on the basis of all the superficial results of faith. It is true that Western culture is based on Christian faith, it is true that our legal system is deeply influenced by Christian moral teachings, it is true that American Democracy is based on the Christian doctrine of the nature of man, but none of these are reasons for believing in God. They are the results of faith, they are the things which are given to us because for two thousand years men and women have believed that God raised up this Jesus and made him both Lord and Christ. And believing, those men and women fought, suffered and died for that conviction.

If this one fact is true, and we preach it believing so, it is the only valid argument for Christian faith. We cannot blame people for being half-hearted and indifferent if we try to appeal to them on the grounds of the superficialities, on the hope of results, on the beauties of nature, on the optimistic belief that God helps those who help themselves, and neglect the central fact and truth of the Gospel.

If this one fact be true, and it is the faith of the church, it is the sole reason for regular worship. We need no other standards, or ideas, or justifications for our devotion to the Church. Those first Christians performed their miraculous task of conversion on the sole basis of their faith that God had acted in raising up "This Jesus, whom evil men slew, and made Him both Lord and Christ," whereof they all were witnesses.

Are we?

O GOD, our Shepherd, give to the Church a new vision and a new charity, new wisdom and fresh understanding, the revival of her brightness and the renewal of her unity; that the eternal message of thy Son, undefiled by the traditions of men, may be hailed as the good news of the new age; through him who maketh all things new, Jesus Christ our Lord.   AMEN

CONSECRATION: THE JUNGLE DISCIPLES
Elisabeth Elliot

In January, 1956, five young American missionaries, leaving their young American wives behind in jungle outposts with friendly Ecuadorian Indians, the Quichuas, many of whom they had converted to Christianity and had taught to read, ventured into the territory of the killer stone-age Aucas, having, for some weeks, flown over their jungles dropping gifts and shouting words of friendship in the Auca language.

These young missionaries were:

Jim Elliot, 25 years old when in 1952 he left the United States, a Wheaton College graduate, for missionary service in Ecuador;

Pete Fleming, 28 years old in 1956, a native of Seattle, a philosophy major at the University of Washington;

Ed McCully of Milwaukee, classmate of Jim Elliot, a law student who turned missionary, deciding in 1950 "to live a life of reckless abandon for the Lord, putting all my energy and strength into it";

Nate Saint, born in 1923 in Philadelphia and since the late 'forties the pilot of the yellow Piper Cub of the Missionary Aviation Fellowship (an interdenominational organization founded by two former Navy pilots whose aim it was to transport evangelical missionaries, their supplies, their sick, to and from remote outposts);

Roger Youderian, born in 1924 on a ranch in Montana, a Montana State College three-scholarship man, an ex-paratrooper with the Army and survivor of the Battle of the Bulge, a man who gave up a potential career as a teacher in agriculture to sail in January, 1953, with his wife and six-month-old daughter for missionary work in South America.

The wives of these men were Elisabeth Elliot, who has written the account of the ill-fated venture of her husband and his four companions in Through Gates of Splendor, from which the following chapter is taken; Olive Fleming; Marilou McCully, mother of three young children, Matthew, Mike and Stevie; Marjorie Saint, radio contact, and mother of two young sons, Stevie and Philip and a daughter Kathie; and Barbara Youderian, mother of a daughter Bethy and son Jerry. Mrs. Elliot is also the mother of a daughter Valerie, born in Ecuador.

The following excerpt in Mrs. Elliot's words, and extracts from the diary of Nate Saint, the young missionary-pilot, recounts the preparations of the five dedicated men and that of their families for the "ground operation" of acquaintanceship with the Aucas, whose only contact hitherto with their outside world had been murderous raids upon their neighboring tribes, the Quichuas and the one time head-shrinking Jivaros.

. . . The time was ripening fast. The men and the other wives and I spent long hours discussing this project of which we had dreamed for so many months and years. Olive Fleming remembered what she had read in Pete's diary of his willingness to give his life for the Aucas. I reminded Jim of what we both knew it might mean if he went. "Well, if that's the way God wants it to be," was his calm reply, "I'm ready to die for the salvation of the Aucas." While still a student in college Jim had written: "He is no fool who gives what he cannot keep to gain what he cannot lose."

Marilou McCully said: "I hope no one feels any pressure is being put on Ed to go. This is a thing for each couple to face by themselves."

Two gift flights remained before the actual ground operation was to begin. On December 23, when the Elliots and Flemings had gone to Arajuno to spend Christmas with the McCullys, Nate Saint flew Jim over the Auca settlement. Seeing the same old man they had noticed before standing in a clearing, they swooped down past him at no more than fifty feet.

"Wow!" said Jim, "That guy's scared stiff!"

Nate agreed. "It's as though they had steeled themselves against doing anything that would express either fear or hostility," he wrote later. "Possibly afraid that they might scare away the chicken that lays the golden eggs. But their eyes don't lie—they're full of terror. Understandable, though. The expression is that of a six-year-old in the front row when the circus clown points a big gun right in his face. He's sure it's all in fun, but . . . oh, brother!

"At the main house the 'chief traffic director'* was in full uniform—shirt and pants—everyone else more typically dressed, or undressed. Jim counted thirteen on hand. On our first swoop past, one of them held up what was apparently to be their gift for us. We dropped them a carrying net containing white cloth, a flashlight, a pair of pants, and other trinkets. What wouldn't we give to see them trying to make sense out of that flashlight!

"Jim announced the take-off of their gift on the line, and I rolled out of the turn to hold it up. It is the heaviest yet. We cruised at sixty-five back to Arajuno, and let the bark-cloth bundle down hard. It hit in some bushes about twenty yards from Ed's house. Contents:

"Cooked fish
Two or three little packets of peanuts
A couple of pieces of cooked manioc
A cooked plantain
Two squirrels, very apparently killed by the hard fall
One parrot, alive but a bit nervous
Two bananas in with the parrot
Two pieces of pottery, clay, busted to bits in the fall
A piece of cooked meat and a smoked monkey tail

"This is by far the most all-out effort at a fair-trade arrangement on the part of the neighbors. We are all delighted. Jim and Ed sampled the meat, and we all ate some of the peanuts. Then, meaning

---

* A seemingly cooperative Auca observed on earlier trips.—Ed.

no ill to the kind folks who mailed all those goodies to us, we sat down and ate the meal that Marilou had prepared."

Even though Pete Fleming had not yet made his final decision, he and Olive with three other couples who would be directly involved in the project were together on the 23rd for discussion. (Roger and Barbara Youderian still were on their station in the southern jungle.) The wives were particularly concerned to know exactly what provisions were to be made for safety [of the men]. It was decided that arms would be carried, concealed, and that if the situation appeared to be getting delicate, they would be shown, simply to let the Aucas know that the white man held the upper hand. If this were not enough, shots would be fired with the intention only of scaring them.

Roger had drawn up a plan of operation. Jim was assigned to the task of prefabricating a house to put up in a tree. This would insure safety at night, especially if a gasoline pressure lamp were kept burning to illumine the area at the foot of the tree. Ed was responsible for collecting items for trade with the Aucas. Roj [Roger Youderian] would make up the first-aid kit, Nate saw to the communications and transportation, Jim took charge of arms and ammunition, and when later on Pete decided that he would go too, he was to be responsible for helping Nate on the flights to and from Arajuno, for flights over the Auca houses when he would shout over the loudspeaker, and for keeping supplies on the beach. Roj prepared a set of code signs to be drawn in the sand on the beach in case of emergency, and drew maps for each man with the code names he had made up for the strategic points.

The [Auca] language material which Jim and I had gathered in previous weeks was organized and memorized by each member of the party. Marj Saint's place was to be at the radio in Shell Mera, standing by at all times when Nate Saint's plane was flying, and keeping set schedules of contact with the men on the ground. It was decided that Barbara would stay in Arajuno, helping Marilou with the preparation of food which Nate was to fly daily to Palm Beach.

The appearance of the Auca at Arajuno, the fact that the Quichuas were guessing a little too shrewdly for comfort, the great encouragement in the drop flights [of gifts]—indeed, even the weather itself—seemed to be catapulting them toward their D-day with now-or-never exigency. Within a month the rainy season would start, flooding the rivers and making landings impossible. The ideal time for establishment of their beachhead in Auca territory would be early January during the full of the moon.

They set the date for Tuesday, January 3, 1956.

Christmas at Arajuno was made as much like Christmas at home as Marilou McCully's genius could make it. She even had a little Christmas tree, made of bamboo and decorated with lights and tinsel. Ed and Jim, who already had "reserved seats" for the trip to Palm Beach, were keyed up. Pete Fleming was still waiting on God in prayer before making his final decision to go.

The other wives and I talked together one night about the possibility of becoming widows. What would we do? God gave us peace of heart, and confidence that whatever might happen, His Word would hold. We knew that "when He putteth forth His sheep, He goeth before them." God's leading was unmistakable up to this point. Each of us knew when we married our husbands that there would never be any question about who came first—God and His work held first place in each life. It was the condition of true discipleship; it became devastatingly meaningful now.

It was a time for soul-searching, a time for counting the possible cost. Was it the thrill of adventure that drew our husbands on? No. Their letters and journals make it abundantly clear that these men did not go out as some men go out to shoot a lion or climb a mountain. Their compulsion was from a different source. Each had made a personal transaction with God, recognizing that he belonged to God, first of all by creation, and secondly by redemption through the death of His Son, Jesus Christ. This double claim on his life settled once and for all the question of allegiance. It was not a matter of striving to follow the example of a great Teacher. To conform to the perfect life of Jesus was impossible for a human being. To these men, Jesus Christ was God, and had actually taken upon Himself human form, in order that He might die, and, by His death, provide not only escape from the punishment which their sin merited, but also a *new kind of life*, eternal both in length and in quality. This meant simply that Christ was to be obeyed, and more than that, that He would provide the power to obey. The point of decision had been reached. God's command "Go ye, and preach the gospel to every creature" was the categorical imperative. The question of personal safety was wholly irrelevant.

On Sunday afternoon, December 18, Nate Saint sat at his typewriter to tell the world why they were going—just in case. In speaking these words he spoke for all: "As we weigh the future and seek the will of God, does it seem right that we should hazard our lives for just a few savages? As we ask ourselves this question, we realize that it is not the call of the needy thousands, rather it is the simple intimation of the prophetic Word that there shall be some from every tribe in His presence in the last day and in our hearts we feel that it is pleasing to Him that we should interest ourselves in making an opening into the Auca prison for Christ.

"As we have a high old time this Christmas, may we who know Christ hear the cry of the damned as they hurtle headlong into the Christless night without ever a chance. May we be moved with compassion as our Lord was. May we shed tears of repentance for these we have failed to bring out of darkness. Beyond the smiling scenes of Bethlehem may we see the crushing agony of Golgotha. May God give us a new vision of His will concerning the lost and our responsibility.

"Would that we could comprehend the lot of these stone-age people who live in mortal fear of ambush on the jungle trail . . . those to whom the bark of a gun means sudden, mysterious death . . . those who think all men in all the world are killers like themselves. If God would grant us the vision, the word sacrifice would disappear from our lips and thoughts; we would hate the things that seem now so dear to us; our lives would suddenly be too short, we would despise time-robbing distractions and charge the enemy with all our energies in the name of Christ. May God help us to judge ourselves by the eternities that separate the Aucas from a comprehension of Christmas and Him, who, though He was rich, yet for our sakes became poor so that we might, through His poverty, be made rich.

"Lord, God, speak to my own heart and give me to know Thy Holy will and the joy of walking in it. Amen."

The epilogue of this hopeful prayer is tragic.

After a successful landing and several seemingly friendly contacts with a couple of the Aucas, and even, on one occasion, the proffer by them of a maiden as a gift, the five men were lost to their radio contact, Marj Saint, and when a rescue helicopter was finally despatched, it found the savage-destroyed remnants of Nate Saint's Piper Cub and the bodies of the five young missionaries, the lances of the attack still in some of their bodies.

The wives of the missionaries have remained at their posts in the neighboring Quichua territory, raising their nine small children and, with new additions to their forces, are continuing their efforts to try to win over against the hostile Auca savages.

LIVING

THE MEANING OF JOY

Paul Tillich

Paul Tillich, German-born philosopher and theologian, author of
many books, was Professor of Philosophical Theology at Union Theo-
logical Seminary in New York City from 1933 until 1955 when he retired, but almost at once he became a member of the faculty of the
Divinity School at Harvard.

When the Lord restored the fortunes of Zion, we were like those who
dream. Then our mouth was filled with laughter, and our tongue with
shouts of joy; then they said among the nations, "The Lord has done
great things for them." The Lord had done great things for us; we are
glad.

Restore our fortunes, O Lord, like the watercourses in the Negeb!
May those who sow in tears reap with shouts of joy! He that goes forth
weeping, bearing the seed for sowing, shall come home with shouts of
joy, bringing his sheaves with him.

PSALM 126

Truly, truly, I say to you, you will weep and lament, but the world
will rejoice; you will be sorrowful, but your sorrow will turn into joy.
When a woman is in travail she has sorrow, because her hour has come;
but when she is delivered of the child, she no longer remembers the
anguish, for joy that a child is born into the world. So you have sorrow
now, but I will see you again and your hearts will rejoice, and no one
will take your joy from you.

JOHN 16:20-22

*These things I have spoken to you, that my joy may be in you, and
that your joy may be full.*

JOHN 15:11

The Bible abounds in admonitions to rejoice. Paul's word to the
Philippians, "again I will say, Rejoice," represents an ever-present
element in Biblical religion. For the men of the Old and New
Testaments the lack of joy is a consequence of man's separation
from God, and the presence of joy is a consequence of the reunion with God.

Joy is demanded, and it can be given. It is not a thing one simply has. It is not easy to attain. It is and always was a rare and
precious thing. And it has always been a difficult problem among
Christians. Christians are accused of destroying the joy of life, this
natural endowment of every creature. The greatest of the modern
foes of Christianity, Friedrich Nietzsche, himself the son of a Protestant minister, has expressed his judgment about Jesus in the
words, "His disciples should look more redeemed." We should subject ourselves to the piercing force of these words and should ask
ourselves, "Is our lack of joy due to the fact that we are Christians,
or to the fact that we are not sufficiently Christian?" Perhaps we
can defend ourselves convincingly against the criticism that we are
people who despise life, whose behavior is a permanent accusation
of life. Perhaps we can show that this is a distortion of the truth.

But let us be honest. Is there not enough foundation for criticism? Are not many Christians—ministers, students of theology,
evangelists, missionaries, Christian educators and social workers, pious laymen and lay-women, even the children of such parents—
surrounded by an air of heaviness, of oppressive sternness, of lack
of humor and irony about themselves? We cannot deny this. Our
critics outside the Church are right. And we ourselves should be
even more critical than they, but critical on a deeper level.

As Christians we know our inner conflicts about accepting or rejecting joy. We are suspicious of the gifts of nature which contribute to joy, because we are suspicious of nature itself, although
we confess that it is Divine creation, knowing what God has spo-

ken about His creation: "Behold, it was very good!" We are suspicious of the creations of culture which contribute to joy because we are suspicious of man's creativity, although we confess that God has commanded man to cultivate the garden of the earth which He has made subject to him. And even if we overcome our suspicions and affirm and accept the gifts of nature and the creations of culture, we often do so with an uneasy conscience. We know that we *should* be free for joy, that as Paul says, "all is ours," but our courage is inferior to our knowledge. We do not dare to affirm our world and ourselves; and if we dare to, in a moment of courage, we try to atone for it by self-reproaches and self-punishments, and we draw upon ourselves malicious criticism by those who never have dared. Therefore, many Christians try to compromise. They try to hide their feeling of joy, or they try to avoid joys which are too intense, in order to avoid self-accusations which are too harsh. Such an experience of the suppression of joy, and guilt about joy in Christian groups, almost drove me to a break with Christianity. What passes for joy in these groups is an emaciated, intentionally childish, unexciting, unecstatic thing, without color and danger, without heights and depths.

It is difficult to deny that this is the state of things in many Christian churches. But now we hear the question from both the Christian and the non-Christian sides: "Is not joy, as observed in the Bible, something completely different from the joy of life, which is lacking in many Christians? Do not the Psalmist and Paul and the Jesus of the Fourth Gospel speak of a joy which transcends the natural joy of life? Do they not speak about the joy in God? Is not the decision to be a Christian a decision for the joy in God instead of for the joy of life?"

The first and simplest answer to these questions is that life is God's, and God is the creative Ground of life. He is infinitely more than any life process. But He works creatively through all of them. Therefore, no conflict is necessary between the joy in God and the joy of life. But this first answer, great and joyful as it is, is not sufficient; for "joy of life" can mean many things.

Joy seems to be the opposite of pain. But we know that pain and joy can exist together. Not joy but pleasure is the opposite of pain. There are people who believe that man's life is a continuous flight from pain and a persistent search for pleasure. I have never seen a human being of whom that is true. It is true only of beings who have lost their humanity, either through complete disintegration or through mental illness. The ordinary human being is able to sacrifice pleasures and to take pain upon himself for a cause, for somebody or something he loves and deems worthy of pain and sacrifice. He can disregard both pain and pleasure because he is directed not towards his pleasure but towards the things he loves and with which he wants to unite. If we desire something because of the pleasure we may get out of it, we may get the pleasure but we shall not get joy. If we try to find someone through whom we may get pleasure, we may get pleasure but we shall not have joy. If we search for something in order to avoid pain, we may avoid pain, but we shall not avoid sorrow. If we try to use someone to protect us from pain, he may protect us from pain but he will not protect us from sorrow. Pleasures can be provided and pain can be avoided, if we use or abuse other beings. But joy cannot be attained and sorrow cannot be overcome in this way. Joy is possible only when we are driven towards things and persons because of what they are and not because of what we can get from them. The joy about our work is spoiled when we perform it not because of what we produce but because of the pleasures with which it can provide us, or the pain against which it can protect us. The pleasure about the fact that *I* am successful spoils the joy about the success itself. Our joy about knowing truth and experiencing beauty is spoiled if we enjoy not the truth and the beauty but the fact that it is *I* who enjoys them.

Power can give joy only if it is free from the pleasure about having power and if it is a method of creating something worthwhile. Love relations, most conspicuously relations between the sexes, remain without joy if we use the other one as a means for pleasure or as a means to escape pain. This is a threat to all human relations. It is not an external law which warns us about certain forms of these relations, but the wisdom born out of past experiences which tells us that some of these relations may give pleasure, but that they do not give joy. They do not give joy because they do not fulfill what we are, and that for which we strive. Every human relation is joyless in which the other person is not sought because of what he is in himself, but because of the pleasure he can give us and the pain from which he can protect us.

To seek pleasure for the sake of pleasure is to avoid reality, the reality of other beings and the reality of ourselves. But only the fulfillment of what we really are can give us joy. Joy is nothing else than the awareness of our being fulfilled in our true being, in our personal center. And this fulfillment is possible only if we unite ourselves with what others really are. It is reality that gives joy, and reality alone. The Bible speaks so often of joy because it is the most realistic of all books. "Rejoice!" That means: "Penetrate from what *seems* to be real to that which is *really* real." Mere pleasure, in yourselves and in all other beings, remains in the realm of illusion about reality. Joy is born out of union with reality itself.

One of the roots of the desire for pleasure is the feeling of emptiness and the pain of boredom following from it. Emptiness is the lack of relatedness to things and persons and meanings; it is even the lack of being related to oneself. Therefore we try to escape from ourselves and the loneliness of ourselves, but we do not reach the others and their world in a genuine relation. And so we use them for a kind of pleasure which can be called "fun." But it is not the creative kind of fun often connected with play; it is, rather, a shallow, distracting, greedy way of "having fun." And it is not by chance that it is that type of fun which can easily be commercialized, for it is dependent on calculable reactions, without passion, without risk, without love. Of all the dangers that threaten our civilization, this is one of the most dangerous ones; the escape from one's emptiness through a "fun" which makes joy impossible.

Rejoice! This Biblical exhortation is more needed for those who have much "fun" and pleasure than for those who have little pleasure and much pain. It is often easier to unite pain and joy than to unite fun and joy.

Does the Biblical demand for joy prohibit pleasure? Do joy and pleasure exclude each other? By no means! The fulfillment of the center of our being does not exclude partial and peripheral fulfillments. And we must say this with the same emphasis with which we have contrasted joy and pleasure. We must challenge not only those who seek pleasure for pleasure's sake, but also those who reject pleasure because it is pleasure. Man enjoys eating and drinking, beyond the mere animal need of them. It is a partial ever-repeated fulfillment of his striving for life; therefore, they are pleasure and give joy of life. Man enjoys the community of men in family, friendship, and the social group. They fulfill some fundamental strivings for life; therefore, they are pleasure and give joy of life.

Yet in all these relations the question arises: Is our way of having these pleasures right or wrong? Do we use them for pleasure's sake because we want to unite in love with all that to which we belong? We never know with certainty. And those of us together with those in the past history of Christianity who have an anxious conscience, prefer to renounce pleasures although they are established as good by creation itself. They hide their anxiety behind parental or social or ecclesiastical prohibitions, calling these prohibitions Divine commands.

They justify their fear to affirm the joy of life by appealing to their conscience, calling it the voice of God, or to the need of discipline and self-control, and selflessness, calling them the "imitation of Christ." But Jesus, in contrast to John the Baptist, was called a glutton and a drunkard by His critics. In all these warnings against pleasure, truth is mixed with untruth. Insofar as they strengthen our responsibility, they are true; insofar as they undercut our joy, they are wrong. Therefore let me give another criterion for accepting or rejecting pleasures, the criterion indicated in our text; the pleasures are good which go together with joy; those are bad which prevent joy. In the light of this norm we should risk the affirmation of pleasures, even if our risk may prove to have been an error. It is not more Christian to reject than to accept pleasure. Let us not forget that the rejection implies a rejection of creation, or as the Church Fathers called it, a blasphemy of the Creator—God. And every Christian should be aware of a fact of which many non-Christians are keenly aware: the suppression of the joy of life produces hatred of life, hidden or open. It can lead to a self-destruction, as many physical and mental diseases prove.

Joy is more than pleasure; and it is more than happiness. Happiness is a state of mind which lasts for a longer or shorter time and is dependent on many conditions, external and internal. In the ancient view it is a gift of the gods which they give and take away again. In the American Constitution, "the pursuit of happiness" is a basic human right. In economic theory the greatest happiness of the greatest possible number of people is the purpose of human action. In the fairy tale, "they lived happily ever after." Happiness can stand a large amount of pain and lack of pleasure. But happiness cannot stand the lack of joy. For joy is the expression of our essential and central fulfillment. No peripheral fulfillments and no favorable conditions can be substituted for the central fulfillment. Even an unhappy state of great joy can transform unhappiness into happiness. What, then, is this joy?

Let us first ask what is its opposite. It is sorrow. Sorrow is the feeling that we are deprived of our central fulfillment, by being deprived of something that belongs to us and is necessary to our fulfillment. We may be deprived of relatives and friends nearest to us, of a creative work and a supporting community which gave us a meaning of life, of our home, of honor, of love, of bodily or mental health, of unity of our person, of a good conscience. All this brings sorrow in manifold forms, the sorrow of sadness, the sorrow of loneliness, the sorrow of depression, the sorrow of self-accusation. But it is precisely this kind of situation in which Jesus tells his disciples that His joy shall be with them and that their joy shall be full. For, as Paul calls it, sorrow can be the "sorrow of the world" which ends in the death of final despair, and it can be Divine sorrow which leads to transformation and joy. For joy has something within itself which is beyond joy and sorrow. This something is called blessedness.

Blessedness is the eternal element in joy, that which makes it possible for joy to include in itself the sorrow out of which it arises, and which it takes into itself. In the Beatitudes, Jesus calls the poor, those who mourn, those who hunger and thirst, those who are persecuted, "blessed." And He says to them: "Rejoice and be glad!" Joy within sorrow is possible to those who are blessed, to those in whom joy has the dimension of the eternal.

Here we must once more reply to those who attack Christianity because they believe that it destroys the joy of life. In view of the Beatitudes they say that Christianity undercuts the joy of *this* life by pointing to and preparing for another life. They even challenge the blessedness in the promised life as a refined form of seeking for pleasure in the future life. Again we must confess that in many Christians, joy in this way is postponed till after death, and that there are Biblical words which seem to support this answer. Nevertheless, it is wrong. Jesus will give His joy to His disciples *now*. They shall get it after He has left them, which means in *this* life. And Paul asks the Philippians to have joy *now*. This cannot be otherwise, for blessedness is the expression of God's eternal fulfillment. Blessed are those who participate in this fulfillment here and now. Certainly eternal fulfillment must be seen not only as eternal which is present, but also as eternal which is future. But if it is not seen in the present, it cannot be seen at all.

This joy which has in itself the depth of blessedness is asked for and promised in the Bible. It preserves in itself its opposite, sorrow. It provides the foundation for happiness and pleasure. It is present in all levels of man's striving for fulfillment. It consecrates and directs them. It does not diminish or weaken them. It does not take away the risks and dangers of the joy of life. It makes the joy of life possible in pleasure and pain, in happiness and unhappiness, in ecstasy and sorrow. Where there is joy, there is fulfillment. And where there is fulfillment, there is joy. In fulfillment and joy the inner aim of life, the meaning of creation, and the end of salvation, are attained.

DEFENCE OF LEISURE

Salvador de Madariaga

Salvador de Madariaga, one of the world's outstanding living liberals, makes his home in Oxford, England, when he is not in some other part of the world lecturing. He was born in Spain in 1886 and educated to be an engineer. After five years as a mining engineer and as technical advisor to the Spanish Northern Railway, he went to London and in 1916 entered journalism. In 1921 he became part of the Secretariat of the League of Nations, then head of the disarmament section. He has also served Spain as Ambassador to the United States and as Ambassador to France. His sister is a member of the faculty at Vassar.

"Don't you ever feel like work?"—a lazy boy was asked—and he answered: "Yes, Sir, but I do without." The hero of this story may appeal to some as a specialist in leisure; for many are those who through an insufficient acquaintance with the real thing, mistake leisure for idleness and even for laziness. It is, of course, nothing of either kind; for idleness is the contrary of action, and laziness its enemy; while action and leisure, despite appearances, are so closely connected as to be unthinkable without each other.

But since this prepossession that mistakes leisure for idleness is so general, we might just as well enter the subject through it. Who knows but that it might reveal some truth after all. It is unusual for everybody to be altogether wrong all the time; and if many people think the same for very long, there is sure to be something in it. For most people, perhaps, leisure is equivalent to "having time on one's hands"; to have, that is, either nothing to do, or less to do than time to do it in. As most people earn their living by working for others (who see to it that the time they buy is well stuffed with work) leisure, in this first sense, can only occur in a man's own time, or, in other words, in the part of his life which he has not sold away. This sense of owning his own time is the source of the pleasure which his idleness gives the idle man.

He soon discovers, however, that he cannot remain idle for long; and proceeds to cast his "leisure" away: either by undertaking some paid work in his "free" hours, therefore by selling part of that life he had not already sold; or by fiddling with some unpaid work for a friend or for himself, such as gardening; or by burning his surplus energies in a game of football, tennis, or golf. Here, the pleasure comes from the feeling of liberty of choice. The leisured man does this but might, if he so wished, do that; unlike what happens in his workshop or office, where his course of action is limited and his time set.

It takes many men to make a world; and among them numerous are those who, as Wordsworth (a good man of leisure) put it, "have felt the weight of too much liberty." For these, order, organization, and sequence in the activities which will eat away their leisure seem a necessity. At this stage, the very liberty of choice that still remained as the mark of leisure as opposed to work has vanished. The once idle man has become busy in his so-called idle hours; and, for all we know, may find his trainer a harder and a more exacting master than his boss. That genius for action which is so typical of the English, and that sense of spontaneous organization which is its natural sequel, have gradually raised British sports to such a pitch of perfection that the man who goes in for any of them, popular or stylish, becomes a slave to training and performance—and may soon find relief in actual work from the grind of his sport. Nor is golf an exception—for golf, the puritan game *par excellence*, confronts the player with himself alone, and calls forth the unhappiest and most humiliating meditations from the sporting conscience of the solitary searcher for lost balls.

In games, however, the man of leisure has still the comfort of working . . . for his pleasure, was I to say—but no. After a few experiences, he has grown too wise to claim that sport is work undertaken for pleasure. His satisfaction, as he soon realizes, comes from the mere fact that he *plays*. Though sport may at times be hard work, it is not work—since it is *play*; and the two are not the same, as everybody knows. Work aims at something other than itself, while play aims at nothing outside its own self. So now, his freedom lost, his time given away, the man of leisure takes comfort in the fact that he is giving away his energies and no longer bartering them for bread and butter. And this is in itself a spiritual liberation. Play is by no means a frivolous activity. Far from it. A society without play would be a society of slaves. I hammer a nail to hang a picture up; but why do I hang the picture up if not to enjoy the sight of it? Smith presses some steel to make a frame to make a car for Jones to go to the office to keep the books of an importing company that ships beef over from Argentina to sell it in Smithfield for a number of Smiths and Joneses to eat for them to press steel to make frames to make cars to go to the office to keep accounts—it makes no sense. It simply makes no sense unless at the end of this chain of utilitarian actions, some wholly *useless* thing comes to enliven it all, and to endow it with some meaning, some light, and some delight.

This meaning, this light, and this delight is that of *being* and no longer merely *doing*; that of *play* and no longer *work*; that of *freedom* and no longer *purpose*.

But there is still some road ahead on the way to the deepest meaning of leisure, that in which it may be said to be so closely connected with action as to be unthinkable without it. Between leisure, thus understood, and action, there is the same relationship as there is in music between silence and sound. Every composer knows how a pause enhances the meaning, value, beauty, of what he has just said and of what he is about to say; let alone the fact that all music rests on a background of silence, without which it would merely add to the general hullabaloo—would, in fact, be unborn and unthinkable.

So with action and leisure. Action is the music of our life. Like music, it starts from a pause of leisure, a silence of activity which our initiative *attacks*; then it develops according to its inner logic, passes its climax, seeks its cadence, ends, and restores silence, leisure again. Action and leisure are thus interdependent; echoing and recalling each other, so that action enlivens leisure with its memories and anticipations, and leisure expands and raises action beyond its mere immediate self and gives it a permanent meaning.

So life goes on; woven of the two trends of leisure and of action, so closely knit together that one might wonder where the one begins and the other ends were it not that their texture is so different that everyone should be able to tell. For, and here is the crux of the matter, the difference between action and leisure is less in the doing than in the mood of doing which, in action, as the very word suggests, is active, while in true leisure it is passive.

This is the secret of the boon that leisure is for human beings; the reason why it is so restful, since it sets the spirit in a different attitude; the cause of its creative virtue, since it opens all the senses and the faculties to the inbreathing of nature and its goings-on and ways; the basis of that strong link between it and action, since leisure turns out to be the breathing in of the will which has been breathed out in activity.

Happy the life that can achieve a balance between action and leisure. Such a life will be as free from the sense of haste, of being driven, so widespread nowadays, as from the sense of wasteful and bored idleness which devours many a heart even in our hectic times. It is perhaps in the search for such a balance that true practical wisdom lies; and in securing it, once achieved, against the constant threats from the world around us, and from ourselves.

But how are we to seek this wisdom and this balance if we hold mistaken notions about it? Now the point to emphasize is that *passivity* is an essential feature of the highest form of leisure. This is hard for active people to understand; who will at once proceed to choke with activity any leisure left by chance to them; and, of course, condemn as idleness or even laziness the true enjoyment of leisure which consists in doing just—nothing. Here is perhaps at last the kernel of truth we had expected to find in so general and persistent a misrepresentation; for at all times and in all places, true connoisseurs of leisure have been for all but the wary-eyed indistinguishable from idlers and lazybones in that they would do nothing at all—not even play a game of tennis, or a hand at bridge.

But the difference is capital. The idler never works, if he can help it. As in the story told at the beginning, if he happens to feel like work (which is unlikely) he does without. The connoisseur of leisure, who will of course do nothing while he is enjoying it, is not only a good worker, but a better worker than most; for he knows of the give and take between the two moods; and will be the more active in his work for the fact that he has been passive in his leisure.

It is, let it be said again, like breathing. The more air you breathe out, the more air you must breathe in. The more you pour yourself into the outer life in your action, the more you must let life pour itself into you during your leisure. That is why the best and highest form of leisure is contemplation, preferably where life is least spoiled and meddled with by man—in the country. Nervy, brittle people, as so many moderns are, mostly through lack of true leisure, will destroy their only possibility of restoring their peace of mind by filling their happily empty days with games, excursions, and what not. The ideal holiday for the truly active man is one doing nothing in beautiful surroundings, drinking nature in quietly through the eyes; and the ideal exercise for this best form of leisure is the old, natural, spontaneous movement of the body—the walk.

For the same reason, the best pastimes for a true enjoyer of leisure who has to stay at home are those that enable the mind and the body to remain as passive as possible: reading by the fireside, for instance, provided the author is not one that goads us into a vigorous opposition. That is why in days of leisure one must avoid any opinionated books; indeed any books on opinion; and select rather those that present the drama, the romance, and the poetry of life before which we remain as passive spectators. Listening to music is an admirable way of spending one's leisure: for music releases the mind, and lets it wander; and, more subtly still, music, by the haunting way in which it recalls our activity, achieves in our soul for a while that marriage of leisure and of action which makes us feel the taste of life. Broadcasting is a godsend for lovers of true leisure, for they can let good music flow in without having to move from their fireside; and (confining to their professional chairs critics and censors whose work it is to take in a musical piece as a whole and understand and explain it) can, if they feel like it, quietly dream out and in again, away from and back to their Mozart or their Beethoven, and even glide into sleep—in which sleep their dreams are sure to be excellent and harmonious, and a true comfort from our machine-controlled life.

For modern life in industrialized nations is in deadly conspiracy against true leisure. To begin with, it works against country and for town life, which, from the point of view of true leisure, could not be worse. Then again these monstrous, overgrown cities of ours gradually drive their dwellers out to their outer edges, so that the precious time the worker might devote to leisure, to sit back and look on at his life, has to be spent on the 8.40 A.M. and the 6.05 P.M. sitting up in a third-class compartment and looking at a newspaper for lack of something better; since cows and meadows are, by relativity, set in motion and made to travel backwards as fast as he does forward.

Not content with this grievous drain on our leisure, our industrial age infiltrates and infects with its economic prejudice every hour and every minute of man's life. Work is turned into a god or a fetish; and, regardless of the fact that it presupposes leisure as day does night, the economic fiends that rule our life (whether socialist or capitalist matters nothing) proceed to destroy leisure by filling it up with activity. What shall we do with this half hour which has squeezed through our nets? Men, being what they are, have fought tooth and nail for the right to sell their work as they thought fit; but seem unable or unwilling to defend their leisure against the encroachments of a work-mad society. And yet, it is the freedom of his leisure that truly makes a man free.

ON THE SHAPE OF WONDER

N. J. Berrill

N. J. Berrill, member of the Royal Society, a renowned embryologist, a professor at McGill University, Montreal, Canada, is the author of Man's Emerging Mind *and other books growing out of his lifetime activities in science. His principal research has been in the field of the development of organisms, and he has his own laboratory for the study of marine life on the Maine coast. He is also the author of* Journey Into Wonder *and* Sex and the Nature of Things.

. . . What the mind does when a person is engrossed in finding sustenance or is working under direction or is in a semi-coma from too much food or from the lack of it is not significant. I am not concerned with the driven or the sleepy mind but with one that is fully alert and free to express itself, for the mind shows its true nature only when it is free to play, free to be itself as fully as possible, just as a child will climb a tree under conditions of vigorous health, mental relaxation and the presence of an arboreal paradise. Our true nature comes to the fore in those activities that give us the greatest joy when we are free from constraint or anxiety, and our true values appear in what, under other circumstances, we are prepared to live for and if necessary die for. The being which emerges may or may not be in the image of God, but at least he is new in this corner of the universe.

Through most of the past we have been slaves to our senses and to a great extent are captives still, although we are no longer bound by smell like the rest of our mammalian kin. We miss a lot but we gain a lot. We have developed touch to an astonishing degree, which allows creative urges their tangible expression. But above all we are indebted to eyes and ears and a sense of action, although our eyes and ears are not the best in the animal kingdom. Yet they are good enough and the amazing newness is of another kind.

We see, but we see more than the light and shadow and color recorded by the retina, more than meaningful forms and movements that mean life or death or sociability—we see a sunset or a rainbow or a flower and call it beauty. We see expression on a face and see radiance within—and call it beauty. We see unfolding growth in a child, in its mind and body, and call it beauty. I know of no other name to call it.

We hear, but the sounds take on meaning though they are but percussions in the air. The mind now weaves them into patterns of symbols that form channels of thought between mind and mind. Speech seems so natural and all pervasive that we forget its import and fail to realize the isolation and awkwardness of thought if sound had no significance. We pool our wisdom in gaseous waves and think nothing of it. Yet sound is beaten into other patterns which cannot be traced to thought. Beaten into rhythms and molded into tones we get a sense of movement, cycles, harmony, and time itself, in forms which speak directly to the spirit and the emotions leaving intelligence untouched. It conveys feeling and loveliness. We call it music, yet what else can it be but beauty?

I know beauty but I do not know what it means. Keats said that beauty is truth and so did the Greeks, although the one was concerned with loveliness and the others mainly with intellect. I do know that whatever beauty is, whether it is the kind that is woven within the mind itself or is perceived without, on this earth only the human mind can sense it. We can shut it out or kill it, and to that extent we die ourselves, but it is every man's birthright and children recognize it instinctively in its simpler forms. And inasmuch as we ourselves, in body, brain or mind, are as integral a part of the universe as any star, it makes little difference whether we say beauty lies only in the mind of the beholder or otherwise. We, each of us, you and I, exhibit more of the true nature of this universe than any dead Saturn or Jupiter, and if beauty is built in to our minds and has nowhere else to live, it still remains beauty and we have even greater reason to cherish it. Yet I do not think this is the case. I believe that somehow, as our brains have grown beyond a certain complexity and size, beauty emerged both as perception and as creation. We know it when we meet it and we create it when we can. And we know it in many forms and not only in sublimated senses—we know it when love becomes selfless and solicitude becomes compassion. We see it in moral stature and in hope and courage. We see it whenever the transcending quality of growth is clear and unmistakable, knowing that only in such growth do we find our own individual happiness.

When you speak of divinity the divine flies out the window, someone said. And I feel it is much the same with beauty and love. We can express them with words but cannot define them—we can only say that this and this are included but that is not, and wordlessly we all recognize the truth of it. Speech is limited, no matter what the language, and here I think we are not unlike a dog who feels intensely the bonds of loyalty and devotion but cannot speak. For in our hearts we understand more than we can possibly talk about.

We know that quality counts far above quantity. We cannot prove it but we can live by it. We know that once a life has begun to grow it should develop to its utmost, and that a flower nipped in the bud or a child dead is wrong. We know that when an animal or a plant becomes extinct, whether lovely or grotesque or simply different, the earth is poorer. We know loss when we destroy beauty for the sake of power or water. We know that when we kill, whatever the provocation or incentive, whether man or beast, harm has been done to more than flesh and blood. Or if we do not then we fall short of being human, and sooner or later we usually know this too. To destroy or repress the growth of body or spirit or recognizable beauty in any of its manifestations is evil. I believe it is the only evil that we know—that instinctively we acknowledge the supreme values of the emergent quality we sense within us and recognize without in all of nature, and insofar as we realize it and hinder its expression we feel guilty of sin, the only sin there is. Conscience was born when this brain of ours reached its present dimensions, and it raises an intriguing question: If our brain should grow larger and better with a corresponding development of mind, will we suffer greater remorse or will we stop sinning against the light? The latter seems to make more sense. . . .

When we are left alone and are not thinking of personal relationships or where the next meal is coming from our thoughts wander into space and time, weave patterns out of the passing present and the life of yesterday, and become both meditative and speculative. Even when idling along, without incentive except for pleasure in being alive, the process is essentially a creating of order out of chaos of immediate and remembered sensory impressions, a persistent and almost effortless process of bringing together a sequence of different facts and happenings from the well of memory. Unless the mind is driven by urgency in a particular direction something akin to reverie goes on incessantly, even in sleep in a disorderly way. Such is the loom on which the tapestries of light are woven, though they are shot through with emotion and vibrate to sound. Yet deep within it you feel there is someone, which is you, who mixes the colors as they feed in and, more significantly, scans the results for meaning and in the rather wistful hope of finding his own image.

Freedom begins here. The freedom to think untrammeled and to speak accordingly, the freedom for thought to soar if possible, and the freedom of the mind to be for the sake of being, in the sense that a thing of beauty is a joy forever and needs no other sanction. And joy comes to the mind when it is most fully aware of beauty in its broadest and deepest sense, and when thought for the sake of thinking is exercised most strongly. There is always satisfaction in doing what you are best designed to do, whether it is climbing a mountain, painting a picture, or solving a problem; and if the achievement is considerable there is always a certain amount of pain—the labor pains that accompany every birth—for only then do you know that you yourself are fully and consciously alive. For the finest performance of the mind a man should work for no reason except that which is the very life within him, for an element of slavery creeps in when the will, whether your own or someone else's, drives the mind to work for other motives. The performance may still be good but it is not so freely given and the difference can be noted. A man may enter science for the sake of benefiting humanity—an unselfish and noble purpose—but unless he becomes completely seduced he will serve both to the satisfaction of neither. You cannot travel freely along a predetermined path, for where freedom lies there is no path. And pure science, like pure art, whether of painting, poetry or music, is self directed and fancy free, and is a creation of individual minds working alone except for sources of inspiration.

I am not here concerned with moral obligations or with any obligation except that of the human spirit to express and recognize itself. You cannot study the course of a homing bird if you keep it captive, nor can you see what evident joy there is in flight if flight is not free. And it is only when the mind is keyed to a high pitch, is directed by intuition controlled by reason, and free of all external restraint, can you see the course it follows and feel its drive toward the heavens. Then it is that science, art, history and religion all seem to converge into a single whole, each portraying a facet with a color of its own yet each reflecting something of the rest. Science, with which I am more intimately involved, is concerned no less than religion and art with truth and beauty, and in some ways is more illuminating since it itself is better understood.

Science at this level, where it is conducted for no rewards and for no useful purpose, is enlightening. It is based on faith, though a faith that is instinctive and not based on any dogma. It is faith that the universe we construct from the impressions of our senses has some correspondence in reality, that we are part of nature and sensible to it. It is faith that by opening the windows of intuition and bringing all the power of reason to bear we can understand the nature of reality to a considerable extent. And it is faith that there is an all-pervading unity throughout all of nature and the universe as a whole, that it all has coherent meaning and is all of one piece including the scientist who attempts to discover and understand it. There is room for neither God nor space outside it, neither broken rules, nor interference, but the whole is both the song of creation and the singer himself—without beginning and without end.

As individual we each contain within us the whole of our individual existence. As humanity we not only add up in a queerly collective sense but embrace the past as well. Man is the whole fantastic event which includes not only what we call the present, together with its potentiality, but also all that has gone before that can be recognized as human, which in turn takes roots in a more extensive being. That we are delving for it so is the same urge, I feel sure, as most people get during their middle or later years to recapture the days of their youth. We know instinctively that it is part of us and not merely idle curiosity, for the desire to repossess, both in the individual and in science, is usually passionate. Yet there is no place that I can see where we can draw a line. The individual becomes one with his species, the species with its kind, and so ever-broadening in space and deepening in time all life becomes one. We are but a phase of it, and a recent one. In essence this is simply the theory of evolution, although that is so much more than a theory for it is primarily our acknowledgement of the unity and the continuity of life. And to me at least it means that the living quality of the human creatures who struggled through the ice age is real, although I can barely sense it; that the age of early mammals is still real because it has already happened; and that the earlier events in the history of earthly life, however vague our notions of them may be, still retain their value. We can find analogy in a symphony, although it is much more than an analogy.

A symphony is a single event from beginning to end, an indivisible whole. Its parts may be separately enjoyable and beautiful but are necessarily incomplete when heard in isolation, while the whole has a content and a majesty which is more than the simple addition of the values and properties of the individual parts. All this is fully recognized. Moreover this is true whether we are considering a symphony as it grew within the creative intensity of a Beethoven or as a re-creation in the mind of a conductor or through the ears of the listeners. The opening movement is not dead and gone because you are listening to later phrases, and the closing measures are only the development of what has already happened. It remains a unity in time or it has no meaning at all, and its musical life is in the whole of it—without present, past or future but only eternal beauty. And I believe this is as true of the total pageant of life as it is of this symphonic expression of life. The past is alive in the same sense as the first part of the symphony; we represent a refrain somewhere along the course; and whether our particular refrain evolves into the major movement or gives way to another is of more concern to us than to the whole: in any case we have been heard and consequently remain immortal. This may be the faith of an individual but it also makes sense, particularly to those who study the development of organisms and are forced to think in four dimensions.

It makes sense in more ways than one, for it also gives reason to my being. I am living my life for the sake of living and not for any thought of entering pearly gates. All that I can be I will be, but for the sake of being. I know that work, love, hope, the search for beauty, self discipline, the vigorous use of reason, all are immediately satisfying and require no justification or purpose other than themselves. The quality of life is paramount and we need to hold to our old concepts of greatness and to cultivate our human garden for its finest flowers.

In the end I believe it is reason that reigns supreme. I do not mean that process of logical reasoning which is a tool of conscious thought but that part of you which craves to understand and, having understood, accepts and governs accordingly. Man is a rational being, much more rational than is generally admitted, but he seems somewhat afraid to trust his reason. Psychoanalysts for instance, who generally fail to acknowledge the role of reason, cure by means of explanation wherever they cure at all, for once reason understands, it creates order where there had been confusion. Potentially it is master of the subconscious hungers of the self. A man under hypnotic influence may give away all his possessions or even accuse himself of a crime which results in his execution, but he will not violate what to him is a moral principle—his sense of right is greater than his instinct for self-preservation. And in industry it is well known that a man will work better under bad conditions than under unjust conditions no matter how physically good the last may be. We are rational in a way that is new in this world, and our reason has the power to govern the whole human personality.

We are underestimating both the craving and the capacity of human beings everywhere to understand the meaning of things, the nature of our world and ourselves, and our particular predicament as individuals and societies. Unless warped and deafened and deadened by propaganda the average human individual has resources and capacities that should cause a tyrant shame. If information is true, or as true as can be, understanding begins and the will to act according to the light eventually follows. I doubt if a collective will is ever very potent but the individual will is powerful indeed and it is vital that it comes from minds whose understanding is based on truth. And inasmuch as each individual view of the truth is inevitably a little different from all others, we need to integrate them for greater wisdom. The collective pool of understanding grows from what is poured into it, but the contributions are those of individuals and the will to act must come from them—as the diversified individuals of a group acting together like those of an orchestra, not as members of a herd following the loudest voice.

We need faith, a faith in ourselves as human beings and not as members of this or that race or religion or state or class of society. We need no faith in supernatural forces. We need only to recognize that our knowledge of the universe through our senses and our knowledge of the universe through our own inward nature show that it is orderly, moral and beautiful, that it is akin to intelligence, that love and hope belong in it as fully as light itself, and that the power and will of the human mind is but a symptom of reality; that we, when we are most human, most rational, most aware of love and beauty, reflect and represent the spirit of the universe. That should be enough. But insofar as we recognize this and fail to live accordingly, we know and do evil in some degree, for the deeper the insight the greater the sin.

THE *MYSTIQUE* OF THE DESERT
Joseph Wood Krutch

*Joseph Wood Krutch, teacher, drama critic, biographer, editor, jour-
nalist, public speaker, and formerly Brander Matthews Professor of
Dramatic Literature at Columbia University, is at present a resident
of Tucson, Arizona, where for more than five years he followed another of his numerous bents—naturalism. One of his latest books is
The Voice of the Desert, A Naturalist's Interpretation, from which
the following excerpt is taken.*

. . . Just as the realm of speculative reason lies beyond the facts
of science, so also, beyond the realm of speculative reason, lies
the realm of emotion. To me that realm is no less important
than the realm of fact or the realm of speculative thought, though
to discuss what one experiences in the realm of emotion one
must either depreciate it and explain it away, as the pure rationalist does, or one must accept what one can only call the *mystique*
as opposed to the *rational* of the human being's intercourse with
the universe around him.

Your Philistine never enters this realm of the mystical. When he
has read the great poem, looked at the great picture, heard the
great music, or even grasped the great theory, he always makes the
same comments in words which lie halfway between exclamation
and question: "So what?" Since neither music, nor poetry, nor
pure theory has practical usefulness and since the mystique of all

three eludes him, his comment-question is perfectly proper. And the only—usually impossible—answer to him lies in the mystique itself.

Though in *The Voice of the Desert* I have presented facts and, at moments, permitted myself metabiological speculations, neither the one nor the other really says all that I would like to be able to say. If Dipodomys never drinks; if the moth desires the candle; if the seed has learned to disregard the wetness of summer while waiting for the wetness of spring; if the cactus has learned to be at home where its ancestors would have perished; who cares? Why, having learned these things, did I not say, "So what" and pass on? The ultimate answer, I think, is to be found only by admitting the mystical element. The reason for my deepest caring does not lie within the scope of biology or even metabiology. One cannot recognize it without being to that extent a mystic.

Of the official mystical writers I am no great reader. The clarity of their visions, the overwhelming certainty of their conviction that ultimate truth has been revealed to them, is foreign to my own experience. At most I have "intimations," not assurances, and I doubt that I could ever go further in recommendation of the complete mystics than William James goes when he bids the ordinary mortal recognize the reality, in some realm, of the phenomena to which the mystics testify, no matter what interpretation we ordinary mortals put upon them. Yet I, and many whose temperaments are no more mystical than mine, do know moments when we draw courage and joy from experiences which lie outside the getting and spending of everyday life.

The occasions of such experiences are many. The commonest and perhaps the least obviously related are these: reading a poem and contemplating a child—human or animal. But the experiences come to different men in many different ways. Some are most likely to be aware of them in solitude, others in crowds; some while looking at the stars, some while watching the waves roll in upon a beach. And whether you call the experience infrarational or superrational, it involves the momentary acceptance of values not definable in terms of that common sense to which we ordinarily accord our first loyalty. And to all such experiences one thing is common. There is a sense of satisfaction which is not personal but impersonal. One no longer asks, "What's in it for me?" because one is no longer a separate selfish individual but part of the welfare and joy of the whole.

Those to whom such mystical experiences are habitual and hence more ordinary than what most people call ordinary life, can often call upon them at will as the religious mystics do by the repetition of a prayer. But to the majority there is no certain formula or ritual—not even a private, much less a communicable, one. At most we can only, for example, plunge into the crowd or retire into a solitude, knowing that sometimes in the one situation or the other we will glimpse out of the corner of our eyes what, if one may believe the true mystics, is usually at the very center of the true mystic's vision.

I happen to be one of those, and we are not a few, to whom the acute awareness of a natural phenomenon, especially of a phenomenon of the living world, is the thing most likely to open the door to that joy we cannot analyze. I have experienced it sometimes when a rabbit appeared suddenly from a bush to dash away to the safety which he values so much, or when, at night, a rustle in the leaves reminds me how many busy lives surround my own. It has also come almost as vividly when I suddenly saw a flower opening or a stem pushing out of the ground.

But what is the content of the experience? What is it that at such moments I seem to realize? Of what is my happiness compounded?

First of all, perhaps, there is the vivid assurance that these things, that the universe itself, really do exist, that life is not a dream; second, that the reality is pervasive and, it seems, unconquerable. The future of mankind is dubious. Perhaps the future of the whole earth is only somewhat less dubious. But one knows that all does not depend upon man, that possibly, even, it does not depend upon this earth. Should man disappear, rabbits may well still run and flowers may still open. If this globe itself should perish, then it seems not unreasonable to suppose that what inspires the stem and the flower may exist somewhere else. And I, it seems, am at least part of all this.

God looked upon the world and found that it was good. How great is the happiness of being able, even for a moment, to agree with Him! And how much easier that is if one is not committed to considering only some one section of the world or of the universe.

Long before I ever saw the desert I was aware of the mystical overtones which the observation of nature made audible to me. But I have never been more frequently or more vividly aware of them than in connection with the desert phenomena. And I have often wondered why.

Were I to believe what certain psychologists have been trying to tell me, the thing which I call a "mystique" and especially what I call "the mystique of the desert" is only the vague aura left behind by certain experiences of infancy and childhood. Should I search my memory of the latter I should certainly find there what nearly every other American or European would: a Christmas card showing Wise Men crossing the desert and also, in some school geography, another picture of rolling dunes, a camel and the caption "Sahara Desert." Both seemed then to be things I should never see; both were remote from the scene of my sorrows—whatever at the moment I found my sorrows to be. "Poof!" say those psychologists. The "mystique" is mysterious no longer. To adjust yourself to your environment would have been a simple matter. Had you been so adjusted you would never have gone to live in the American Southwest. And you would not give a damn whether Dipodomys drinks or not.

If those psychologists are right, then I am glad that I, at least, was not "adjusted" to everything and hence incapable of giving a damn about anything whatsoever. But I am not sure that they are right. Curiosity is not always the result of conditions and there are words at which most imaginations kindle. Among them are all those words which suggest the untamed extravagances or the ultimate limits of nature in any one of her moods. We may prefer to live amid hills and meadows, fields and woodlots, or even, for that matter, surrounded by steel and concrete. But "wilderness," "jungle," and "desert" are still stirring words, as even movie-makers know. And it is just possible that they will continue to be such after the last Christmas card having anything to do with Christmas has disappeared from the shops and after school geographies have consented to confine themselves exclusively to "things relevant to the child's daily life." Perhaps the mind is not merely a blank slate upon which anything may be written. Perhaps it reaches out spontaneously toward what can nourish either intelligence or imagination. Perhaps it is part of nature and, without being taught, shares nature's intentions.

THE IDLER AND HIS WORKS
George Santayana

George Santayana, born in Spain of a Spanish father and a Spanish mother who was born in Scotland and raised in Virginia, died in his sleep at the age of 88 on September 26, 1952, in a nursing home of a Catholic convent in Rome. For twenty-three years he taught philosophy at Harvard, but retired to live in Europe in 1912 where he continued his writings—essays, poetry, a novel, autobiography, and the many volumes of his classic works, The Life of Reason, and The Realms of Being.

The essay in this book was found by Daniel Cory, his secretary and disciple and long-time friend, in an old valise with other writings labeled "Unpublished" and "Important." The self-appraisal of his own life work is considered by Mr. Cory a masterpiece of its kind in summing up a literary life's labors and "attempting to evaluate them from the standpoint of posterity." The piece was written in Rome sometime between 1942 and 1944.

Many other persons and places, not mentioned in my autobiography, have played important parts in my life and left their ghosts, at night, in my dreams: but they had better remain there. I have recorded only such fragments of biography as still interested my waking mind, or perhaps might serve some antiquary curious about the times or the types that I have painted with care. Many of them, although potent influences over me in my private capacity, may seem insignificant and tiresome to a reader who thinks of me as an author: and how else should a reader think of me? Yet it is not at all as an author or as a professional philosopher that I think of myself. I have written a great many books and a great many reviews and articles. Astonishing bibliographies of them have been compiled, astonishing, I mean, to me; I wonder how I found time for wasting so much ink and paper.

I have seldom been conscious of working hard. Most of my writing has been an instinctive pleasure, a playful impulse, as in running down a grassy slope or exploring a woodland path. The things wrote themselves; and when I dropped the pen, and rose from my writing-table, I seemed to awake from a trance and to be myself again. Yet that other dreaming, industrious self, weaving words eagerly together, and excogitating arguments and opinions as if he were an animated book, is doubtless the self that I am supposed to be and that, in an autobiography, I should have been expected to write about.

No doubt that industrious, playful, automatic self was an original part of me, and a persistent part. I am happy in mental idleness, with manual work. I envy the housemaids, so common in Southern Europe, who sing as they scrub. I feel that there is something sane and comfortable in the old women who sit knitting or turning over the roasting chestnuts at the street corners. I like to spend drowsy hours drawing, cleaning or making something, or even mending my clothes. Pleasant is solitude among manageable things. And among manageable things, the most manageable for me are words.

All my life, since I regained my freedom, I have passed the morning writing. The theme had been chosen in a moment of inspiration. The chapter, perhaps the paragraph was already begun. Nothing was required but to turn on the current, if only the current would come, and continue the flow of language. The material act of writing entertained me; also the semimaterial act of arranging and rearranging the words. Often the thought was rekindled in the process, transformed, sharpened, corrected; and out came an epigram or a terse formula for something that had perhaps been floating in my mind for years.

Various peculiarities and faults of my writings are due to this mechanical and dreamful way of composing them. All is improvised, as in poetry: hence, unless there is a drastic revision, so much repetition, so much that is desultory, rambling, inconclusive. No strict program, no order was predetermined, no precise limits or scope. Such a method or lack of method would have been fatal had there not been sharp definition in my thought, clear principles in my judgments. As it is, though the surface be sometimes confused, as in a tapestry, the figures at a little distance stand out clearly enough; and I think that, at least in my later works, a sympathetic reader will not be seriously troubled by my meanderings. The mountains and the sea are never out of sight. I don't stop to reconsider what comes to me as I write, and I consult no authorities; but I have read much and reflected long before I begin writing.

As regards the subject matter, my work might be divided into two strands, the poetic and the academic. There may be poetic touches and irresponsible flights sometimes in the academic books, and academic themes even in the poetry: yet the two were originally quite distinct. My verses and my private philosophizing belonged to me, expressed me, and were addressed essentially to nobody else; the academic subjects were suggested or imposed by circumstances, and I appear there in the costume and under the mask of an assumed character. The acting is sincere enough, but the part is conventional. My life does not appear in my works until we turn to the "Poems," "Soliloquies in England," "Dialogues in Limbo," and "The Last Puritan." In these my inmost feelings, and the places and persons concerned in my real life, supply the subject and control the expression. It is not a question of complete portraits either of myself or of others. All has been recast in a crucible, and there appear only possibilities, dream-images of my surroundings and passions, such as the mind retains more willingly than the accidental and imperfect realities.

In the academic books, besides the rhetorical veneer that I have spoken of, there is a tendency to infuse more and more of myself into the apprehension of the world and of its opinions, until in "Realms of Being" the picture of them becomes itself a confession and an image of the mind that composed it. Not that I have intentionally indulged the imagination here, as in the poems and the novel: on the contrary, I have studied to be austere and sceptical and to discount the human mind and its bias as far as possible. But this love of the bare truth, this intellectual asceticism, is itself a human passion and the secret of a regenerate life: so that the more I strip myself of myself, the better I bring to light that something in me that is more myself than I am—the spirit. I believe there is substantial, though relative truth in my philosophy, since it is merely the confession of sincere and fundamental assumptions, which a living being can hardly avoid; and I hope that some more powerful and betterknit mind may arise, and restate those views as I ought to have stated them. But that could be done in a single volume, without any of the accidental trappings that encumber my compositions. All my technical writings could then be forgotten to advantage, even as my own mind prefers to forget them.

When by chance I open one of my books, especially one of the earlier ones, it seems to me the work of some other man; and I am surprised if I come to something that sounds like what I should say myself. In general the tone and tenor remain quite foreign to me. Not that I have changed my opinions. I should still say the same things, did the same questions present themselves to me in the same terms. But those terms belonged to a fundamentally foreign morality. I said in them, as well as I could, what I honestly felt; yet they constituted a literary and diplomatic veil to my latent intelligence. I seemed cold (as Bertrand Russell has observed) when my heart was burning away beneath the embers; and it has taken the greater part of a long life for me to extricate my meaning from my words, find the center of my survey, and form fresh categories and a fresh vocabulary.

Ancient philosophy was a great aid to me in this: the more I retreated in time, and the farther east I looked, the more I discovered my own profound and primitive convictions. The conventional moralizing and the prim esthetic judgments of my earlier books need not be contradicted; the literary psychology in them may even be confirmed; but all this needs to be grounded in physical facts and at the same time shown to be purely relative to special phases of human life and to special predicaments. The surface of human experience must not be taken for its ground or for its own motive power. It is all an effect of subhuman or superhuman forces.

The liberal, empirical, psychological philosophy into which I was plunged was miserably artificial, like a modern town laid out in squares. There was nothing subterranean acknowledged in it, no ultimate catastrophe, no jungle, no desert, and no laughter of the Gods. Mankind lived lost in the fog of self-consciousness, persuaded that it was creating itself and the whole universe. They had forgotten their religion; and their philosophy, when they had one, was a glorification of their vanity and of their furious impulse to make money, to make machines, and to make war. What would come of it, except perhaps to make them all alike? In my solitude I watched their mechanical arts not without admiration: they were clever children making their own toys, and as busy at it as birds building their nests or worms burrowing their holes. Verily they have their reward, if they enjoy the process. But may they not be rather multiplying their troubles, and missing the natural pleasures and dignity of man? These pleasures and dignity lie in seeing and thinking, in living with an understanding of the place and destiny of life.

Now reflection convinces me that what is called experience, the obvious and inescapable pressure of sensation, is intrinsically a dream, something arbitrary, fugitive, unsubstantial, coming out of nothing and ending in nothing. Yet since this dream is endured, and to some extent may be surveyed and remembered, there is something else on the hither side of it which I call the spirit; a witness, but not an agent, since spirit can neither bring the dream about nor avoid it nor understand why it should come. This coming, however, is a terrible assault to the spirit, for it awakes in ter-

ror and tears; so that on the further side of the dream and anteced-
ent to it, there is something dynamic, obscure to the spirit, but over-
whelmingly powerful and real, which I call matter, but which, if
you prefer, you may call God. Spirit here and matter or God there,
are not phenomena; they are not distinguishable and recognizable
features in the dream, but an outlying power in the one case and an
observant intellect in the other, which is not observed but is ana-
lytically implied in the fact of observation and in the act of com-
paring one part of the dream with another and noting its inconstancy and confusion.

The terms employed in this apprehension of experience remain
mere images or words, but for intelligence they become signs for
something beneath or beyond them, matter, God, or spirit, of
which they manifest the presence, power, and method of action.
Such manifestation, however, is not exhaustive, as if the words or
images were alone real, and signified nothing further. They do not
define their object but only indicate it. Nothing existent can be de-
fined. Definition defines only the idea, the word, or the image: the
object is transcendent. Matter, God, or spirit have to be posited beyond. Only such substances, powers, or faculties can have any depth
or persistence or can render our visions and definitions valid or true
of anything beyond themselves.

Such was the summary system of categories by which in the end
I cleared my mind, at least in principle and in intention, of all foreign confusion. In fact, however, the books in which I worked out
that system—"Scepticism and Animal Faith" and "Realms of Being"
—are terribly overloaded with accidental matters, the mud and the
weeds that clung to me as I struggled out of the bog. Nevertheless,
I hope that a benevolent reader will shed these impedimenta as he
advances, and will retain at the end a clear sense of my radical position. It is not at all new or artificial. I did not reach it by invention
or hypothesis but by retreat from all inventions and hypotheses to
the inevitable assumptions and the obvious terms of all apprehension.

Then I found myself reverting to a system like those of the first
Greek philosophers, who looked at the world boldly, without reli-

gious preconceptions, yet found it to be much the same world that the Indians described in their religious meditations. But the Indian like the Christian philosophers were encumbered with fantastic notions, suggested by moral predicaments to an unrestrained imagination; and it is necessary to remove these problems to the moral and poetical sphere where they belong. They are human problems and a man may well find them more interesting and important than cosmology, but this poetic or moral enthusiasm in him will not change the real conditions of his life, or the source and development of that enthusiasm itself; so that even in the interests of his private spiritual progress, he will do well in the first place not to deceive himself about his natural status. Nothing could be farther from me than a desire to quench the imagination; on the contrary I would preserve it in all its freedom and originality. But it should not profess to be perception or science, if it would not become madness.

My philosophical system, being thus discovered within me, was latent in all the earlier phases of my opinions; and I think there is very little in my first writings that cannot be inserted into my mature system. Yet I was not clearly aware, when I wrote those innocent phrases, in what sense exactly they ought to be understood; so that some uncertainty and confusion seems to hang about my words. The words came from the heart, I was always sincere; but the heart was reacting upon alien impressions, and not speaking freely out of its clear depths. It would be necessary in each case to understand the circumstances and the connections in which such thoughts came into my mind; and then the spontaneous side of my reaction, which alone would express my innate philosophy, could be disengaged.

In my first prose book, "The Sense of Beauty," the argument is uninspired and academic; I was writing the book for a practical purpose. Yet it was I that was writing it; so that in the incidental touches and in the style there is more of me than in the doctrine. I speak as if the sense of beauty were compounded of ingredients, so much sugar, so much lemon, and so much water making the proper lemonade. But sensations are moments of spirit, they cannot endure, they cannot be compounded; and the whole "chemistry of mind" goes on in the psyche, in the life of the body, from which the richest and subtlest intuition issues pure and whole, like the sound of a bell, or the voice singing. I had not yet read Arisobe sufficiently or understood that the psyche is the life of the body as a whole, in its unity and direction, partially and incidentally expressed in consciousness. When I spoke of "objectified pleasure," apart from the false subsistence apparently attributed to feelings, as if they could be tossed about like dice in a dicebox, there was nevertheless a true sense of the nerve of perception, which is transcendent intent or indication: the psyche receives an impression, and the intellect and will respond with a belief. So in the presence of things harmonious with its life, the psyche luxuriates, and is suffused with a vital pleasure; a part of this pleasure may be proper to the act of seeing or hearing, which at the same time evokes a visual or musical image: and since this image is a recognizable object our joy in it comes as the sense of its beauty, not as a sense of our pleasure. The beauty is probably the first thing felt by the lover, before the form in which it dwells becomes distinct and articulate in his vision. So the sun attracts and dazzles us, before we can focus the eyes on its color or its shape.

In turning to criticism, as I did in "Interpretations of Poetry and Religion," I began to rescue the part that was my own from the borrowed part of my philosophy. The themes were public, and principally drawn from English literature and philosophy; but now the judgments passed, and the criterion that inspired them, were frankly not English. What were they? We cannot say that they were Spanish or Catholic, yet they lay in that direction; in that direction and beyond, in the humanism not of the Renaissance but of antiquity. The Renaissance was not a rebirth but a reproduction of relics; the seeds of antiquity had not been replanted in the soil of Christendom, so that they might bloom afresh into a new and complete life. There had been merely a revival, a restoration—patches of antiquity inserted in the torn garment of the Christian mind. Now in my criticism, I was falling back upon pre-Christian, merely human standards; yet these in one sense even more Christian than the

English standard of appreciation. They condemned "the poetry of barbarism," the worship of impulse, enterprise, effort, and blind adventure. They were anti-romantic, anti-idealistic, and demanded a "life of reason."

The long book in which I expounded what I conceived a life of reason to be suffered from the very faults that my criticism condemned: it was too impulsive, too pretentious, too casual, and based on too little learning. Admiration of ancient Greece and modern England insinuated a didactic tone into the political part, and made me seem a prophet of I don't know what Utopia. This tone pleased people in America, especially the young Jews, and perhaps caused the book to become well-known in that circle when otherwise it might have been altogether neglected. It also caused the book to be misinterpreted, as if it had been inspired by romantic idealism, and not grounded, as it was meant to be, on a materialistic view of nature and life.

Such a view does not exclude the possibility of all sorts of beautiful and surprising developments in the universe. The natural world is indefinitely fertile; but its fertility is not directed by the human will; it is not governed, except in man, by human interests. The sentiment that it would justly inspire about human life and human hopes would be extremely sober. Beings that arise are likely to find means of subsistence and a chance to propagate their kind, because otherwise they would never have arisen; but in no particular case, and at no particular time, can a race or an individual be sure of continued good fortune; and no specific hope about distant issues is ever likely to be realized. The ground shifts, the will of mankind deviates, and what the father dreamt of, the children neither fulfil nor desire.

My political fancy had undergone two love affairs, two seasons in which I almost believed that I had discovered the ideal in the real. Greece and England had seemed to me, in different directions, to have come near it. I called it the life of reason. By this I meant that on the one hand, the world had been conceived sanely in effect, though in poetical or rhetorical terms; on the other hand the art of life had been developed in two different directions, each of them satisfying. But satisfying to whom? In Greece to the Greeks and in England to the English? Or in both, ideally, to me? On this point I had not come to clearness. If I meant that the ideals suggested to me by Greece and England, somehow fused together, seemed to me to satisfy all the just demands of human nature, then my long book on "The Life of Reason" should have painted a concrete picture of a perfect society. I should have constructed another Utopia. But I possessed neither the varied knowledge nor the firm principles requisite for such a performance. My book was only a semi-historical semi-judicial review of the most familiar forms of society, religion, art, and science in the Western world; and while a rational criterion of moral judgment did underlie the whole discussion, this criterion was not clearly set forth or strictly applied.

My mind was allowed to float lazily amongst plausible opinions. I intended, however, to be a consistent naturalist, and I ought to have smiled a little at my casual enthusiasms, seeing that all ideals are but projections of vital tendencies in animal organisms. Therefore, since animal organisms are of many variable sorts, the direction and goal of progress always remain optional and subject to revision. This would have reduced my lovely Greece and my lovely England to local episodes in the history of manners and morals. Their rightness would have been avowedly only relative, even if it had been complete. But it had been sadly incomplete. Soon experience in the case of England and a little more reading in the case of Greece brought my two political love affairs to an end.

This book, though loosely composed and imperfectly digested, still marks an advance from convention to radical sincerity. I perceived that morality is something normal, and that religion, like perception, clothes in spontaneous sensuous or imaginative signs the real presence of pressing dangers and favorable opportunities. The material world and our animal nature, far from being obstacles in our way, are indispensable conditions for the pursuit and safe possession of any good; indispensable indeed for the discrimination of good from evil, or their existence at all. There must be something not chosen that chooses, something not desired that desires. This dynamic surge, this primeval automatism, within us and without, sustains the whole ideal structure of our language, our thoughts, and our interests, keeps them consecutive, and brings forth the fruits that we promise ourselves and the catastrophes that we wish to avoid.

Of historical illustration for this thesis the best I had to offer were drawn from religion. There I had more information and more experience than in other spheres. I was at home in the workings of *la fonction fabulatrice*. Moreover, I knew the difference between well-grounded inspired myths, innocently mistaken for revelations, and the vapid fancies of stray poets. In both cases we suffer illusion, because passion, and often action, reacts upon an image as if it were a physical object. But the illusion proper to waking perception and to wise myths, when once discovered, drives us all the more confidently and successfully upon the real object; whereas the illusion proper to idle musings and dreams leaves us cheated and disaffected towards reality. A great religion need not fear philosophic criticism, which will liberate its moral and speculative substance from the poetic images in which it first appeared. Ultimate truths are more easily and adequately conveyed by poetry than by analysis. This is no reason for forbidding analysis, but it is a reason for not banishing poetry.

My later books teach the same lesson, but by a different approach. They may seem to move in the opposite direction; yet only because they start from an opposite quarter in making for the same goal. This goal is a good life, according to our nature and circumstances; and it may be missed either by ignoring it or misconceiving our true circumstances or else by ignoring or misconceiving our true nature and proper good. Now for a mind coming to philosophy from religion and poetry, as I did, and as did the first Greek philosophers, the pressing reform seems to be to criticize anthropomorphism in religion and fable in science; to insist that life, reason, and spirit are something natural, and that it is only by facing our true environment, and making the best of it, that we can develop them well. Therefore, those early Greek philosophers, who were great poets and prophets of nature, figured as sour enemies of mythology:

and so I too, whose turn of mind was always poetical and religious, seemed to discard all inspiration and idealism.

Yet when naturalism in regard to circumstances had been firmly rooted in my mind, the other half of the total problem spontaneously came to the fore. What, in this natural world, is the nature and possible virtue of man? On what, without folly and intimate disaster, can he set his heart? And I was constrained to reply: Only on the life of reason, only on union with the truth, only on ideal sympathy with that irrepressible spirit which comes to light in all living beings, flowering differently in each, and moving in each towards a special perfection. And allowing for the different background introduced by my naturalism, this was very like the reply given by the most radical religious teachers, idealists, and mystics: so that I might seem to be moving away from my earlier doctrine and reverting to the traditions I had rejected. Yet I was not in the least reverting to the illusions about circumstances that accompanied those traditions; I was merely placing the spirit, the motives, and the discipline found in those traditions back where they belonged: for they were all voices of nature, elicited by human predicaments.

How rich and how full of significance in regard to the natural world and to human life in it this spiritual music may be, I have attempted to show once more in my book on "The Idea of Christ in the Gospels, or God in Man." There is less presumption than we might at first suspect in taking Christ for a model after having identified him with God. Reason differs from perception and sentiment precisely in transcending our human egotism and aspiring to understand things as they are in themselves and to love in them the good that they love. This aspiration of reason extends inevitably to sharing the vision and judgments of God; in other words, to transporting ourselves into the presence of the truth and to living, as Aristotle says, as much as possible in the eternal. Omniscience can neither lose nor expect anything, and lives exclusively in the vision of all things under the form of eternity. A corollary of this teaches us that it is only ideally that things can enter the mind. When passing events enter the mind they stick there: they become ideas of those events. Now it is in memory and imagination that we know the world: while we move in it, if memory and inspiration do not retain any images of it, we are simply a part of the moving world and know nothing of it. Physical life perforce keeps time with the rest of the physical world and is in flux like it. But reason bridges those gaps and makes a panorama of those variations. Though it is impossible for us to live our lives all at once, we may cultivate a sense of its totality, and of the totality and truth of things. In that measure we shall have lived, as it were, in the presence of God, and in as full harmony with his vision and will as our human nature allows.

Let me repeat, however, that I do not propose this sublimation of the life of reason as something obligatory: no man can achieve it completely, and most men can hardly practice it at all. I see nothing wrong or sad in that. It is right that most of what we are and of what we think should be lost for ever. Eternal damnation overtakes it justly. Society will judge some minds to be too flighty and others to be too rigid or too mystical; but those judgments have only a relative authority. It may be true that such habits are inconvenient for certain purposes: but no man's and no society's convenience can remake or limit the world. It is always lawful for a butterfly to be a butterfly, and it is lawful for a man like La Fontaine to be proud of being a butterfly, as when he says:

Je suis chose légère et vole à tout suject:
Je vais de fleur en fleur et d'objet en objet.

Yet the butterflies had better not form a league to exterminate the sages. The sages will smile upon them, and survive.

In spite of being so much in sympathy with the sages, I am well aware of not having been one of them. As a person I was too self-indulgent and not heroic enough: as a writer I was too miscellaneous: as a thinker I was born at the wrong time and bred in the wrong way. I like to hope that someone may later revive parts of my philosophy in more favorable circumstances. Yet for my own happiness I was philosophical enough. In a commonplace psyche I kept alive a spark of pure spirit which cast an impartial light, as far as it could reach, over the *universitas rerum*. This light cannot be blamed for the quality of the objects it found to shine upon: nor can it be taxed with inconstancy for shining only spasmodically, since that is the fault of the psyche and of the world in which it was formed. Pure spirit is no complete being: only a capacity to feel and to think upon occasion. Its light must be subdued to the quality of the things it touches. Yet in touching anything, no matter how foul, the light itself is not contaminated.

In my various books I have discussed things at very unequal removes from the fountain of spirit within me. But that center was truly philosophical. I can identify my self heartily with nothing in me except with the flame of spirit itself. Therefore the truest picture of my inmost being would show none of the features of my person, and nothing of the background of my life. It would show only the light of understanding that burned within me and, as far as it could, consumed and purified all the rest.

FEELING

THE REINTEGRATION OF HONOR
Gabriel Marcel

Gabriel Marcel, member of the Institute of France and a winner of the Grand Prix de Littérature of the Académie Française, is a critic and playwright as well as philosopher. He was born in 1887 and lives in Paris. He is the author of Being and Having, Man Against Mass Society *and other works.*

Coming home the other evening from an excellent Bach concert, I thought to myself, "Here is something that restores to one a feeling that one might have thought lost, or perhaps something more than a feeling, an assurance: the assurance that it is an honor to be a man." It is important to notice that everything seems to be in alliance today to destroy this notion of human honor, as to destroy all other notions that reflect an aristocratic morality. People affect to believe that an aristocracy can only be a caste and that the caste-system as such is a mode of existence condemned by history. Now, while we may readily agree that a closed caste-system appears to us today as something indefensible, on the other hand we must utterly deny that the idea of aristocracy implies any system of this sort. We should also, of course, note that the way is being visibly prepared for the coming of a kind of world oligarchy, that of "the managers" in Burnham's sense, the technocrats. Yet it is very doubtful whether such an oligarchy can be regarded as an aristocracy, since one does not see on what genuinely spiritual principle it would claim to base itself.

What sort of a thing is this "honor" of which the awareness was awakened in me the other night after hearing a few concertos by Bach? It is certainly not easy to make its nature clear; but it seems to me that we have to bring in the idea of an immediate awareness of a kind of fundamental straightness; and as always in such cases, to clarify our notion, we are forced in the first instance to think of it in terms of what is contrary to it.

What the notion of honor seems radically to exclude, then, is anything at the level of accommodation or connivance; at the level of flattery; and also at the level of ambiguity or equivocation, in so far as a perverted mind may be led deliberately to cultivate these. I mean that the idea of honor is linked to that of a man's word and also to the fact that his word should have a single, plain meaning. But it is just this, perhaps, that is the note of an aristocracy in the only acceptable sense of the word—the kind of aristocracy which may not only lack material resources but be unable to boast of noble ancestry. If the Spanish people, for instance, are so generally respected and admired by those who have come in contact with them, is that not precisely because, in spite of their well-known poverty, they have retained that native quality and the pride that goes with it? The pride I am thinking of is something very different from the pride, the arrogance, which is a deadly sin; though it is often in danger of being confused with it. It seems to me that a "proper pride" of this sort is always connected with the sense of an, as it were, innate and inalienable independence; and such a pride therefore stands in strange contrast with that spirit of claiming one's due which is so typical of democracies. For that spirit is out to claim not *what it has*, but *what it ought to have*. Now, for the man of "proper pride" this contrast between what he has and what he ought to have does not exist; he would feel, in a sense, that he was lowering himself by claiming his due.

It is not to be denied that such pride may be the source of a stiffness, a lack of suppleness, not very compatible with the conditions of social life, as we tend to conceive them today. We ought also to acknowledge without any reserves that if, from the point of view of social justice, real progress in certain very restricted fields has been achieved, that has been possible only because during the last hundred years the workers have repeatedly claimed their due from the so-called directing classes, classes at most times only too ready to refuse to allow their privileges even to be discussed. But it cannot be denied, on the other hand, that the development of the spirit of claiming one's due can coincide with a kind of moral degradation. To be certain of this, I have only to think of these friendly gatherings of university teachers at which the serious technical problems arising out of the job of teaching itself are never touched on, but only questions of salary increases and cost-of-living allowances. In a quite general sense, it does seem to me undeniably true that by a sad paradox the sense of professional honor has tended to diminish to the extent to which the members of each profession have become aware of their power as a pressure-group; and one expression of this fact is the extent to which what one can only call collective blackmail has become a generalized phenomenon during the last ten or twenty years.

From another but not unconnected point of view, we can see that the man of "proper pride" is a man who does not allow his word to be doubted. For *his word is himself*, one might be tempted to say that it is his only real possession, and honor is just the awareness of this indefectible quality, of one's word as being what is called in equations an invariable. From this fact one might infer that honor is always linked to a deep sense, a sense that cannot be uprooted, of *being*; for between being and the word there does exist, as Heidegger has shown in Germany and that profound but little-known thinker, Brice Parain, in France, an irrefragable unity. One should not draw the conclusion from this, of course, that honor in itself implies anything resembling an articulate religious faith. Among the best of the Spanish anarchists, on the contrary, honor was able to ally itself with an atheism which in its depths, for that matter, was perhaps nothing more than a mere refusal; the rejecting of a condition of feudal servitude which, of course, a sufficiently evolved theology would have recognized as incompatible with the fundamental principles of the Christian faith, with the freedom of the children of God. There is no more serious problem than that of knowing how Church membership, while retaining its strictly religious value, can avoid degenerating into a condition of feudal servitude incompatible with honor.

It must, to be sure, seem strange to illustrate a reflection set going by hearing the music of Bach with examples partly drawn from the life of the Spanish soul. But in thinking out a situation so complex and in some ways so agonizing as that of contemporary man, there may be an advantage in starting off from several different focal topics at once. Between these it will not require very profound reflection to discover a secret kinship.

Into Bach, it seems to me, as into the very structure of the Spanish soul, we must see how impossible it is to introduce anything like the opposition, so current among French rationalists, between reason and faith. In one sense, no music can be more satisfying to the reason than that of Bach, but on the other hand this satisfaction, which so soon transcends itself to become a higher state, obviously represents a response to some gift which reason reduced to its mere self would never have been able to lavish on us. In fact, for that matter, can reason ever really give us anything? It can only exploit and transform—and sometimes also reduce and dissolve, the latter in the case where its exercise becomes purely critical. But it is false to claim that, because of its own status, reason is in some sense obliged to defend itself against gifts whose source it does not know and to refuse them rather as one might refuse contraband merchandise. Reason, though it recognizes itself as overwhelmed by the music of Bach, expands itself, on the contrary, to welcome that light; for, in its depths, reason has a presentiment, though a very indistinct one, that this light is of the same nature as reason itself, and I am ready to affirm that reason makes it a point of honor to proclaim this identity, *to whose origin and nature nevertheless it has no clue.*

Honor in such a case is really linked to gratitude—a wonderful word, and a word into whose deeper sense, it seems to me, thinkers have too rarely penetrated. In what sense does the ungrateful man sin against honor? Is it not that he is in some sense a betrayer, that he breaks a certain tie, profiting basely from the fact that his benefactor—let us ignore for the moment certain rather unpleasant over-tones which that word may have—has carefully avoided asking him for any sort of acknowledgement of his debt? But the man of honor will feel himself all the more under an obligation just because that official acknowledgement of a debt does not exist; he would con-sider it an act of utter baseness to say that he feels his obligation is nothing because nothing has been asked of him. It seems to him that the exact converse is true. One might say, I think, that an ethic of honor is not only an ethic of fidelity but that it is also an ethic of gratitude, and that, in the extreme case, this gratitude assumes an ontological character, since it is a gratitude for having been allowed to exist, that is to say, fundamentally, for having been created. It is against such an ethic or such a metaphysics that the nihilist is sin-ning when he declares that he never asked to be alive: there, we are at the roots of the impiety which tends to diffuse itself generally today even into the bonds of family life themselves—and at the roots also, on the other hand, of a very dangerous attitude in par-ents, which is, as it were, an attempt to counterbalance this impiety, and which manifests itself sometimes as a weak and flattering soft-ness towards their children, deriving from a bad conscience, or from an actual sense of shame which seems to attach itself today to the fact that one has given life, that one has literally inflicted life on somebody who did not ask for it.

One might pursue similar reflections about the disappearance of the sense of hospitality today, at least in the countries which have been submerged by technical progress. We ought, of course, to be accurate in our way of stating this: to be sure, famous visitors, well-known scholars, writers, or artists are usually very well received in all countries. But by the sense of hospitality, I mean above all the sort of piety which is shown in the East to the unknown guest—simply because he is a guest, because he has entrusted himself to a man and his dwelling.

But these are the very bonds between man and man that are tending to disappear in a world where individuals, reduced to their abstract elements, are more and more merely juxtaposed, and where the only hierarchies that remain are founded either on money or on educational qualifications whose human significance is practically nil.

Honor, in every case, appears to be linked to a certain noble and generous simplicity in the fundamental human relationships.

TRANSLATED FROM THE FRENCH BY G. S. FRASER

REVERENCE FOR LIFE

Albert Schweitzer

Albert Schweitzer, surgeon, theologican, musicologist, missionary and philosopher, and recipient in 1952 of the Nobel Peace Prize, is a native of Alsace, where he was born January 14, 1875, the son of a Lutheran minister. He was educated at the University of Strasbourg, the Sorbonne at Paris and the University of Berlin. After a beginning in science and art and the publication of his first book (on the religious philosophy of Immanuel Kant) he took up the study of medicine in 1905 in order to spend the rest of his life as a doctor in Africa. Most of his books have been written in the jungle mission and hospital which he founded with his wife, when he reached Africa in 1913 where he has lived almost continuously ever since. The excerpt in this book is taken from his autobiography, Out of My Life and Thought.

What is Reverence for Life, and how does it arise in us?

If man wishes to reach clear notions about himself and his relations to the world, he must ever again and again be looking away from the manifold, which is the product of his thought and knowledge, and reflect upon the first, the most immediate, and the continually given fact of his own consciousness. Only if he starts from this can he arrive at a thinking world-view.

Descartes makes thinking start from the sentence "I think; so I must exist" (*Cogito, ergo sum*), and with his beginning thus chosen he finds himself irretrievably on the road to the abstract. Out of this empty, artificial act of thinking there can result, of course, nothing which bears on the relation of man to himself, and to the universe. Yet in reality the most immediate act of consciousness has some content. To think means to think something. The most immediate fact of man's consciousness is the assertion: "I am life which wills to live, in the midst of life which wills to life," and it is as will-to-live in the midst of will-to-live that man conceives himself during every moment that he spends in meditating on himself and the world around him.

As in my will-to-live there is ardent desire for further life and for the mysterious exaltation of the will-to-live which we call pleasure, while there is fear of destruction and of that mysterious depreciation of the will-to-live which we call pain: so too are these in the will-to-live around me, whether it can express itself to me, or remains dumb.

Man has now to decide what his relation to his will-to-live shall be. He can deny it. But if he bids his will-to-live change into will-not-to-live, as is done in Indian and indeed in all pessimistic thought, he involves himself in self-contradiction. He raises to the position of his world and life view something unnatural, something which is in itself untrue, and which cannot be carried to completion. Indian thought, and Schopenhauer's also, is full of inconsistencies because it cannot help making concessions time after time to the will-to-live which persists in spite of all world and life denial, though it will not admit that the concessions are really such. Negation of the will-to-live is self-consistent only if it is really willing actually to put an end to physical existence.

If man affirms his will-to-live, he acts naturally and honestly. He confirms an act which has already been accomplished in his instinctive thought by repeating it in his conscious thought. The beginning of thought, a beginning which continually repeats itself, is that man does not simply accept his existence as something given, but experiences it as something unfathomably mysterious. Life-affirmation is the spiritual act in which he ceases to live unreflectively and begins to devote himself to his life with reverence, in order to raise it to its true value. To affirm life is to deepen, to make more inward, and to exalt the will-to-live.

At the same time the man who has become a thinking being feels a compulsion to give to every will-to-live the same reverence for life that he gives to his own. He experiences that other life in his own. He accepts as being good: to preserve life, to promote life, to raise to its highest value life which is capable of development; and as being evil: to destroy life, to injure life, to repress life which is capable of development. This is the absolute, fundamental principle of the moral, and it is a necessity of thought.

The great fault of all ethics hitherto has been that they believed themselves to have to deal only with the relations of man to man. In reality, however, the question is what is his attitude to the world and all life that comes within his reach. A man is ethical only when life, as such, is sacred to him, that of plants and animals as that of his fellow-men, and when he devotes himself helpfully to all life that is in need of help. Only the universal ethic of the feeling of responsibility in an ever-widening sphere for all that lives—only that ethic can be founded in thought. The ethic of the relation of man to man is not something apart by itself: it is only a particular relation which results from the universal one.

The ethic of Reverence for Life, therefore, comprehends within itself everything that can be described as love, devotion, and sympathy whether in suffering, joy, or effort.

The world, however, offers us the horrible drama of Will-to-Live divided against itself. One existence holds its own at the cost of another: one destroys another. Only in the thinking man has the Will-to-Live become conscious of other will-to-live, and desirous of solidarity with it. This solidarity, however, he cannot completely bring about, because man is subject to the puzzling and horrible law of being obliged to live at the cost of other life, and to incur again and again the guilt of destroying and injuring life. But as an ethical being he strives to escape whenever possible from this necessity, and as one who has become enlightened and merciful to put a stop to this disunion (*Selbstentzweiung*) of the Will-to-Live so far as the influence of his own existence reaches. He thirsts to be permitted to preserve his humanity, and to be able to bring to other existences release from their sufferings.

The Reverence for Life, therefore, which has arisen in the thinking Will-to-Live, contains world- and life-affirmation and the ethical fused together. Its aim is to create values, and to realize progress of different kinds which shall serve the material, spiritual, and ethical development of men and mankind. While the unthinking modern world- and life-affirmation stumbles about with its ideals of power won by discovery and invention, the thinking world- and life-affirmation sets up the spiritual and ethical perfecting of mankind as the highest ideal, and an ideal from which alone all other ideals of progress get their real value.

Through ethical world- and life-affirmation we reach a power of reflection which enables us to distinguish between what is essential in civilization and what is not. The stupid arrogance of thinking ourselves civilized loses its power over us. We venture to face the truth that with so much progress in knowledge and power true civilization has become not easier but harder. The problem of the mutual relationship between the spiritual and the material dawns upon us. We know that we all have to struggle with circumstances to preserve our humanity, and that we must be anxiously concerned to turn once more towards hope of victory the almost hopeless struggle which many carry on to preserve their humanity amid unfavorable social circumstances.

A deepened, ethical will to progress which springs from thought will lead us back, then, out of uncivilization and its misery to true civilization. Sooner or later there must dawn the true and final Renaissance which will bring peace to the world.

TRANSLATED BY C. T. CAMPION

A VISIT TO MORIN

Graham Greene

Graham Greene, born October 2, 1904, the son of a headmaster of a Hertfordshire school in England, has written fiction which he has called "entertainments" and from which such films have been made as Brighton Rock, The Third Man, This Gun For Hire, and others. He has also preoccupied himself in other of his novels, The Heart of the Matter, The End of the Affair, for example, with doctrinal issues of the Catholic church. He was converted to Catholicism some years ago and his plays, notably The Living Room and The Potting Shed have especially involved the moral problems of man today.

Le Diable au Ciel—there it was on a shelf in the Colmar bookshop, causing a memory to reach for me from the past of twenty years ago. One didn't often in the 1950's see Pierre Morin's novels on display, and yet here were two copies of his once famous book, and looking along the rows of paper bindings I discovered others, as though there existed in Alsace a secret Cave like those hidden cellars where wines were once preserved from the enemy for the days when peace would return.

I had admired Pierre Morin when I was a boy, but I had almost forgotten him. He was even then an older writer on the point of abandonment by his public, but the language class in an English public school is always a long way behind the Paris fashions. We happened at Collingworth to have a Roman Catholic master who belonged to the generation which Morin had pleased or offended. He had offended the orthodox Catholics in his own country and pleased the Liberal Catholics abroad; he had pleased too the Protestants who believed in God with the same intensity that he seemed to show, and he used to find enthusiastic readers among non-Christians who, when once they had accepted imaginatively his premises, perhaps detected in his work the freedom of speculation which put his fellow Catholics on their guard. How fresh and exciting his work had appeared to my schoolmaster's generation; and to me, brought up in a lower form on *Les Misérables* and the poems of Lamartine, he was a revolutionary writer. But it is the fate of revolutionaries that the world accepts them. The excitement has gone from Morin's pages. Only the orthodox read him now, when the whole world seems prepared to believe in a god, except strangely enough—but I will not anticipate the point of my small anecdote which may yet provide a footnote to the literary history of Morin's day. When I publish it no harm can be done. Morin will be dead in the flesh as well as being dead as a writer, and he has left, so far as I am aware, no descendants and no disciples.

I yet recall with pleasure those French classes presided over by a Mr. Strangeways from Chile. At these senior classes we no longer studied syntax—at which Mr. Strangeways was in any case weak. Mr. Strangeways read aloud to us and we read aloud to him, but after five minutes we would launch into literary criticism, pulling to pieces with youthful daring—Mr. Strangeways like so many schoolmasters remained always youthful—the great established names and building up with exaggerated appreciation those who had not yet "arrived." Of course Morin had arrived years before, but of that we were unaware in our brick prison five hundred miles from the Seine—he hadn't reached the school textbooks: where we didn't understand his meaning, there were no editor's notes to kill speculation.

"Can he really believe that?" I remember exclaiming to Mr. Strangeways when a character in *Le Diable au Ciel* made some dark and horrifying statement on the Atonement or the Redemption; and I remember Mr. Strangeways' blunt reply, flapping the sleeves of his short black gown like a vermin of the night, "But I believe it too, Dunlop." He went on to indicate that we were unconcerned with what the author believed. The author had chosen as his viewpoint the character of an orthodox Catholic—all his thoughts therefore must be affected, as they would be in life, by his orthodoxy. Morin's technique forbade him to play a part in the story himself: even to show irony would be to cheat, though perhaps we might detect something of Morin's view from the fact that the orthodoxy of Durobier was extended to the farthest possible limits, so that at the close of a book we had the impression of a man stranded on a long strip of sand from which there was no possibility of advance, and to retreat toward the shore would be to surrender. "Is this true or is it not true?" His whole creed was concerned in the answer.

"You mean," I asked Mr. Strangeways, "that perhaps Morin does not believe?"

"I mean nothing of the kind. No one has seriously questioned his Catholicism, only his prudence. Anyway that's not true criticism. A novel is made up of words and characters. Are the words well chosen and do the characters live? All the rest belongs to literary gossip. You are not in this class to learn how to be gossip writers."

And yet in those days I would have liked to know. Sometimes Mr. Strangeways, recognizing my interest in Morin, would lend me Roman Catholic literary periodicals which contained notices of the novelist's work that often offended his principle of leaving the author's views out of account. I found Morin was sometimes accused of Jansenism—whatever that might be: others called him an Augustinian—a name which meant as little to me, and in the better printed and bulkier reviews I thought I detected a note of grievance. He believed all the right things, they could find no specific fault, and yet—it was as though some of his characters accepted a dogma so wholeheartedly that they drew out its implications to the verge of absurdity, while others examined a dogma as though they were constitutional lawyers determined on confining it to a kind of legal minimum. Durobier, I am sure, would have staked his life on a literal Assumption: at some point in history, somewhere in the latter years of the first century A.D., the body of the Virgin had floated skyward, leaving an empty tomb. On the other hand there was a character called Sagrin, in one of the minor novels, perhaps *Le Bien Pensant*, who believed that the holy body had rotted in the grave like other bodies. The strange thing was that both views seemed to possess irritating qualities to Catholic reviewers, and yet both proved to be equally in accordance with the dogmatic pronouncement when it came. One could claim therefore that they were orthodox, yet the orthodox critics seemed to scent heresy like a rat dead somewhere under the boards, at a spot they could not locate.

These, of course, were ancient criticisms, fished out of Mr. Strangeways' cupboard full of old French magazines dating back to his long-lost sojourn in Paris some time during the late twenties, when he had attended lectures at the Sorbonne and drunk beer at the Dôme. The word "paradox" was frequently used with an air of disapproval. Perhaps after all the orthodox were proved right, for certainly I was to discover just how far Morin carried in his own life the sense of paradox.

2

I am not one of those who revisit their old school, or what a disappointment I should have proved to Mr. Strangeways who must by now be on the point of retirement. I think he had pictured me in the future as a distinguished writer for the weeklies on the subject of French literature—perhaps even as the author of a scholarly biography of Corneille. In fact, after an undistinguished war record, I obtained a post, with the help of influential connections, in a firm of wine merchants. My French syntax, so neglected by Mr. Strangeways, had been improved by the war and proved useful to the firm, and I suppose I had a certain literary flair which enabled me to improve on the rather old-fashioned style of the catalogues. The directors had been content for too long with the jargon of the Wine Society—"An unimportant but highly sympathetic wine for light occasions among friends." I introduced a more realistic note and substituted knowledge for knowingness. "This wine comes from a small vineyard on the western slopes of the Mont Soleil range. The soil in this region has Jurassic elements, as the vineyard is on the edge of the great Jurassic fissure which extends across Europe from the Urals, and this encourages the cultivation of a small, strong, dark grape with a high sugar content less liable than more famous wines to the chances of weather." Of course it was the same "unimportant" wine, but my description gave the host more material for his vanity.

Business had brought me to Colmar—we had found it necessary to change our agent there, and as I am a single man and find the lonely Christmases of London sad and regretful, I had chosen to combine my visit with the Christmas holiday. One does not feel alone abroad: I imagined drinking my way through the festival itself in some *bierhaus* decorated with holly, myself invisible behind the fumes of cigars. A German Christmas is Christmas par excellence: singing, sentiment, gluttony.

I said to the shop assistant, "You seem to have a good supply of M. Morin's books."

"He is very popular," she said.

"I got the impression that in Paris he is no longer much read."

"We are Catholics here," she said with a note of reproof. "Besides, he lives near Colmar, and we are very proud he chose to settle in our neighborhood."

"How long has he been here?"

"He came immediately after the war. We consider him almost one of us. We have all his books in German also—you will see them over there. Some of us feel he is even finer in German than in French. German," she said, scrutinizing me with contempt as I picked up a French edition of *Le Diable au Ciel*, "has a better vocabulary for the profundities."

I told her I had admired M. Morin's novels since my school days. She softened toward me then, and I left the shop with M. Morin's address—a village fifteen miles from Colmar. I was uncertain all the same whether I would call on him. What really had I to say to him to excuse the vulgarity of my curiosity? Writing is the most private of all the arts, and yet few of us hesitate to invade the writer's home. We have all heard of that one caller from Porlock, but hundreds of callers every day are ringing doorbells, lifting receivers, thrusting themselves into the secret room where a writer works and lives.

I doubt whether I should have ventured to ring M. Morin's bell, but I caught sight of him two days later at the Midnight Mass in a village outside Colmar; it was not the village where I had been told he lived, and I wondered why he had come such a distance alone. Midnight Mass is a service which even a nonbeliever like myself finds inexplicably moving. Perhaps there is some memory of childhood which makes the journey through the darkness, the lighted windows and the frosty night, the slow gathering of silent strangers from the four quarters of the countryside moving and significant.

There was a crib to the left of the door as I came in—the plaster baby sprawled in the plaster lap, and the cows, the sheep and the shepherd cast long shadows in the candlelight. Among the women kneeling, there was an old man whose face I seemed to remember: a round head like a peasant's, the skin wrinkled like a stale apple, with the hair gone from the crown. He knelt, bowed his head, and rose again. There had just been time, I suppose, for a formal prayer, but it must have been a very short one. His chin was stubbled white like the field outside; and there was so little about him to suggest a member of the French Academy, I might have taken him for the peasant he appeared to be, in his suit of respectable and shiny black and his black tie like a bootlace, if I had not been attracted by the eyes. The eyes gave him away: they seemed to know too much and to have seen farther than the seasons and the fields: of a very clear, pale blue, they continually shifted focus looking close and looking away, observant, sad and curious like those of a man caught in some great catastrophe which it is his duty to record, but which he cannot bear to contemplate without a break for any length of time. It was not, of course, during his short prayer before the crib that I had time to watch Morin so closely, but when the congregation was shuffling up toward the altar for Communion, Morin and I found ourselves alone among the empty chairs. It was then I recognized him, per-

haps from memories of old photographs in Mr. Strangeways' reviews, I do not know, but I was convinced of his identity, and I
wondered what it was that kept this old distinguished Catholic
from going up with the others, at this Mass of all Masses in the
year, to receive the Sacrament. Had he perhaps inadvertently
broken his fast, or was he a man who suffered from scruples and
did he believe that he had been guilty of some act of uncharity or
greed? There could not be many serious temptations, I thought,
for a man who must be approaching his eightieth year. And yet I
would not have believed him to be scrupulous; it was from his own
novels I had learned of the existence of this malady of the
religious, and I would never have supposed the creator of Durobier
to have suffered from the same disease as his character. However, a
novelist may sometimes write most objectively of his own failings.

We sat there alone at the back of the church. The air was as
cold and still as a frozen tree and the candles burned straight on
the altar and God, so they believed, passed along the altar rail.
This was the birth of Christianity: outside in the dark was old savage Judea, but in here the world was only a few minutes old. It
was the Year One again, and I felt the old sentimental longing to
believe as those, I suppose, believed who came back one by one
from the rail, with lips set like closed doors around the dissolving
wafer, and crossed hands. If I had said to one of them "teach me
why you believe," what would the answer have been? I thought
perhaps I knew, for once in the war—driven by fear and disgust at
the sight of the dead—I had spoken to a Catholic chaplain in just
that way. He didn't belong to my unit, he was a busy man—it isn't
the job of a chaplain in the line to instruct or convert and he was
not to blame that he could convey nothing to an outsider like
myself of his faith. He lent me two books—one a penny catechism
with its catalogue of preposterous questions and answers, smug and
explanatory: mystery like a butterfly killed by cyanide, stiffened
and laid out with pins and paper strips; the other a sober enough
study of gospel dates. I lost them both in a few days, with three
bottles of whiskey, my jeep and the corporal whose name I had not
had time to learn before he was killed, while I was peeing in the

green canal close by. I don't suppose I'd have kept the books much longer anyway. They were not the kind of help I needed, nor was the chaplain the man to give it to me. I remember asking him if he had read Morin's novels. "I haven't time to waste with him," he said abruptly.

"They were the first books," I said, "to interest me in your faith."

"You'd have done much better to read Chesterton," he said.

So it was odd to find myself there at the back of the church with Morin himself. He was the first to leave and I followed him out. I was glad to go, for the sentimental attraction of a Midnight Mass was lost in the long ennui of the Communions.

"M. Morin," I said in that low voice we assume in a church or hospital.

He looked quickly, and I thought defensively, up.

I said, "Forgive my speaking to you like this, M. Morin, but your books have given me such great pleasure." Had the man from Porlock employed the same banal phrases?

"You are English?" he asked.

"Yes."

He spoke to me then in English. "You write yourself? Forgive my asking, but I do not know your name."

"Dunlop. But I don't write. I buy and sell wine."

"A profession more worthy of respect," M. Morin said. "If you would care to drive with me—I live only ten kilometers from here —I think I could show you a wine you may not have encountered."

"Surely it's rather late, M. Morin. And I have a driver. . . ."

"Send him home. After Midnight Mass I find it difficult to sleep. You would be doing me a kindness." When I hesitated he said, "As for tomorrow, that is just any day of the year, and I don't like visitors."

I tried to make a joke of it. "You mean it's my only chance?" and he replied, "Yes" with seriousness. The doors of the church swung open and the congregation came slowly out into the frosty glitter, pecking at the holy water stoop with their forefingers, chatting cheerfully again as the mystery receded, greeting neighbors. A wailing child marked the lateness of the hour like a clock. M. Morin strode away and I followed him.

3

M. Morin drove with clumsy violence, wrenching at his gears, scraping the right-hand hedgerows as though the car were a new invention and he a courageous pioneer in its use. "So you have read some of my books?" he asked.

"A great many, when I was a schoolboy. . . ."

"You mean they are fit only for children?"

"I mean nothing of the sort."

"What can a child find in them?"

"I was sixteen when I began to read them. That's not a child."

"Oh well, now they are only read by the old—and the pious. Are you pious, Mr. Dunlop?"

"I'm not a Catholic."

"I'm glad to hear that. Then I shan't offend you."

"Once I thought of becoming one."

"Second thoughts are best."

"I think it was your books that made me curious."

"I'll not take responsibility," he said. "I'm not a theologian." We bumped over a little branch railway-track without altering speed and swerved right through a gateway much in need of repair. A light hanging in a porch shone on an open door.

"Don't you lock up," I asked him, "in these parts?"

He said, "Ten years ago—times were bad then—a hungry man was frozen to death near here on Christmas morning. He could find no one to open a door: there was a blizzard, but they were all at church. Come in," he said angrily from the porch, "are you looking round, making notes of how I live? Have you deceived me? Are you a journalist?"

If I had had my own car with me I would have driven away. "M. Morin," I said, "there are different kinds of hunger. You seem only to cater to one kind." He went ahead of me into a small study—a desk, a table, two comfortable chairs, and some bookshelves oddly bare—I could see no sign of his own books. There was a bottle of brandy on the table, ready perhaps for the stranger and the blizzard that would never again come together in this place.

"Sit down," he said, "sit down. You must forgive me if I was discourteous. I am unused to company. I will go and find the wine I spoke of. Make yourself at home." I had never seen a man less at home himself. It was as if he were camping in a house that belonged to another.

While he was away, I looked more closely at his bookshelves. He had not rebound any of his paperbooks and his shelves had the appearance of bankrupt stock: small tears and dust and the discoloration of sunlight. There was a great deal of theology, some poetry, very few novels. He came back with the wine and a plate of salami. When he had tasted the wine himself, he poured me a glass. "It will do," he said.

"It's excellent. Remarkable."

"A small vineyard twenty miles away. I will give you the address before you go. For me, on a night like this, I prefer brandy." So perhaps it was really for himself and not for the stranger, I thought, that the bottle stood ready.

"It's certainly cold."

"It was not the weather I meant."

"I have been looking at your library. You read a lot of theology."

"Not now."

"I wonder if you would recommend. . . ." But I had less success with him than I had with the chaplain.

"No. Not if you want to believe. If you are foolish enough to want that you must avoid theology."

"I don't understand."

He said, "A man can accept anything to do with God until scholars begin to go into the details and the implications. A man can accept the Trinity, but the arguments that follow. . . ." He gave a gesture of rejection. "I would never try to determine some point in differential calculus with a two times two table. You end by disbelieving the calculus." He poured out two more glasses and drank his as though it were vodka. "I used to believe in Revelation, but I never believed in the capacity of the human mind."

"You used to believe?"

"Yes, Mr. Dunlop—was that the name?—used. If you are one of those who comes seeking belief, go away. You won't find it here."

"But from your books. . . ."

"You will find none of them," he said, "on my shelves."

"I noticed you have some theology."

"Even disbelief," he said with his eye on the brandy bottle, "needs bolstering somehow." I noticed that the brandy very quickly affected him, not only his readiness to communicate with me, but even the physical appearance of his eyeballs. It was as if the little blood-cells had been waiting under the white membrane to burst at once like buds with the third glass. He said, "Can you find anything more inadequate than the scholastic arguments for the existence of God?"

"I'm afraid I don't know them."

"The arguments from an agent, from a cause?"

"No."

"They tell you that in all change there are two elements, that which is changed and that which changes it. Each agent of change is itself determined by some higher agent. Can this go on ad infinitum? Oh no, they say, that would not give the finality that thought demands. But does thought demand it? Why shouldn't the chain go on forever? Man has invented the idea of infinity. In any case how trivial any argument based on what human thought demands must be. The thoughts of you and me and Monsieur Dupont. I would prefer the thoughts of an ape. Its instincts are less corrupted. Show me a gorilla praying and I might believe again."

"But surely there are other arguments?"

"Four. Each more inadequate than the other. It only needs a child to say to these theologians, why?—why not? Why not an infinite series of causes? Why should the existence of a good and a better imply the existence of a best? This is playing with words. We invent the words and make arguments from them. The better is not a fact: it is only a word and a human judgment."

"You are arguing," I said, "against someone who can't answer you back. You see, M. Morin, I don't believe either. I am curious, that's all."

"Ah," he said, "you've said that before—curious. Curiosity is a great trap. They used to come here in their dozens to see me. I used to get letters saying how I had converted them by this book or that. Long after I had ceased to believe myself I was a carrier of belief, like a man can be a carrier of disease without being sick. Women especially." He added with disgust, "I had only to sleep with a woman to make a convert." He turned his red eyes toward me and really seemed to require an answer when he said, "What sort of a Rasputin life was that?" The brandy by now had really taken a hold: I wondered how many years he had been waiting for some stranger without faith to whom he could speak with frankness.

"Did you never tell this to a priest? I always imagined in your faith. . . ."

"There were always too many priests," he said, "around me. The priests swarmed like flies. Near me and any woman I knew. First I was an exhibit for their faith. I was useful to them, a sign that even an intelligent man could believe. That was the period of the Dominicans who liked the literary atmosphere and good wine. Then afterward when the books stopped, and they smelled something—gamy—in my religion, it was the turn of the Jesuits, who never despair of what they call a man's soul."

"And why did the books stop?"

"Who knows? Did you never write verses for some girl when you were a boy?"

"Of course."

"But you didn't marry the girl, did you? The unprofessional poet writes of his feelings and when the poem is finished he finds his love dead on the page. Perhaps I wrote away my belief like the young man writes away his love. Only it took longer—twenty years and fifteen books."

He held up the wine. "Another glass?"

"I would rather have some of your brandy." Unlike the wine it was a crude and common mark, and I thought again: for a beggar's sake or his own? I said, "All the same you go to Mass."

"I go to Midnight Mass on Christmas Eve," he said. "The worst of Catholics goes then—even those who do not go at Easter. It **is** the Mass of our childhood. And of mercy. What would they **think** if I were not there? I don't want to give scandal. You must **realize** I wouldn't speak to any one of my neighbors as I have spoken **to** you. I am their Catholic author, you see. Their academician. I never wanted to help anyone to believe, but God knows I wouldn't take a hand in robbing them. . . ."

"I was surprised at one thing when I saw you there, M. Morin."

"Yes?"

I said rashly, "You and I were the only ones who didn't **take** Communion."

"That is why I don't go to the church in my own village. **That** too would be noticed and cause scandal."

"Yes, I can see that." I stumbled heavily on (perhaps the brandy had affected me, too). "Forgive me, M. Morin, but I wondered **at** your age what kept you from Communion. Of course, now I know the reason."

"Do you?" Morin said. "Young man, I doubt it." He looked **at** me across his glass with impersonal enmity. He said, "You don't understand a thing I have been saying, do you? What a story you would make of this if you were a journalist, and yet there wouldn't be a word of truth. . . ."

I said stiffly, "I thought you made yourself perfectly clear **that** you had lost your faith."

"Do you think that would keep anyone from the Confessional? You are a long way from understanding the Church or the human mind, Mr. Dunlop. Why, it is one of the most common confessions of all for a priest to hear—almost as common as adultery. 'Father, I have lost my faith.' The priest, you may be sure, makes it himself often enough at the altar before he receives the Host."

I said—I was angry in return now, "Then what keeps you away? Pride? One of your Rasputin women?"

"As you so rightly thought," he said, "women are no longer a problem at my age." He looked at his watch, "Two-thirty, perhaps I ought to drive you back."

"No," I said. "I don't want to part from you like this. It's the drink that makes us irritable. Your books are still important to me. I know I am ignorant. I am not a Catholic and never shall be, but in the old days your books made me understand that at least it might be possible to believe. You never suddenly closed the door in my face as you are doing now. Nor did your characters, Durobier, Sagrin." I indicated the brandy bottle. "I told you just now—people are not only hungry and thirsty in that way. Because you've lost your faith. . . ."

He interrupted me ferociously. "I never told you that."

"Then what have you been talking about all this time?"

"I told you I had lost my belief. That's quite a different thing. But how are you to understand?"

"You don't give me a chance."

He was obviously striving to be patient. He said, "I will put it this way. If a doctor prescribed you a drug and told you to take it every day for the rest of your life and you stopped obeying him and drank no more, and your health decayed, would you not believe in your doctor all the more?"

"Perhaps. But I still don't understand you."

"For twenty years," Morin said, "I excommunicated myself voluntarily. I never went to Confession. I loved a woman too much to pretend to myself that I would ever leave her. You know the condition of absolution? A firm purpose of amendment. I had no such purpose. Five years ago my mistress died and my sex died with her."

"Then why couldn't you go back?"

"I was afraid. I am still afraid."

"Of what the priest would say?"

"What a strange idea you have of the Church. No, not of what the priest would say. He would say nothing. I dare say there is no greater gift you can give a priest in the Confessional, Mr. Dunlop, than to return to it after many years. He feels of use again. But can't you understand? I can tell myself now that my lack of belief is a final proof that the Church is right and the faith is true. I had cut myself off for twenty years from grace and my belief withered as the priests said it would. I don't believe in God and His Son and His angels and His saints, but I know the reason why I don't believe and the reason is—the Church is true and what she taught me is true. For twenty years I have been without the Sacraments and I can see the effect. The wafer must be more than wafer."

"But if you went back. . . ."

"If I went back and belief did not return? That is what I fear, Mr. Dunlop. As long as I keep away from the Sacraments, my lack of belief is an argument for the Church. But if I returned and they failed me, then I would really be a man without faith, who had better hide himself quickly in the grave so as not to discourage others." He laughed uneasily. "Paradoxical, Mr. Dunlop?"

"That is what they said of your books."

"I know."

"Your characters carried their ideas to extreme lengths. So your critics said."

"And you think I do too?"

"Yes, M. Morin."

His eyes wouldn't meet mine. He grimaced beyond me. "At least I am not a carrier of disease any longer. You have escaped infection. Time for bed, Mr. Dunlop. Time for bed. The young need more sleep."

"I am not as young as that."

"To me you seem very young."

He drove me back to my hotel and we hardly spoke. I was thinking of the strange faith which held him even now after he had ceased to believe. I had felt very little curiosity since that moment of the war when I had spoken to the chaplain, but now I began to wonder again. M. Morin considered he had ceased to be a carrier, and I couldn't help hoping he was right. He had forgotten to give me the address of the vineyard, but I forgot to ask him when I said good night.

RELUCTANT CONVERT

C. S. Lewis

C. S. Lewis, lecturer on English literature at Magdalen College, Oxford, is the author of The Screwtape Letters which, since 1942, has brought him widening fame. The book is one of epistles written "by an elderly Devil named Screwtape to his ambitious nephew Wormwood, advising on the best way of winning to eternal perdition the soul of a certain 'patient' living in the world today." Wormwood inclining to go out for spectacular wickedness is reminded by the wiser uncle that the safest road to hell is "the gradual one," the real thing that matters is the extent to which you separate the man from the Enemy (God). Mr. Lewis followed the Letters with several other short but illuminating volumes, all in a style which C. E. M. Joad has characterized as one which "makes righteousness readable." Mr. Lewis has stated that he "gave up Christianity at about fourteen. Came back to it when getting on for thirty. It was not an emotional conversion: almost purely philosophical. I didn't want to. I'm not in the least the religious type. I want to be let alone, to feel I'm my own master; but since the facts seemed to be just the opposite I had to give in."

> The one principle of hell is—"I am my own."
> —GEORGE MAC DONALD.

In the summer of 1922 I finished Greats. As there were no philosophical posts going, or none that I could get, my long-suffering father offered me a fourth year at Oxford during which I read English so as to get a second string to my bow. . . .

No sooner had I entered the English School than I went to George Gordon's discussion class. And there I made a new friend. The very first words he spoke marked him out from the ten or twelve others who were present; a man after my own heart, and that too at an age when the instantaneous friendships of earlier youth were becoming rather rare events. His name was Nevill Coghill. I soon had the shock of discovering that he—clearly the most intelligent and best-informed man in that class—was a Christian and a thoroughgoing supernaturalist. There were other traits that I liked but found (for I was still very much a modern) oddly archaic; chivalry, honor, courtesy, "freedom," and "gentillesse." One could imagine him fighting a duel. He spoke much "ribaldry" but never "villeinye." Barfield was beginning to overthrow my chronological snobbery (the uncritical acceptance of the intellectual climate common to our own age and the assumption that whatever has gone out of date is on that account discredited); Coghill gave it another blow. Had something really dropped out of our lives? Was the archaic simply the civilized, and the modern simply the barbaric? It will seem strange to many of my critics who regard me as a typical *laudator temporis acti* that this question should have arisen so comparatively late in my life. But then the key to my books is Donne's maxim, "The heresies that men leave are hated most." The things I assert most vigorously are those that I resisted long and accepted late.

These disturbing factors in Coghill ranged themselves with a wider disturbance which was now threatening my whole earlier outlook. All the books were beginning to turn against me. Indeed, I must have been as blind as a bat not to have seen, long before, the ludicrous contradiction between my theory of life and my actual experiences as a reader. George MacDonald had done more to me than any other writer; of course it was a pity he had that bee in his bonnet about Christianity. He was good *in spite of it*. Chesterton had more sense than all the other moderns put together; bating, of course, his Christianity. Johnson was one of the few authors whom I felt I could trust utterly; curiously enough, he had the same kink. Spenser and Milton by a strange coincidence had it too. Even among ancient authors the same paradox was to be found. The most religious (Plato, Aeschylus, Virgil) were clearly those on whom I could really feed. On the other hand, those writers who did not suffer from religion and with whom in theory my sympathy ought to have been complete—Shaw and Wells and Mill and Gibbon and Voltaire—all seemed a little thin; what as boys we called "tinny." It wasn't that I didn't like them. They were all (especially Gibbon) entertaining; but hardly more. There seemed to be no depth in them. They were too simple. The roughness and density of life did not appear in their books.

Now that I was reading more English, the paradox began to be aggravated. I was deeply moved by the *Dream of the Road*; more deeply still by Langland; intoxicated (for a time) by Donne; deeply and lastingly satisfied by Thomas Browne. But the most alarming of all was George Herbert. Here was a man who seemed to me to excel all the authors I had ever read in conveying the very quality of life as we actually live it from moment to moment; but the wretched fellow, instead of doing it all directly, insisted on meditating it through what I would still have called "the Christian mythology." On the other hand most of the authors who might be claimed as precursors of modern enlightenment seemed to me very small beer and bored me cruelly. I thought Bacon (to speak frankly) a solemn, pretentious ass, yawned my way through Restoration Comedy, and, having manfully struggled on to the last line of *Don Juan*, wrote on the end-leaf "Never again." The only non-Christians who seemed to me really to know anything were the Romantics; and a good many of them were dangerously tinged with something like religion, even at times with Christianity. The upshot of it all could nearly be expressed in a perversion of Roland's great line in the *Chanson*—

Christians are wrong, but all the rest are bores.

The natural step would have been to inquire a little more closely whether the Christians were, after all, wrong. But I did not take it.

I thought I could explain their superiority without that hypothesis. Absurdly (yet many Absolute Idealists have shared this absurdity) I thought that "the Christian myth" conveyed to unphilosophic minds as much of the truth, that is of Absolute Idealism, as they were capable of grasping, and that even that much put them above the irreligious. Those who could not rise to the notion of the Absolute would come nearer to the truth by belief in "a God" than by disbelief. Those who could not understand how, as Reasoners, we participated in a timeless and therefore deathless world, would get a symbolic shadow of the truth by believing in a life after death. The implication—that which I and most other undergraduates could master without extraordinary pains would have been too hard for Plato, Dante, Hooker, and Pascal—did not yet strike me as absurd. I hope this is because I never looked it squarely in the face . . .

When I began teaching for the English Faculty, I made two other friends, both Christians (these queer people seemed now to pop up on every side) who were later to give me much help in getting over the last stile. They were H. V. V. Dyson (then of Reading) and J. R. R. Tolkien. Friendship with the latter marked the breakdown of two old prejudices. At my first coming into the world I had been (implicitly) warned never to trust a Papist, and at my first coming into the English Faculty (explicitly) never to trust a philologist. Tolkien was both.

Realism had been abandoned; the New Look* was somewhat damaged; and chronological snobbery was seriously shaken. All over the board my pieces were in the most disadvantageous positions. Soon I could no longer cherish even the illusion that the

---

* An attitude consciously adopted during his first two years at Oxford in which there was to be "no more pessimism, no more self-pity, no flirtations with any idea of the supernatural, no romantic delusions. In a word, like the heroine of *Northanger Abbey*, I formed the resolution 'of always judging and acting in future with the greatest good sense.' And good sense meant, for me at that moment, a retreat, almost a panic-stricken flight, from all that sort of romanticism which had hitherto been the chief concern of my life. . . ."

initiative lay with me. My Adversary began to make His final moves.

The first Move annihilated the last remains of the New Look. I was suddenly impelled to re-read (which was certainly no business of mine at the moment) the *Hippolytus* of Euripides. In one chorus all that world's end imagery which I had rejected when I assumed my New Look rose before me. I liked, but did not yield; I tried to patronize it. But next day I was overwhelmed. There was a transitional moment of delicious uneasiness, and then—instantaneously—the long inhibition was over, the dry desert lay behind, I was off once more into the land of longing, my heart at once broken and exalted as it had never been since the old days at Bookham. There was nothing whatever to do about it; no question of returning to the desert. I had simply been ordered—or, rather, compelled—to "take that look off my face." And never to resume it either.

The next Move was intellectual, and consolidated the first Move. I read in Alexander's *Space Time and Deity* his theory of "Enjoyment" and "Contemplation." These are technical terms in Alexander's philosophy; "Enjoyment" has nothing to do with pleasure, nor "Contemplation" with the contemplative life. When you see a table you "enjoy" the act of seeing and "contemplate" the table. Later, if you took up Optics and thought about Seeing itself, you would be contemplating the seeing and enjoying the thought. In bereavement you contemplate the beloved and the beloved's death and, in Alexander's sense, "enjoy" the loneliness and grief; but a psychologist, if he were considering you as a case of melancholia, would be contemplating your grief and enjoying psychology. We do not "think a thought" in the same sense in which we "think that Herodotus is unreliable." When we think a thought, "thought" is a cognate accusative (like "blow" in "strike a blow"). We enjoy the thought (that Herodotus is unreliable) and, in so doing, contemplate the unreliability of Herodotus.

I accepted this distinction at once and have ever since regarded it as an indispensable tool of thought. A moment later its consequences—for me quite catastrophic—began to appear. It seemed to me self-evident that one essential property of love, hate, fear, hope, or desire was attention to their object. To cease thinking about or attending to the woman is, so far, to cease loving; to cease thinking about or attending to the dreaded thing is, so far, to cease being afraid. But to attend to your own love or fear is to cease attending to the loved or dreaded object. In other words the enjoyment and the contemplation of our inner activities are incompatible. You cannot hope and also think about hoping at the same moment; for in hope we look to hope's object and we interrupt this by (so to speak) turning round to look at the hope itself. Of course the two activities can and do alternate with great rapidity; but they are distinct and incompatible. This was not merely a logical result of Alexander's analysis, but could be verified in daily and hourly experience. The surest means of disarming an anger or a lust was to turn your attention from the girl or the insult and start examining the passion itself. The surest way of spoiling a pleasure was to start examining your satisfaction. But if so, it followed that all introspection is in one respect misleading. In introspection we try to look "inside ourselves" and see what is going on. But nearly everything that was going on a moment before is stopped by the very act of our turning to look at it. Unfortunately this does not mean that introspection finds nothing. On the contrary, it finds precisely what is left behind by the suspension of all our normal activities; and what is left behind is mainly mental images and physical sensations. The great error is to mistake this mere sediment or track or by-product for the activities themselves. That is how men may come to believe that thought is only unspoken words, or the appreciation of poetry only a collection of mental pictures, when these in reality are what the thought or the appreciation, when interrupted, leave behind—like the swell at sea, working after the wind has dropped. Not, of course, that these activities, before we stopped them by introspection, were unconscious. We do not love, fear, or think without knowing it. Instead of the twofold division into Conscious and Unconscious, we need a three-fold division: the Unconscious, the Enjoyed, and the Contemplated.

This discovery flashed a new light back on my whole life. I saw that all my waitings and watchings for Joy, all my vain hopes to find some mental content on which I could, so to speak, lay my finger and say, "This is it," had been a futile attempt to contemplate the enjoyed. All that such watching and waiting ever *could* find would be either an image (Asgard, the Western Garden, or what not) or a quiver in the diaphragm. I should never have to bother again about these images or sensations. I knew now that they were merely the mental track left by the passage of Joy— not the wave but the wave's imprint on the sand. The inherent dialectic of desire itself had in a way already shown me this; for all images and sensations, if idolatrously mistaken for Joy itself, soon honestly confessed themselves inadequate. All said, in the last resort, "It is not I. I am only a reminder. Look! Look! What do I remind you of?"

So far, so good. But it is at the next step that awe overtakes me. There was no doubt that Joy was a desire (and, in so far as it was also simultaneously a good, it was also a kind of love). But a desire is turned not to itself but to its object. Not only that, but it owes all its character to its object. Erotic love is not like desire for food, nay, a love for one woman differs from a love for another woman in the very same way and the very same degree as the two women differ from one another. Even our desire for one wine differs in tone from our desire for another. Our intellectual desire (curiosity) to know the true answer to a question is quite different from our desire to find that one answer, rather than another, is true. The form of the desired is in the desire. It is the object which makes the desire harsh or sweet, coarse or choice, "high" or "low." It is the object that makes the desire itself desirable or hateful. I perceived (and this was a wonder of wonders) that just as I had been wrong in supposing that I really desired the Garden of the Hesperides, so also I had been equally wrong in supposing that I desired Joy itself. Joy itself, considered simply as an event in my own mind, turned out to be of no value at all. All the value lay in that of which Joy was the desiring. And that object, quite clearly, was no state of my own mind or body at all. In a way, I had proved this by elimination. I had tried everything in my own mind and body; as it were, asking myself, "Is it this you want? Is it this?" Last of all I had asked if Joy itself was what I wanted; and, labelling it "aesthetic experience," had pretended I could answer Yes. But that answer too had broken down. Inexorably Joy proclaimed, "You want—I myself am your want of—something other, outside, not you nor any state of you." I did not yet ask, Who is the desired? only What is it? But this brought me already into the region of awe, for I thus understood that in deepest solitude there is a road right out of the self, a commerce with something which, by refusing to identify itself with any object of the senses, or anything whereof we have biological or social need, or anything imagined, or any state of our own minds, proclaims itself sheerly objective. Far more objective than bodies, for it is not, like them, clothed in our senses; the naked Other, imageless (though our imagination salutes it with a hundred images), unknown, undefined, desired.

That was the second Move; equivalent, perhaps, to the loss of one's last remaining bishop. The third Move did not seem to me dangerous at the time. It consisted merely in linking up this new *éclaircissement* about Joy with my idealistic philosophy. I saw that Joy, as I now understood it, would fit in. We mortals, seen as the sciences see us and as we commonly see one another, are mere "appearances." But appearances of the Absolute. In so far as we really are at all (which isn't saying much) we have, so to speak, a root in the Absolute, which is the utter reality. And that is why we experience Joy: we yearn, rightly, for that unity which we can never reach except by ceasing to be the separate phenomenal beings called "we." Joy was not a deception. Its visitations were rather the moments of clearest consciousness we had, when we became aware of our fragmentary and phantasmal nature and ached for that impossible reunion which would annihilate us or that self-contradictory waking which would reveal, not that we had had, but that we were, a dream. This seemed quite satisfactory intellectually. Even emotionally too; for it matters more that Heaven should exist than that we should ever get there. What I did not notice was that I had passed an important milestone. Up till now my thoughts had been centrifugal; now the centripetal movement had begun. Considerations arising from quite different parts of my experience were beginning to come together with a click. This new dovetailing of my desire-life with my philosophy foreshadowed the day, now fast approaching, when I should be forced to take my "philosophy" more seriously than I ever intended. I did not foresee this. I was like a man who has lost "merely a pawn" and never dreams that this (in that state of the game) means mate in a few moves.

The fourth Move was more alarming. I was now teaching philosophy (I suspect very badly) as well as English. And my watered Hegelianism wouldn't serve for tutorial purposes.* A tutor must make things clear. Now the Absolute cannot be made clear. Do you mean Nobody-knows-what, or do you mean a superhuman mind and therefore (we may as well admit) a Person? After all, did Hegel and Bradley and all the rest of them ever do more than add mystifications to the simple, workable, theistic idealism of Berkeley? I thought not. And didn't Berkeley's "God" do all the same work as the Absolute, with the added advantage that we had at least some notion of what we meant by Him? I thought He did. So I was driven back into something like Berkeleyanism; but Berkeleyanism with a few top-dressings of my own. I distinguished this philosophical "God" very sharply (or so I said) from "the God of popular religion." There was, I explained, no possibility of being in a personal relation with Him. For I thought He projected us as a dramatist projects his characters, and I could no more "meet" Him, than Hamlet could meet Shakespeare. I didn't call Him "God" either; I called Him "Spirit." One fights for one's remaining comforts.

Then I read Chesterton's *Everlasting Man* and for the first time saw the whole Christian outline of history set out in a form that seemed to me to make sense. Somehow I contrived not to be too

* Not, of course, that I thought it a tutor's business to make converts to his own philosophy. But I found I needed a position of my own as a basis from which to criticize my pupils' essays.

badly shaken. You will remember that I already thought Chesterton the most sensible man alive "apart from his Christianity." Now, I veritably believe, I thought—I didn't of course *say*; words would have revealed the nonsense—that Christianity itself was very sensible "apart from its Christianity." But I hardly remember, for I had not long finished *The Everlasting Man* when something far more alarming happened to me. Early in 1926 the hardest boiled of all the atheists I ever knew sat in my room on the other side of the fire and remarked that the evidence for the historicity of the Gospels was really surprisingly good. "Rum thing," he went on. "All that stuff of Frazer's about the Dying God. Rum thing. It almost looks as if it had really happened once." To understand the shattering impact of it, you would need to know the man (who has certainly never since shown any interest in Christianity). If he, the cynic of cynics, the toughest of the toughs, were not—as I would still have put it—"safe," where could I turn? Was there then no escape?

The odd thing was that before God closed in on me, I was in fact offered what now appears a moment of wholly free choice. In a sense. I was going up Headington Hill on the top of a bus. Without words and (I think) almost without images, a fact about myself was somehow presented to me. I became aware that I was holding something at bay, or shutting something out. Or, if you like, that I was wearing some stiff clothing, like corsets, or even a suit of armour, as if I were a lobster. I felt myself being, there and then, given a free choice. I could open the door or keep it shut; I could unbuckle the armour or keep it on. Neither choice was presented as a duty; no threat or promise was attached to either, though I knew that to open the door or to take off the corslet meant the incalculable. The choice appeared to be momentous but it was also strangely unemotional. I was moved by no desires or fears. In a sense I was not moved by anything. I chose to open, to unbuckle, to loosen the rein. I say, "I chose," yet it did not really seem possible to do the opposite. On the other hand, I was aware of no motives. You could argue that I was not a free agent, but I am more inclined to think that this came nearer to being a perfectly free act than most that I have ever done. Necessity may not be the opposite of freedom, and perhaps a man is most free when, instead of producing motives, he could only say, "I am what I do." Then came the repercussion on the imaginative level. I felt as if I were a man of snow at long last beginning to melt. The melting was starting in my back—drip-drip and presently trickle-trickle. I rather disliked the feeling.

The fox had been dislodged from Hegelian Wood and was now running in the open, "with all the woe in the world," bedraggled and weary, hounds barely a field behind. And nearly everyone was now (one way or another) in the pack; Plato, Dante, MacDonald, Herbert, Barfield, Tolkien, Dyson, Joy itself. Everyone and everything had joined the other side. Even my own pupil Griffiths—now Dom Bede Griffiths—though not yet himself a believer, did his share. Once, when he and Barfield were lunching in my room, I happened to refer to philosophy as "a subject." "It wasn't a *subject* to Plato," said Barfield, "it was a *way*." The quiet but fervent agreement of Griffiths, and the quick glance of understanding between these two, revealed to me my own frivolity. Enough had been thought, and said, and felt, and imagined. It was about time that something should be done.

For of course there had long been an ethic (theoretically) attached to my Idealism. I thought the business of us finite and half-unreal souls was to multiply the consciousness of Spirit by seeing the world from different positions while yet remaining qualitatively the same as Spirit; to be tied to a particular time and place and set of circumstances, yet there to will and think as Spirit itself does. This was hard; for the very act whereby Spirit projected souls and a world gave those souls different and competitive interests, so that there was a temptation to selfishness. But I thought each of us had it in his power to discount the emotional perspective produced by his own particular selfhood, just as we discount the optical perspective produced by our position in space. To prefer my own happiness to my neighbour's was like thinking that the nearest telegraph post was really the largest. The way to recover, and act upon, this universal and objective vision was daily and hourly to remember our true nature, to reascend or return into that Spirit which, in so far as we really were at all, we still were. Yes; but I now felt I had better try to do it. I faced at last (in MacDonald's words) "something to be neither more nor less nor other than *done*." An attempt at complete virtue must be made.

Really, a young Atheist cannot guard his faith too carefully. Dangers lie in wait for him on every side. You must not do, you must not even try to do, the will of the Father unless you are prepared to "know of the doctrine." All my acts, desires, and thoughts were to be brought into harmony with universal Spirit. For the first time I examined myself with a seriously practical purpose. And there I found what appalled me: a zoo of lusts, a bedlam of ambitions, a nursery of fears, a hareem of fondled hatreds. My name was legion.

Of course I could do nothing—I could not last out one hour—without continual conscious recourse to what I called Spirit. But the fine, philosophical distinction between this and what ordinary people call "prayer to God" breaks down as soon as you start doing it in earnest. Idealism can be talked, and even felt; it cannot be lived. It became patently absurd to go on thinking of "Spirit" as either ignorant of, or passive to, my approaches. Even if my own philosophy were true, how could the initiative lie on my side? My own analogy, as I now first perceived, suggested the opposite: if Shakespeare and Hamlet could ever meet, it must be Shakespeare's doing.* Hamlet could initiate nothing. Perhaps, even now, my Absolute Spirit still differed in some way from the God of religion. The real issue was not, or not yet, there. The real terror was that if you seriously believed in even such a "God" or "Spirit" as I admitted, a wholly new situation developed. As the dry bones shook and came together in that dreadful valley of Ezekiel's, so now a philosophical theorem, cerebrally entertained, began to stir and heave and throw off its gravecloths, and stood upright and became

---

* i.e. Shakespeare could, in principle, make himself appear as Author within the play, and write a dialogue between Hamlet and himself. The "Shakespeare" within the play would of course be at once Shakespeare and one of Shakespeare's creatures. It would bear some analogy to Incarnation.

a living presence. I was to be allowed to play at philosophy no longer. It might, as I say, still be true that my "Spirit" differed in some way from "the God of popular religion." My Adversary waived the point. It sank into utter unimportance. He would not argue about it. He only said, "I am the Lord"; "I am that I am"; "I am."

People who are naturally religious find difficulty in understanding the horror of such a revelation. Amiable agnostics will talk cheerfully about "man's search for God." To me, as I then was, they might as well have talked about the mouse's search for the cat. The best image of my predicament is the meeting of Mime and Wotan in the first act of *Siegfried; hier brauch' ich nicht Spärer noch Späher, Einsam will ich* . . . (I've no use for spies and snoopers. I would be private. . . .)

Remember, I had always wanted, above all things, not to be "interfered with." I had wanted (mad wish) "to call my soul my own." I had been far more anxious to avoid suffering than to achieve delight. I had always aimed at limited liabilities. The supernatural itself had been to me, first, an illicit dram, and then, as by a drunkard's reaction, nauseous. Even my recent attempt to live my philosophy had secretly (I now knew) been hedged round by all sorts of reservations. I had pretty well known that my ideal of virtue would never be allowed to lead me into anything intolerably painful; I would be "reasonable." But now what had been an ideal became a command; and what might not be expected of one? Doubtless, by definition, God was Reason itself. But would He also be "reasonable" in that other, more comfortable, sense? Not the slightest assurance on that score was offered me. Total surrender, the absolute leap in the dark, were demanded. The reality with which no treaty can be made was upon me. The demand was not even "All or nothing." I think that stage had been passed, on the bus-top when I unbuckled my armour and the snow-man started to melt. Now, the demand was simply "All."

You must picture me alone in that room in Magdalen, night after night, feeling, whenever my mind lifted even for a second from my work, the steady, unrelenting approach of Him whom I so earnestly desired not to meet. That which I greatly feared had at last come upon me. In the Trinity Term of 1929 I gave in, and admitted that God was God, and knelt and prayed: perhaps, that night, the most dejected and reluctant convert in all England. I did not then see what is now the most shining and obvious thing; the Divine humility which will accept a convert even on such terms. The Prodigal Son at least walked home on his own feet. But who can duly adore that Love which will open the high gates to a prodigal who is brought in kicking, struggling, resentful, and darting his eyes in every direction for a chance of escape? The words *compelle intrare*, compel them to come in, have been so abused by wicked men that we shudder at them; but, properly understood, they plumb the depth of the Divine mercy. The hardness of God is kinder than the softness of men, and His compulsion is our liberation.

2

For it is one thing to see the land of peace from a wooded ridge . . . and another to tread the road that leads to it.
—ST. AUGUSTINE, CONFESSIONS, VII, XXI

It must be understood that the conversion recorded . . . was only to Theism, pure and simple, not to Christianity. I knew nothing yet about the Incarnation. The God to whom I surrendered was sheerly non-human. . . .

The last stage in my story, the transition from mere Theism to Christianity, is the one on which I am now least informed. Since it is also the most recent, this ignorance may seem strange. I think there are two reasons. One is that as we grow older we remember the more distant past better than what is nearer. But the other is, I believe, that one of the first results of my Theistic conversion was a marked decrease (and high time, . . .) in the fussy attentiveness which I had so long paid to the progress of my own opinions and the states of my own mind. For many healthy extroverts self-examination first begins with conversion. For me it was almost the other way round. Self-examination did of course continue. But it was (I suppose, for I cannot quite remember) at stated intervals, and for a practical purpose; a duty, a discipline, an uncomfortable thing, no longer a hobby or a habit. To believe and to pray were the beginning of extroversion. I had been, as they say, "taken out of myself." If Theism had done nothing else for me, I should still be thankful that it cured me of the time-wasting and foolish practice of keeping a diary. (Even for autobiographical purposes a diary is nothing like so useful as I had hoped. You put down each day what you think important; but of course you cannot each day see what will prove to have been important in the long run.*)

As soon as I became a Theist I started attending my parish church on Sundays and my college chapel on weekdays; not because I believed in Christianity, nor because I thought the difference between it and simple Theism a small one, but because I thought one ought to "fly one's flag" by some unmistakable overt sign. I was acting in obedience to a (perhaps mistaken) sense of honour. The idea of churchmanship was to me wholly unattractive. I was not in the least anti-clerical, but I was deeply anti-ecclesiastical. That curates and archdeacons and churchwardens should exist, was admirable. They gratified my Jenkinian love of everything which has its own strong flavour. And (apart from Oldie) I had been fortunate in my clerical acquaintances; especially in Adam Fox, the Dean of Divinity at Magdalen, and in Arthur Barton (later Archbishop of Dublin) who had been our Rector at home in Ireland. (He, by the by, had once suffered under Oldie at Belsen. Speaking of Oldie's death, I had said to him, "Well, we shan't see him again." "You mean," he answered with a grim smile, "we hope we shan't.") But though I liked clergymen

---

* The only real good I got from keeping a diary was that it taught me a just appreciation of Boswell's amazing genius. I tried very hard to reproduce conversations, in some of which very amusing and striking people had taken part. But none of these people came to life in the diary at all. Obviously something quite different from mere accurate reporting went to the presentation of Boswell's Langton, Beauclerk, Wilkes, and the rest.

as I liked bears, I had as little wish to be in the Church as in the zoo. It was, to begin with, a kind of collective; a wearisome "get-together" affair. I couldn't yet see how a concern of that sort should have anything to do with one's spiritual life. To me, religion ought to have been a matter of good men praying alone and meeting by twos and threes to talk of spiritual matters. And then the fussy, time-wasting botheration of it all! the bells, the crowds, the umbrellas, the notices, the bustle, the perpetual arranging and organising. Hymns were (and are) extremely disagreeable to me. Of all musical instruments I liked (and like) the organ least. I have, too, a sort of spiritual *gaucherie* which makes me unapt to participate in any rite.

Thus my churchgoing was a merely symbolical and provisional practice. If it in fact helped to move me in the Christian direction, I was and am unaware of this. My chief companion on this stage of the road was Griffiths, with whom I kept up a copious correspondence. Both now believed in God, and were ready to hear more of Him from any source, Pagan or Christian. In my mind (I cannot now answer for his, and he has told his own story admirably in *The Golden String*) the perplexing multiplicity of "religions" began to sort itself out. The real clue had been put into my hand by that hard-boiled Atheist when he said, "Rum thing, all that about the Dying God. Seems to have really happened once"; by him and by Barfield's encouragement of a more respectful, if not more delighted, attitude to Pagan myth. The question was no longer to find the one simply true religion among a thousand religions simply false. It was rather, "Where has religion reached its true maturity? Where, if anywhere, have the hints of all Paganism been fulfilled?" With the irreligious I was no longer concerned; their view of life was henceforth out of court. As against them, the whole mass of those who had worshipped— all who had danced and sung and sacrificed and trembled and adored—were clearly right. But the intellect and the conscience, as well as the orgy and the ritual, must be our guide. There could be no question of going back to primitive, untheologised and unmoralised, Paganism. The God whom I had at last acknowledged was one, and was righteous. Paganism had been only the childhood of religion, or only a prophetic dream. Where was the thing full grown? or where was the awaking? (*The Everlasting Man* was helping me here.) There were really only two answers possible: either in Hinduism or in Christianity. Everything else was either a preparation for, or else (in the French sense) a *vulgarisation* of, these. Whatever you could find elsewhere you could find better in one of these. But Hinduism seemed to have two disqualifications. For one thing, it appeared to be not so much a moralised and philosophical maturity of Paganism as a mere oil-and-water coexistence of philosophy side by side with Paganism unpurged; the Brahmin meditating in the forest, and, in the village a few miles away, temple-prostitution, *sati*, cruelty, monstrosity. And secondly, there was no such historical claim as in Christianity. I was by now too experienced in literary criticism to regard the Gospels as myths. They had not the mythical taste. And yet the very matter which they set down in their artless, historical fashion—those narrow, unattractive Jews, too blind to the mythical wealth of the Pagan world around them—was precisely the matter of the great myths. If ever a myth had become fact, had been incarnated, it would be just like this. And nothing else in all literature was just like this. Myths were like it in one way. Histories were like it in another. But nothing was simply like it. And no person was like the Person it depicted; as real, as recognisable, through all that depth of time, as Plato's Socrates or Boswell's Johnson (ten times more so than Eckermann's Goethe or Lockhart's Scott), yet also luminous, lit by a light from beyond the world, a god. But if a god—we are no longer polytheists—then not a god, but God. Here and here only in all time the myth must have become fact; the Word, flesh; God, Man. This is not "a religion," nor "a philosophy." It is the summing up and actuality of them all.

As I have said, I speak of this last transition less certainly than of any which went before it, and it may be that in the preceding paragraph I have mixed thoughts that came later. But I can hardly be wrong about the main lines. Of one thing I am sure. As I drew near the conclusion, I felt a resistance almost as strong as my previous resistance to Theism. As strong, but shorter-lived, for I understood it better. Every step I had taken, from the Absolute to "Spirit" and from "Spirit" to "God," had been a step towards the more concrete, the more imminent, the more compulsive. At each step one had less chance "to call one's soul one's own." To accept the Incarnation was a further step in the same direction. It brings God nearer, or near in a new way. And this, I found, was something I had not wanted. But to recognise the ground for my evasion was of course to recognise both its shame and its futility. I know very well when, but hardly how, the final step was taken. I was driven to Whipsnade one sunny morning. When we set out I did not believe that Jesus Christ is the Son of God, and when we reached the zoo I did. Yet I had not exactly spent the journey in thought. Nor in great emotion. "Emotional" is perhaps the last word we can apply to some of the most important events. It was more like when a man, after long sleep, still lying motionless in bed, becomes aware that he is now awake. And it was, like that moment on top of the bus, ambiguous. Freedom, or necessity? Or do they differ at their maximum? At that maximum a man is what he does; there is nothing of him left over or outside the act. As for what we commonly call Will, and what we commonly call Emotion, I fancy these usually talk too loud, protest too much, to be quite believed, and we have a secret suspicion that the great passion or the iron resolution is partly a put-up job.

They have spoiled Whipsnade since then. Wallaby Wood, with the birds singing overhead and the bluebells underfoot and the Wallabies hopping all round one, was almost Eden come again.

But what, in conclusion, of Joy? for that, after all, is what the story has mainly been about. To tell you the truth, the subject has lost nearly all interest for me since I became a Christian. I cannot, indeed, complain, like Wordsworth, that the visionary gleam has passed away. I believe (if the thing were at all worth recording) that the old stab, the old bittersweet, has come to me as often and as sharply since my conversion as at any time of my life whatever. But I now know that the experience, considered as a state of my own mind, had never had the kind of importance I once gave it.

It was valuable only as a pointer to something other and outer. While that other was in doubt, the pointer naturally loomed large in my thoughts. When we are lost in the woods the sight of a signpost is a great matter. He who first sees it cries, "Look!" The whole party gathers round and stares. But when we have found the road and are passing signposts every few miles, we shall not stop and stare. They will encourage us and we shall be grateful to the authority that set them up. But we shall not stop and stare, or not much; not on this road, though their pillars are of silver and their lettering of gold. "We would be at Jerusalem."

Not, of course, that I don't often catch myself stopping to stare at roadside objects of even less importance.

WONDERING

SPIRIT

Edmund W. Sinnott

Edmund W. Sinnott, Harvard 1908, is one of the leading botanists of America. He has taught at the University of Connecticut, Columbia and Yale where he is at present Sterling Professor of Botany. He has written several books including Cell and Psyche, Two Roads to Truth, *and* The Biology of the Spirit. *"Spirit" is taken from his latest book entitled* Matter, Mind and Man, *in Harper & Brothers' World Perspectives Series edited by Ruth Nanda Anshen.*

That such a thing as the human spirit exists at all will be denied by many. It seems to them an idea so flavored with mysticism, so reminiscent of those ancient, unenlightened days before man's growing reason had freed him from superstition, that it no longer is worthy of serious attention. To such objectors we may reply that his psychical life has various aspects, and that one of them—by many thought of as the most significant of all—needs a particular name by which it can be distinguished. In the sense in which it will here be used, the term "spirit" need have no mystical overtones and certainly no taint of superstition. It is simply one special aspect of man as a living being.

Goal-seeking in a primitive mind translates itself directly to behavior. What a savage wants to do he *does* at once if it is possible; but since far more goals exist within his mind than can be gained, or even pursued, at the same time, most of them stay latent there as things desired, to be gained at some time in the future by appropriate acts of behavior when opportunity offers. He likes eating meat, let us say, and enjoys the pleasures of the chase or the grimmer ones of combat. The company of his mate delights him, and the warmth of the family fire. These are all goals which from time to time he tries to reach, but when he is not doing so they linger in the background of his mind as things he would like to do. In intellects more refined, such goals become translated into clearer images of things that might be, a body of desires, hopes, interests and ideals. They interfuse most of man's mental life. The wish in a real sense thus is father to the thought. Our minds are colored by the presence there of such goals, unrealized, often unconscious, but powerfully affecting what we do. As the magnetic pole pulls the needle of the compass toward it, so they direct the course of our thoughts and actions. They form the basis of our values.

The experience of these desires is rarely a neutral and passionless feeling, a cool and intellectual affair. Sometimes, indeed, it seems to be such, as is his who comes to appreciate a masterpiece of art or literature by dissection and analysis, or who embraces a religious creed from purely rational conviction. Far more commonly, however, these cravings transcend mere rational justification. They are experienced with a warmth, intensity and vividness that are the source of those strong feelings of attraction and aversion which are such vital elements in human life. Goal-seeking and purposiveness at this level are transmuted into emotions—love, hate, fear, aspiration, anxiety, delight in beauty, reverence and many more. They are what chiefly distinguish man from a machine and give to his existence the zest and fire and richness that lift it so far above mere rationality.

The emotions of primitive man were doubtless those that had proved advantageous for his survival. Darwin described many instances of this. Despite the bloody evolutionary road that man has traveled, however, a remarkable thing about these emotional attitudes of his is that they include not only those appropriate for a species that has fought its way up, but that so often they are directed to qualities and objectives of a different sort, ones that the universal judgment of the race regards as higher than mere brutish goals. As man grows out from barbarism there rise in him, wherever he is or to whatever race he may belong, cravings for beauty and rightness, love and truth, reverence for something greater than himself that dwells in nature. His interpretation of these qualities may differ widely with time and culture and geography. For a while he may abandon them in part and slip back toward savagery again, but throughout his history man always has returned to these as to his highest values. At his best, something within him seems *naturally* to seek such goals. This conclusion may seem overly optimistic for a time like ours, but in the perspective of history I believe it can be justified. Like Christian in his pilgrimage through Bunyan's allegory, he always lifts his eyes to something higher.

Emotions are subjective; sensed within, and expressed outwardly only by their physiological accompaniments—the faster pulse, the quickened breath, the flushing of the cheek. Nothing like them, we may safely say, happens to a machine, even the most complex. Their beginnings can be inferred among the higher animals, but emotions are far more varied in man's life and mark him off from all the brute creation. He still has animal appetites and passions, to be sure, but these higher cravings are peculiarly his own. Hunger for food he knows, but also hunger for the very different nourishment of beauty. Sexual passion is his, as in the brutes, but he can transform it to the noblest of the emotions, love. Pouring up to consciousness from his unconscious mind, that deep source of purpose and desire within him, these loftier emotions mark a level that is higher than physical goal-seeking and quite different from intelligence and reason. "These deep-seated inborn urgencies and desires, arising spontaneously in the mind but subject to a wide measure of direction, often dragging man down to the level of the beasts but coming to flower as the highest expressions of what he is and what he might become, one may rightly call, I think, the human *spirit*."

Let us define our terms here somewhat more precisely. What *is* man's spirit, really, we may ask? How does it differ from his mind?

his self? his soul? More than all, is it related to any spiritual thing outside, perhaps to a Divine Spirit that dwells in nature?

These are questions impossible to answer satisfactorily. Since what we have called the spirit is an aspect of the living human being, however, the sciences of life and mind should not pretend a lack of interest in it. Spirit has been such a vital element in the life of man from the days of witch doctors until our own that whatever the biologist can say about it should be welcome. At best, this never can be very much, but the foundation that the man of science here can lay may serve for an edifice that will shelter not only himself but the philosopher and the man of faith, as well.

The various expressions of man's psychical life cannot be very sharply distinguished. *Mind* we may assume to cover all the psychical aspects of the human organism. The *self* is his particular individual being as he experiences it. The *soul* is the essence of the self, the precious part of man, looked on by many as his immortal portion. *Intelligence* is that aspect of the mind which sees the relationships of things and draws from them logical conclusions. *Spirit*, as the word here is used, denotes an aspect of the psychical whole that is different from any of these, though not sharply marked off from them. It is like instinct but at a higher level. It includes the stream of deeper feelings and emotions that stir within us, but it is more even than these. It is not mere stirring, mere emotion, but is directed *toward* some object—admiration for a work of art or a piece of music that draws us on to see it or to hear it played; delight in a poem that sets us to reading it; love of a person that makes us want to be with him or to think of him; hatred or fear of something, that fills us with a desire to crush it or avoid it; reverence for whatever is awesome and sublime that brings us to our knees in worship. These feelings may occur at many levels of intensity, from peaceful contemplation of a sunset to the fiery passion of an evangelist or the mystic's ecstasy. In all these cases there is feeling, a stirring of the heart; but unless this feeling is directive, unless it leads us toward that object by which the feeling is aroused, unless it *aspires* to do something, it is not a manifestation, I believe, of what is rightly to be called the spirit.

This quality brings the spirit down, you see, to that same biological fact of goal-seeking and directiveness that we have been discussing. This is a common denominator that binds together all manifestations of life and makes of an organism, even a man with his almost infinite diversity, a single whole. Through the blindly questing embryo that builds random matter into a patterned body, through the marvelous regulations of behavior that one sees in instinct, and through the orderly purposiveness of rational thought, this goal-seeking runs like a golden thread. Why should we not recognize the same fact in the more mysterious realm of deeper, unreasoned aspiration? Since man here, too, is seeking to reach goals, must not these goals be foreshadowed in some way within the organization of that stuff which is the basis of his very life? Whatever spirit is, whatever it may mean for an understanding of man's nature and the problems of philosophy and of religion, whatever it may finally portend for his hope and destiny, it has a relationship with matter through its birth in the regulatory processes of protoplasm.

If this conception of the spirit as rooted in protoplasmic regulation is a true one, it can do something to bring this supreme but nebulous part of man down from the cloudy regions of metaphysics and theology and at least put a biological foundation under it. Bergson rightly says, I think, that the life of the body is on the road to the life of the spirit, and that we have erred in the past by trying to isolate spirit from the rest of life, thus making it unreal and ineffective.

This conception of the spirit, however, ingenious though one may admit it is, will certainly not pass unchallenged. Philosophers of both materialism and of religion may be expected to object vigorously to it, though on quite different grounds.

The evolutionist will hasten to point out that the emotions—for in the end, he says, it all comes down to that—have had their origin in the slow course of man's ascent. They have been fashioned by competition and natural selection, just as have all other human traits. Did not Darwin himself write a book on the expression of emotions in animals which showed their gradual development among the vertebrates and their usefulness for survival? Love, for example, is either an extension of the reproductive urge which brings the sexes together and without which life would not continue, or of the maternal instinct so necessary in the nourishment and protection of the young until they can care for themselves. Even in human societies, family solidarity and the ties that bind individuals into a common group are of great value for survival. The warm emotion of love has a necessary and reasonable place in the life of man, and to explain it no mysterious "goal" is required. Moral qualities in general are of such obvious social value that they would have been developed for this reason alone. And, at the other extreme, rage, hate and fear are accompanied by physiological reactions (in glandular activity and in nervous and muscular changes) which increase the individual's combative potential or aid him to escape from danger. Their evolutionary usefulness is obvious.

Other emotions receive similar explanations. Courage, curiosity, sympathy, anxiety, shame and others may all be understood as serviceable traits. Even where their immediate value for survival is not obvious, if such qualities are present it must be assumed that at some time or other, in the complex processes of competition and adaptation, they have proved their usefulness.

The physiologist, too, can present abundant evidence that for several of the emotions, at least, a definite biochemical basis has been established. In anger, adrenalin is poured into the bloodstream and stimulates muscular activity. Prolactin, the "mother-love hormone," is clearly related to the display of maternal instincts. Drugs of various sorts produce important emotional effects and may even lead to ecstasies and delights resembling those experienced by mystics. For all such, as presumably for every activity of the mind, there is a chemical cause.

Emotions are the particular province of the psychologist, and he joins his scientific brethren in assuring us that there is a definite physical basis for them. They are related to activities in the thalamus. As in all mental states they are derived from the complex interplay of stimulus and response. Often they are the outcome of conditioning, as when a shock of fear is produced by an air-raid signal even after war is long since past. Much is now known of the causes of the emotions, and psychology denies that there is anything which might be called mystical or supernatural about them.

In answer to these objections it may be replied that in the suggestions here proposed as to the origin of spiritual qualities nothing mystical or supernatural is assumed, in the sense of facts outside the realm of law. Unexplained they may be but surely not to be thought of as having no possible explanation. The germ of the emotions, and thus of qualities that have here been termed spiritual, is certainly present among animals. In the complex adaptiveness of life they doubtless have often been of value and preserved by the action of natural selection. There are many instances, however, where their usefulness has certainly not been proved. Darwin himself cites cases of helpfulness between members of different species, which would hardly provide material for natural selection. The many instances where animals seem to be amused or to experience enjoyment could hardly be so explained unless a happy animal is more likely to survive! The desire for beauty seems especially hard to attribute to the influence of natural selection. In man's history, certainly, it must often have been a hindrance, not a help. Many high civilizations that paid homage to it and diverted some of their energies thereto have been toppled down by rude barbarians who kept their weapons bright. Dedication to a moral code that stresses altruism and self-sacrifice may actually be a handicap to survival in a rough and selfish world. At all events, knowledge of evolution is still so incomplete that we are by no means justified in assuming that every trait that exists must do so by virtue of some usefulness that it possesses. We certainly would not be willing to accept this explanation in the field of social evolution, or to agree that "whatever is, is right."

The problem of the physiological and psychological bases of emotions, and thus of spiritual qualities, is simply a part of the ancient question of the body-mind relationship. At least it may be argued that if the material environment, inside and outside the human organism, is such that invariably there are produced in men

those attributes that we have here called spiritual, my main argument—that these qualities are inherent in man—is essentially con-
ceded. Although no confident philosophy of mechanism will admit
that the physico-chemical system that man is can ever have qualities that deserve the name of spiritual, the human *spirit* remains
the most embarrassing fact that this philosophy must face, for it
implies either a spiritual element in man or the emergence from
matter and energy of high qualities that materialism has no reason
to expect to find there.

The objections to the hypothesis from the other side, the advo-
cates of a religious philosophy, are no less vehement. To a man of
faith the conception of his spirit as simply the sum of his emotions
and desires seems so inadequate as to be almost meaningless for an
interpretation of religion. Spirit, he says, is something that pervades
the entire universe. Men are born of it, are filled with it and walk
after it. God himself is spirit. What connection can possibly exist
between these august facts and any processes, however curious and
interesting they may be, that can be found in such a material system as protoplasm is? The two belong to different universes of discourse. "Those that are born of the flesh are flesh, and those that
are born of the spirit are spirit." The teaching of the gospel is that
we must be lifted out of our physical, mundane, biological existence and be born again into a new and *spiritual* world. It is neither good science nor good religion to talk about a biological
basis for the spirit. Emotions are important and when rightly used
can be of value in man's religious life; but Spirit, the word with a
capital letter, the key to man's salvation and the seal of his true nature as a child of God, the great creative Presence that in the darkness of the First Day moved upon the face of the waters—this
surely is so far above the level of biology or psychology or any other
science formulated by the wit of man that it is preposterous to
think of them together. . . .

And at this point the argument temporarily may rest. The position here defended is briefly this: that neither protoplasm itself nor
man, its highest expression, are neutral systems in which whatever
happens is the result only of outer forces, but that specific inner

ones are also effective; that the character and organization of living stuff is such that goals are set up within it which are characteristic and specific at all levels, though subject in their particular quality and effect to the influence of the environment; that the progressive advance in these goals during evolution, though in large measure certainly the result of natural selection, has been due in part to specific tendencies in protoplasm itself; and, most important of all, that the direction in which these goals have advanced is such that in man they tend to create the high ideals of beauty, right, truth and the Divine which in a real sense may be called spiritual. Spirit in man is a result of the autonomous, creative quality that is his. Like the wind, it moves where it lists; but whence it comes, and whither it goes, we do not know.

If these ideas are correct, conclusions of some moment can be drawn from them both for philosophy and for religion.

First, the goals set up within our living stuff, from its lowest level to its highest, determine the course of our desires. When not translated into action, these goals, as we have seen, become latent in the mind as wishes, aspirations and ideals. Man is not neutral about the environment in which he lives. Some things he likes and some things he does not. He is continually making *value judgments* about them. Values are things about which one hears much today. These are of many sorts and at different levels, from purely physical preferences and desires to those we may call spiritual. Values are goals. The most distinctive traits a person has are not so much what he is, in body and mind, as the things and qualities he values. These, in a sense, are what he is. His physical life, his behavior, his philosophy and his religion will finally depend on what it is he *wants*. This is the basis of his self. In any attempt to learn what man's real nature is, a study of his values is therefore of paramount importance. If these are imposed upon him entirely from without, he may truly be said to have no real character of his own, for what he is bears only the stamp of his environment. If they arise within himself, however (modified though they may be by many factors), they are a prolific and dependable source of information about him.

The fact that everywhere, as man has advanced from barbarism, there grew in him the high spiritual values we have been discussing surely tells us something that is significant as to what he is. Men differ greatly in their values. In some of them these never reach a high level, or if they do, they are crowded out by lower ones. For most people, however, spiritual goals, though never completely realized, remain as the supreme values of their lives. That man loves beauty, seeks righteousness, pursues truth and reverences the Divine, and does so not primarily from outer compulsion or inner necessity but because these are things he earnestly *desires*, should put us in good heart about his future. A creature with ideals like these must have rudiments within him of something that is truly god-like.

It is just here that one who seeks to build a bridge between the physical life of man and that higher existence of the spirit which is religion's theme can find a place to put it. Such a bridge exists, I think, in protoplasm, for this is the point where the material complexities of bodily life are so coordinated that goals arise in it—by what means we know not—which, like surveyors in a wilderness, mark out the course that it will follow. This started with the development of the body, passed on through the growth of the mind and the triumphant rise of reason, and finally pushed out into the mysterious territories of the spirit. It is in this goal-seeking character of protoplasm that matter and spirit meet. Whether spirit is born here from the complexities of matter or whether spirit at this critical point becomes associated with it and directs the course that matter takes is an important question for philosophy.

No one has yet an answer to this problem. The point I wish to make is that the case for spirit as a specific reality is stronger than has generally been admitted. It need not rest alone on inner conviction, faith and the authority of revelation, important though these may be, but can look to the basic fact of biology—goal-seeking—for evidence of something that may truly be called spiritual. This position, to be sure, must assume that life and at least the rudiments of spirit are coextensive; that life, mind and spirit essentially are one. To understand the nature of life we shall never succeed, I think, by seeking to interpret it solely through the laws of physics and chemistry which we now know, but we shall need to discover new laws, perhaps a new *kind* of law, for life. When we find these, we shall not only solve the deepest problem in biology and the ancient enigma of the relation between mind and body but shall also dimly begin to understand how spirit, mysterious as it now seems to be, can come to dwell in the flesh.

Important though emotion is in the spirit, the *highest* manifestation of spirit is far more than goal-seeking. It is a moving experience of desires and aspirations carrying an inner certainty of their own high character and with power at times to lift us out of ourselves. Men of all qualities and kinds, though never many of them, have had high mystical experiences and report upon them with surprising unanimity. As William James has said, "In Hinduism, in Neoplatonism, in Sufism, in Christian Mysticism, in Whitmanism, we find the same recurring note, so that there is about mystical utterances an eternal unanimity which ought to make a critic stop and think, and which brings it about that the mystical classes have, as has been said, neither birthday nor native land."*

A sense of exaltation, a longing for an intimate communion with a greater Spirit felt to be near and a certainty of conviction that the experience, brief though it usually is, has given a true picture of reality, is felt by all of them. Such high ecstasies are the lot of only a few, but lesser ones are the common experience of the devotees of all religions. They are the loftiest expressions of spiritual goal-seeking. The foundation of religion is the conviction with which such states report the existence of an unseen world with which it is possible for man to hold communion. Whether these spiritual insights tell the truth or are mere illusions has long been debated, but a substantial number of philosophers and even a psychologist or two like William James believe that they lead us at least into a realm of reality not accessible by reason alone. This means, in the terms we have been using, that these high goals that are set up within us come somehow into contact with the same

* William James, *The Varieties of Religious Experience* (New York: Longmans, Green & Company, 1911), p. 419.

sort of spiritual reality in the universe outside. Such is the great leap of intuition that religion has always made, an adventurous but confident essay of faith that it *is* possible to link our physical world with a far richer one of spirit inaccessible to man's senses. That such a leap may not be completely blind is suggested by the hypothesis presented here. Spirit is but the highest expression of *life*, and life is still as unexplained as spirit is. The final problems of biology and of religion may well turn out to be the same. The vivid inner experience of life at its highest in these aspirations and spiritual insights born in the processes of protoplasm throw light on the operation of that remarkable organized living system we call man.

Man's spirit is first of all a questing and aspiring thing, seeking in the world outside for something to satisfy its inner longing. That there exists a means by which this satisfaction can be gained —a reservoir of spirit on which a man may draw—is suggested by the very longing itself. Nature is not frustrating. For every goal that draws us on, the thing desired exists. That we are hungry or cold implies that food and warmth are to be had. Sometimes it may be that we cannot reach them, but they are there. All lower goals set up in protoplasm can be attained. It would be strange indeed if men were continually tantalized by urgent desires within them which could never be fulfilled. Does not the existence in our hearts of longings for spiritual satisfaction imply that means for satisfying these indeed exist? Must we believe that only here is an explorer deluded by a mirage and that there is nothing that can quench his spirit's thirst? Thus to frustrate men is never nature's way.

If all this is so, religion's ancient insistence can be justified—that insights of the spirit give us a valid picture of truth through a knowledge of it quite different from that which intellect provides. Spirit is the part of man that seems to be in immediate contact with reality and that can feel directly what its very substance is. In many things, of course, rational intelligence is the only safe highway to the truth. But where this no longer can be followed, as in the deepest questions that men face, the other road of spiritual insight, says religion, also provides access to it, and in the end is the most reliable of all. If man's spirit actually *is* in contact with what William James calls "a more of the same kind outside," if man's spiritual goals are not empty dreams but directed toward things that actually exist, then religion's stout assertion has the support of something besides faith alone.

To the materialist and the positivist this conclusion is the veriest moonshine. For them, report of sense and reason are the only verities, and spirit, with whatever it may claim to reveal, is all illusion. These inner feelings and desires, they say, of which we here have made so much, are notoriously subject to outer influences— to oxygen supply, the liver's health, blood chemistry, drugs and many other things. To build a philosophy on evidence from such a source as this is fantastic foolishness. The words of Thomas Henry Huxley still express the opinion of many when he remarks that "anyone who is acquainted with the history of science will admit that its progress, in all ages, meant, and now more than ever means, the extension of the province of what we call matter and causation, and the concomitant gradual banishment from all regions of human thought of what we call spirit and spontaneity."*

It would be comforting indeed to be sure we knew the truth. Man's quest for certainty is his most eager one. To assume that life is simple in the sense that it depends on the known principles of matter and of energy is the easy way to certainty about it. To do so ignores the uncomfortable problems, especially that most obscure of all—how goals arise in living stuff and thus how aspirations of the spirit come to birth. To assume that a thing is simple when it actually is not so, however, is to delude one's self. It certainly is true that circumstances both within the organism and without affect its insights and desires, just as the magnetic needle may be deflected from true pointing to the pole, but we do not count the compass valueless because of this. Instinctive longings of the human spirit may doubtless sometimes be hallucinations, but to maintain that they must therefore always be completely value-

* T. H. Huxley, *Methods and Results,* as quoted by E. W. F. Tomlin, *Living and Knowing* (London: Faber and Faber, 1955).

less is to hold too dogmatic an opinion about a matter which is far more complex than the confident materialist is willing to admit. Both science and theology are too naïve when they assert that only *their* answers can be true. "There are more things in heaven and earth, Horatio, than are dreamt of in your philosophy."

Life is still the final problem and we do well to admit that we are far from a final solution of it and may not even be on the road which will surely take us there. Today is not a time for easy dogmatism in science or religion. If a reasonable possibility exists, as I believe it does, that what we have called the spirit is life's highest manifestation; that through it we can make a direct, and not simply a logical, contact with the nature of life itself; and that life thus sensed is continuous with a greater source of life from whence it comes—then we should be negligent indeed if we ignored what the spirit has to tell. Through it we may be able to look deeply into the very heart of reality and discover truths that are inaccessible by any other means. Life is a continual seeking after goals, and in following the ones the spirit knows we become explorers in that wide realm which is man's native country and to which he is ever striving to return.

Matter, life, mind and spirit are somehow tied together in intimate association. This reaches its highest level of complexity in the activities that go on within the human brain. Wilder Penfield, a foremost student of the brain, thus concludes a recent paper on this remarkable organ: "It is obvious that nerve impulse is somehow converted into thought and that thought can be converted into nerve impulse. And yet all this throws no light upon the nature of that strange conversion. Before certain problems the scientist will always stand in awe. Perhaps he may be forced to make another approach—to what was called in old time 'the heart.' However far our successors in these studies may go, it is my belief that the machine will never fully explain the man, nor mechanisms the nature of the spirit."*

* Wilder Penfield, *Some Observations on the Functional Organization of the Human Brain.* Proc. Amer. Phil. Soc. 98:297, 1954.

THE MYSTERY

W. Somerset Maugham

W. Somerset Maugham, in the concluding sections of The Summing Up, has described his intellectual search for a philosophy of life and a course of "right action" in keeping with it, and ends his autobiography with a quotation from Fray Luis de Leon: "The beauty of life, he says, is nothing but this, that each should act in conformity with his nature and his business."

Mr. Maugham, an Englishman, born in Paris in 1874, for a time engaged in medicine before he became a professional writer and he often refers in his autobiography to the problem of evil as he encountered it in the forms of poverty, crime and disease. A philosophy of life, he found also, was implicit even in the most thoughtless. Whereas most people are permitted to lead their lives on the basis of a "confused body of ideas and feelings," in his case "I sought to make a pattern of mine and from an early age tried to find out what were the elements I had to deal with."

When his parents died he went to live in England with an uncle who was a clergyman, a childless man of 50, and although he became impressionably religious and even earnestly prayed and expected a cure for his stammering, he turned away from the Church of England upon his disillusionment with the clergy he had encountered, convinced that his uncle was a selfish man who cared for nothing but his own comfort and that his masters at King's School, also clergymen, were "stupid and irascible." He undertook a long course of reading

in religion, ethics and philosophy, and some of his later thoughts on
these subjects he has incorporated in The Summing Up.

. . . Every artist wishes to be believed in, but he is not angry
with those who will not accept the communication he offers. God
is not so reasonable. He craves so urgently to be believed in that
you might think he needed your belief in order to reassure himself
of his own existence. He promises rewards to those who believe
in him and threatens with horrible punishment those who do not.
For my part I cannot believe in a God who is angry with me because I do not believe in him. I cannot believe in a God who is
less tolerant than I. I cannot believe in a God who has neither
humor nor common sense. Plutarch long ago put the matter
succinctly. "I would much rather," he writes, "have men say of me
that there never was a Plutarch, nor is now, than to say that Plutarch is a man inconstant, fickle, easily moved to anger, revengeful
for trifling provocations and vexed at small things."

But though men have ascribed to God imperfections that they
would deplore in themselves that does not prove that God does
not exist. It proves only that the religions that men have accepted
are but blind alleys cut into an impenetrable jungle and none
of them leads to the heart of the great mystery. Arguments have
been adduced to prove the existence of God, and I will ask the
reader to have patience with me while I briefly consider them. One
of them assumes that man has an idea of a perfect being; and since
perfection includes existence a perfect being must exist. Another
maintains that every event has a cause and since the universe exists it must have a cause and this cause is the Creator. A third, the
argument from design, which Kant said was the clearest, oldest and
best suited to human reason, is thus stated by one of the characters in Hume's great dialogues "the order and arrangement of nature, the curious adjustment of final causes, the plain use and intention of every part and organ; all these bespeak in the clearest
language an intelligent cause or Author." But Kant showed con-
clusively that there was no more to be said in favor of this argu-

ment than in that of the other two. In their place he propounded another. In a few words it is to the effect that without God there is no guarantee that the sense of duty, which presupposes a free and real self, is not an illusion and therefore that it is morally necessary to believe in God. This has been generally thought more creditable to Kant's amiable nature than to his subtle intelligence. The argument which to me seems more persuasive than any of these is one that has now fallen out of favor. It is known as the proof *e consensu gentium*. It asserts that all men from the remotest origins have had some sort of belief in God and it is hard to think that a belief that has grown up with the human race, a belief that has been accepted by the wisest men, the sages of the East, the philosophers of Greece, the great Scholastics, should not have a foundation in fact. It has seemed to many instinctive and it may be (one can only say, it may be, for it is far from certain) that an instinct does not exist unless there is a possibility of its being satisfied. Experience has shown that the prevalence of a belief, no matter for how long it has been held, is no guarantee of its truth. It appears, then, that none of the arguments for the existence of God is valid. But of course you do not disprove his existence because you cannot prove it. Awe remains, man's sense of helplessness, and his desire to attain harmony between himself and the universe at large. These, rather than the worship of nature or of ancestors, magic or morality, are the sources of religion. There is no reason to believe that what you desire exists, but it is a hard saying that you have no right to believe what you cannot prove; there is no reason why you should not believe so long as you are aware that your belief lacks proof. I suppose that if your nature is such that you want comfort in your trials and a love that sustains and encourages you, you will neither ask for proofs nor have need of them. Your intuition suffices.

Mysticism is beyond proof and indeed demands no more than an indwelling conviction. It is independent of the creeds, for it finds sustenance in all of them, and it is so personal that it satisfies every idiosyncrasy. It is the feeling that the world we live in is but part of a spiritual universe and from this gains its significance: it is the sense of a present God who supports and comforts us. The mystics have narrated their experience so often, and in terms so similar, that I do not see how one can deny its reality. Indeed, I have myself had on one occasion an experience that I could only describe in the words the mystics have used to describe their ecstasy. I was sitting in one of the deserted mosques near Cairo when suddenly I felt myself rapt as Ignatius of Loyola was rapt when he sat by the river at Manresa. I had an overwhelming sense of the power and import of the universe, and an intimate, a shattering sense of communion with it. I could almost bring myself to say that I felt the presence of God. It is doubtless a common enough sensation and the mystics have been careful to ascribe value to it only if its influence was clearly seen in its results. I have a notion that it can be occasioned by other causes than the religious. The saints themselves have been willing to admit that the artists may have it, and love, as we know, can produce a state so like it that the mystics have found themselves drawn to use the phrases of lovers to express the beatific vision. I do not know that it is more mysterious than that condition, which the psychologists have not yet explained, when you have a strong feeling that you have at some past time been through an experience that you are in the act of undergoing. The ecstasy of the mystic is real enough, but it is valid only for himself. Mystic and sceptic agree in this, that at the end of all our intellectual efforts there remains a great mystery.

Faced with this, awed by the greatness of the universe and malcontent with what the philosophers told me, and what the saints, I have sometimes gone back, beyond Mohammed, Jesus and Buddha, beyond the gods of Greece, Jehovah and Baal, to the Brahma of the Upanishads. That spirit, if spirit it may be called, self-created and independent of all other existence, though all that exists, exists in it, the sole source of life in all that lives, has at least a grandeur that satisfies the imagination. But I have been busy with words too long not to be suspicious of them, and when I look at those I have just written I cannot but see that their meaning is tenuous. In religion above all things the only thing of use is an objective truth. The only God that is of use is a being who is personal, supreme and good, and whose existence is as certain as that two and two make four. I cannot penetrate the mystery. I remain an agnostic, and the practical outcome of agnosticism is that you act as though God did not exist.

THE SENSE OF WORSHIP

Victor Gollancz

Drawn from his autobiography, My Dear Timothy, which took the form of letters to his grandson, the following is an excerpt from one of the rare testaments of the contemporary spirit, that of Victor Gollancz, British man of letters, publisher, prominent before the war in consolidating British resistance to Hitler, organizer in 1942 of the National Committee for Rescue from Nazi Terror, from 1945 to 1949 Chairman of the Save Europe Now movement, recently Chairman of the (British) National Campaign for the Abolition of Capital Punishment, and at present Chairman of the Jewish Society for Human Service. In My Dear Timothy, Mr. Gollancz told of his boyhood in a strictly orthodox Jewish household, his education at Oxford, and his final acceptance of Christianity (in his own meaning of the word), a step deeply reflected upon and one he made without, in the end, discounting or disparaging the long traditions of his race, holding that "if traditional Judaism failed of its intention, the intention was of a beauty very rare, if not unexampled, in the history of religion."

My Dear Timothy:

. . . Now I must return to the Person of Christ. I find myself at once in the greatest difficulty; for after sitting a long day before my library fire and brooding over the past, I am no nearer disentangling what I felt at Oxford—about the Incarnation: it is of this that I must speak—from what I felt subsequently and what I feel today. All I can do, I think, is to tell you what I have gradually come to feel about it; and I ought to wait a bit, perhaps a week or so, before making the attempt, because although my emotion is very precise I do not at the moment see how I can formulate it.

A way to do so came to me on Monday night, about twenty-four hours after I had written the preceding paragraph, as I stood for a few minutes by the open window at Ladbroke Grove just before going to bed. I had switched off the light, and as I put my head out over the Square and smelled the leaves and the earth and the soft warm rain that was falling, I was moved once again, moved it may be for the millionth time, by an ineffable emotion of worship and gratitude. And as I lay in bed afterwards this is what I thought:

(1) I have always felt a vast, single, living bliss *behind* everything. I have always been certain it is *there*.

(2) I have always felt a life and a bliss *in* everything—I mean in every particular, in stones and chairs and mantelpieces and paper as well as in what is ordinarily called life: and it is through my meeting with these particulars, living and what are usually thought of as other than living, that I establish communion, feel myself mingled, with the bliss beyond.

(3) There is in me an imperative need, not only to establish communion, not only to merge myself, but also to worship. Or perhaps I should not speak of an imperative need, but should simply say that I *have* always worshipped—my life has been filled with a sense of worship, my being has been worshipful about the sum of things. I have worshipped the vast, single, living bliss beyond—that has been the central fact of my life; and I have worshipped it at once in and through the whole body of particulars, and in and through such single particulars—every single such single particular—as good deeds on the one hand and sticks and stones on the other.

(4) In religious language, I come to God through the world: in Platonic language I come to the Idea through the particulars. I don't mean that I deduce the Idea from the particulars: I mean that it is in the particulars that I feel and love the Idea. And Christ (whether

the historic Christ or the Christ in our hearts—I shall soon deal with that) is the Supreme Particular.

(5) I worship the beyond in and through the particulars, but do not worship the particulars themselves. Not the "ordinary" particulars. I do worship the Supreme Particular, as I worship the beyond. I worship Him as very close, very friendly, very accessible: I worship Him in the way Blake tells of, the way common, I suppose, to all Christians:

> "Then I see the Saviour over me,
> Spreading his beams of love, and dictating the words of this mild
>   song . . .
> I am not a God afar off, I am a brother and a friend;
> Within your bosoms I reside, and you reside in me;
> Lo! we are One; forgiving all Evil; Not seeking recompense . . ."

(6) Christ, the Supreme Particular, is, for me, a concrete individual, one Person, with a man's nature: but typical of men as no other man is typical. His nature is essentially ours—ours, not merely a model for ours (though it is that as well): which is another way of saying that our nature is essentially His—that this is what we really are, the rest being error and misunderstanding. To the extent to which we realise this—to the extent to which we "believe in" Him, we are in Him. He is each one of us—every man—all but completely released from bondage to error and unreality; to the error and unreality of self-centredness as opposed to communion, of what Blake calls "selfhood":

> "O Saviour, pour upon me thy Spirit of meekness and love,
>   Annihilate the Selfhood in me, be thou all my life,
>   Guide thou my hand which trembles exceedingly upon the rock of
>   ages."

"Be thou all my life"—that is the crux.

Most men, in this sense, do die in Adam, and those of them who "believe in" Christ do live again in Him.

And all this being so, worship by a man of Christ as the Supreme Particular is worship both of God and of humanity.

This treatment of the Incarnation is of course completely subjective, and will be criticised accordingly. You must decide for yourself whether the criticism is valid. What I have been saying, you may think, amounts to no more than this: that I have need of a Supreme Particular, and that when I call Christ that Particular all I mean is that Particular for me. Very well; I shall not demur. And if you go on to ask "But why Christ? Why not Krishna, or some other Avatar?", the answer is simple: on the boy born in Elgin Avenue to his own special heritage, and developing as he has slowly developed through a variety of specific experiences, Christ's teaching has made an impact as of the *utterly* true, Christ's personality has made an impact as of the *utterly* adorable, Christ's living and dying has made an impact as of the *utterly* good. I tremble as I add, but in honesty I must, that when I say utterly good I mean utterly good within human possibilities. (This is not such bad theology, either.) I do not regard Him as finally flawless. And even as I tremble I know that Christ will forgive me, for He would wish me to be divinely critical even about, perhaps specially about, Himself. But then again, I wonder: is it perhaps my own imperfection, my human imperfection, that allows me to see imperfection where nothing but perfection exists?

So my Christ, my Supreme Particular, could be no other, if I was to have one, than Christ. If I had been an Indian, Sri Krishna might have made the same impact on me. For I think that there are several Christs, but only one for each person. There are Christs, perhaps, not our Christ and yet our Christ, on earths and in dimensions of which we know nothing:

"With this ambiguous earth
His dealings have been told us. These abide:
The signal to a maid, the human birth,
The lesson, and the young Man crucified.

"But not a star of all
The innumerable host of stars has heard
How He administered this terrestrial ball.
Our race have kept their Lord's entrusted Word.

"Of His earth-visiting feet
None knows the secret, cherished, perilous,
The terrible, shamefast, frightened, whispered, sweet,
Heart-shattering secret of His way with us.

"No planet knows that this
Our wayside planet, carrying land and wave,
Love and life multiplied, and pain and bliss,
Bears, as chief treasure, one forsaken grave.

"Nor, in our little day,
May His devices with the heavens be guessed,
His pilgrimage to thread the Milky Way,
Or His bestowals there be manifest.

"But, in the eternities,
Doubtless we shall compare together, hear
A million alien Gospels, in what guise
He trod the Pleiades, the Lyre, the Bear.

"O be prepared, my soul!
To read the inconceivable, to scan
The million forms of God those stars unroll
When, in our turn, we show to them a Man." *

What a God it is who has given us, not only the "ordinary" particulars, but a Supreme Particular! And what a universe it is that can boast, not of one Supreme Particular, but of many!

Being the sort of person I am, if Christ had not existed I might almost have been tempted to invent Him. It may even be (though I don't believe it, Toynbee's great excursus notwithstanding) that,

* By Alice Meynell.

in one sense, men *have* invented Him: it may be, I mean, that the Gospel story is a mere amalgam of various happenings that have occurred, or have been imagined to occur, in many different places at many different times. Well, what of it? Then God, we should have to say, has put a Person, a Life and a Death into human consciousness, as a paradigm of the Way. On the one reading (to express it in its orthodox form) God was born, by God's grace, very man in a manger: on the other, God is born, by God's grace, very man in men's hearts: and I cannot for the life of me see why the one Christ should be any less "real," any less to be worshipped, than the other.

Or we should have to say, looking at it now from a slightly different angle, that out of the depths of its consciousness—out of the love and understanding in its heart—humanity has bodied forth a myth that incarnates the ultimate truth. Christ would then exist— would always have existed, would forever exist ("Before Abraham was, I am") as essential, as Divine, Humanity. Is that non-existence?

Beethoven "invented" the Quartet in C Sharp Minor, opus 131: that is to say, God put it into Beethoven's consciousness, with Beethoven's co-operation. Doesn't it then exist? Isn't it "real"? Listen to it, my dear Timothy, next time you have the chance (for you are certain to love music) and answer me.

I was delighted, the other day, to come across this passage in a book by Sri Aurobindo, the Hindu philosopher and saint who recently died:

"Such controversies as the one that has raged in Europe over the historicity of Christ would seem to a spiritually-minded Indian largely a waste of time; he would concede to it a considerable historical, but hardly any religious importance; for what does it matter in the end whether a Jesus son of the carpenter Joseph was actually born in Nazareth or Bethlehem, lived and taught and was done to death on a real or trumped-up charge of sedition, so long as we can know by spiritual experience the inner Christ, live uplifted in the light of His teaching and escape from the yoke of the natural

Law by that atonement of man with God of which the crucifixion is the symbol? If the Christ, God made man, lives within our spiritual being, it would seem to matter little whether or not a son of Mary physically lived and suffered and died in Judea."

No, it would matter a great deal, because we are flesh and blood, and to part with a Christ of our own flesh and blood would be grievous. And yet in another sense I would go even a little further than Aurobindo. Whether or not the Incarnation—unique or otherwise—is, in the popular sense, a fact, scepticism about it would appear to be more reasonable if Christ is "historical," as you know I believe Him to be, than if He is not. If He is "historical," there is nothing far-fetched in the idea that people have drawn false deductions from a remarkable life and death. But if the Gospel narrative is a myth, it is difficult to understand how it can have come into being except by way of explaining what would then be, so to speak, a fact in its own right: the incarnation of God—his incarnation, unique or otherwise, as Christ—in innumerable men's hearts. Roughly by the same token, various parallelisms—and in particular the recurrent "dying God" beliefs—would appear to confirm Christianity, at least in one interpretation of it, rather than the reverse.

Such, then, is what I feel about the Incarnation: a matter partly of knowledge—of immediate experience—and partly of mood, and not at all one of "faith" or dogmatic precision. And it's no good people telling me that it's all very vague (simpletons!) and that I *ought* to have dogmas. I am merely describing. It is not a question of what ought to be, but of what is. The reality, for me, is that I adore Christ. Whatever may be the truth about the Gospel story, whatever may be the metaphysics of the matter, He lives and reigns for me eternally; and whether or not I should hesitate to call Him Lord, I can assuredly call Him Master.

MY RELIGION

Helen Keller

Helen Keller, who has lived and worked for more than 75 years deaf and blind as a result of an illness suffered at nineteen months, was born at Tuscumbia, Alabama in 1880, a descendant on her father's side from a colonial governor of Virginia and related on her mother's side to the Adams and Everett families of New England. She began her education under a remarkable woman, Miss Sullivan (Mrs. John A. Macy) in 1887 and continued as her student until Miss Sullivan's death in 1936. What she has done since fills a column in Who's Who. Besides her innumerable activities for various societies for the blind and deaf, her lectures on behalf of the handicapped in all parts of the world, she is the author of a number of books many of which in one way or another have detailed the methods by which a handicapped person participates in the fullness of life. Her most recent venture, at the age of 76, was a six-nation tour of Iceland, Finland, Sweden, Norway, Denmark and Switzerland as a counselor on international relations for the American Foundation for Overseas Blind and for the State Department's International Education Exchange Service. When at home she lives in Westport, Conn.

Once affliction was looked upon as a punishment from God—a burden to be borne passively and piously. The only idea of helping the victims of misfortune was to shelter them and leave them to meditate and live as contentedly as possible in the valley of the shadow. But now we understand that a sequestered life without aspiration enfeebles the spirit. It is exactly the same as with the body. The muscles must be used, or they lose their strength. If we do not go out of our limited experience somehow and use our memory, understanding, and sympathy, they become inactive. It is by fighting the limitations, temptations, and failures of the world that we reach our highest possibilities. That is what Swedenborg* calls renouncing the world and worshipping God.

Sick or well, blind or seeing, bond or free, we are here for a purpose and however we are situated, we please God better with useful deeds than with many prayers or pious resignation. The temple or church is empty unless the good of life fills it. It is not the stone walls that make it small or large, but the brave soul's light shining round about. The altar is holy if only it represents the altar of our heart upon which we offer the only sacrifices ever commanded—the love that is stronger than hate and the faith that overcometh doubt.

A simple, childlike faith in a Divine Friend solves all the problems that come to us by land or sea. Difficulties meet us at every turn. They are the accompaniment of life. They result from combinations of character and individual idiosyncrasies. The surest way to meet them is to assume that we are immortal, and that we have a Friend who "slumbers not, nor sleeps," and who watches over us and guides us—if we but let Him. With this thought strongly intrenched in our inmost being, we can do almost anything we wish and need not limit the things we think. We may help ourselves to all the beauty of the universe that we can hold. For every hurt there is recompense of tender sympathy. Out of pain grow the violets of patience and sweetness, the vision of the Holy Fire that touched the lips of Isaiah and kindled his life into spirit, and the contentment that comes with the evening star. The marvellous richness of human experience would lose something of rewarding joy if there were no limitations to overcome. The hilltop hour would not be half so wonderful if there were no dark valley to traverse.

* Emanuel Swedenborg, 1688-1772, Swedish scientist, philosopher and theologian.

I have never believed that my limitations were in any sense punishments or accidents. If I had held such a view, I could never have exerted the strength to overcome them. It has always seemed to me that there is a very special significance in the words of "the Epistle of Paul to the Hebrew": "If we are chastened, God dealeth with us as with sons." Swedenborg's teachings bear me out in this view. He defines the greatly misunderstood word chastening or chastisement, not as punishment, but as training, discipline, refinement of the soul.

The *True Christian Religion* is full of stimuli for faith in our God-given powers and self-activity. The chapters "Faith" and "Free-will" are a powerful declaration that we should never surrender to misfortunes or circumstances or even to our faults hopelessly, passively—as if we were but carved images with our hands hanging down, waiting for God's Grace to put us into motion. We should give no quarter to spiritual slavery. We should take the initiative, look into ourselves fearlessly, search out new ideas of what to do, and ways to develop our will-power. Then God will give us enough light and love for all our needs.

Now, limitations of all kinds are forms of chastening to encourage self-development and true freedom. They are tools put into our hands to hew away the stone and flint which keep the higher gifts hidden away in our being. They tear away the bandage of indifference from our eyes, and we behold the burdens others are carrying, and we learn to help them by yielding to the dictates of a pitying heart.

The example of the newly blinded man is so concrete, I wish to use it as a type for all life-training. When he first loses his sight, he thinks there is nothing left for him but heartache and despair. He feels shut out from all that is human. Life to him is like the ashes on a cold hearth. The fire of ambition is quenched. The light of hope is gone out. The objects in which he once took delight seem to thrust out sharp edges at him as he gropes his way about. Even those who love him act unwittingly as an irritant to his feelings because he can no longer give them the support of his labor. Then comes some wise teacher and friend and assures him he can work with his hands and to a considerable degree train his hearing to take the place of sight. Often the stricken man does not believe it, and in his despair interprets it as a mockery. Like a drowning person he strikes blindly at anyone that tries to save him. Nevertheless, the sufferer must be urged onward in spite of himself, and when he once realizes that he can put himself again in connection with the world, and fulfil tasks worthy of a man, a being he did not dream of before unfolds itself within him. If he is wise, he discovers at last that happiness has very little to do with outward circumstances, and he treads his dark way with a firmer will than he ever felt in the light.

Likewise those who have been mentally blinded "in the gradual furnace of the world" can, and must, be pressed to look for new capabilities within themselves and work out new ways to happiness. They may even resent faith that expects nobler things from them. They say in effect, "I will be content if you take me for what I am —dull, or mean, or hard, or selfish." But it is an affront to them and to the eternal dignity of man so to acquiesce. How often it comes over us that there is much in us which our nearest friends cannot know—more than we dare or care or are able to lay bare, more of feeling, more of power, more of manhood. How little we know ourselves! We need limitations and temptations to open our inner selves, dispel our ignorance, tear off disguises, throw down old idols, and destroy false standards. Only by such rude awakenings can we be led to dwell in a place where we are less cramped, less hindered by the ever-insistent External. Only then do we discover a new capacity and appreciation of goodness and beauty and truth.

From such experience we may gain a wonderful interpretation of the Lord's words: "Verily, verily, I say unto you, he that receiveth whomsoever I send receiveth me." We may know that in every limitation we overcome and in the higher ideals we thus attain the whole kingdom of Love and Wisdom is present. In this way we learn that the real way to grow is by aspiring beyond our limitations, by wishing sublimely for great things and striving to achieve them. We grow in our increasing consciousness of the deeper meaning of the outer life in which we have always lived.

The eye grows by learning to see more in particular objects. To man's physical sight the earth looks flat, and the stars are the same to us that they were to the ancients. Yet science has opened up infinite new wonders and glories in these phenomena! A child sees in the things about him only what he wants or does not want, but when a Newton recognizes the falling of the apple as the expression of a universal force in Nature, he sees far beyond ordinary sight. It is the same with our spirits. We grow as we discern more fully the possibilities of new life wrapped up in daily contacts. But when we forget or ignore this vital fact, the senses lead us astray. That is why limitations are necessary to bring before us the greatness of inner life offered us in the circumstances of our lives, and show us our God-given opportunities.

The constant service of Swedenborg lies in such thoughts as these. He shows us that in every event and every limitation we have a choice, and that to choose is to create. We can decide to let our trials crush us, or we can convert them to new forces of good. We can drift along with general opinion and tradition, or we can throw ourselves upon the guidance of the soul within and steer courageously toward truth. We cannot tell from the outside whether our experiences are really blessings or not. They are cups of poison, or cups of healthful life, according to what we ourselves put into them. The choices offered us are never so much between what we may or may not do, as between the principles from which we act when we are thwarted and limited. Earth is not intended to be an altogether delightful abode any more than it is to be a place of wrath. Since the soil brings forth thistles, and roses have thorns, why should man's life not have its trials. It is not strange, or cruel. It is the urge of God that impels us to enlarge our lives and keep strong for that higher destiny which cannot be accomplished within the limits of earth. Only by striving for what is beyond us do we win expansion and joy. Let us, then, take up that limitation which each one has, and follow the example of Him who bore upon his frail human shoulders the cross of the world, that He might become a luminous and inspiring influence, communicating life-giving thoughts and desires to the weak, the tempted, and the despondent.

I do not know if it is the "mystic" sense I possess; but certainly it is perceptive. It is the faculty that brings distant objects within the cognizance of the blind so that even the stars seem to be at our very door. This sense relates me to the spiritual world. It surveys the limited experience I gain from an imperfect touch world, and presents it to my mind for spiritualization. This sense reveals the Divine to the human in me, it forms a bond between earth and the Great Beyond, between now and eternity, between God and man. It is speculative, intuitive, reminiscent. There is not only an objective physical world, but also an objective spiritual world. The spiritual has an outside as well as an inside, just as the physical has an inside and an outside. Each has its own phase of reality. There is no antagonism between these two planes of life, except when the material is used without regard to the spiritual which lies within and above it. The distinction between them is explained by Swedenborg in his theory of discrete degrees. He illustrates this by saying that the physical world is perceived by a sensory apparatus that is of the same substance as the physical world, while the spiritual world is perceived by a sensory apparatus that is of the same substance as that of the spiritual world.

My life is so complicated by a triple handicap of blindness, deafness, and imperfect speech that I cannot do the simplest thing without thought and effort to rationalize my experiences. If I employed this mystic sense constantly without trying to understand the outside world, my progress would be checked, and everything would fall about me in chaos. It is easy for me to mix up dreams and reality, the spiritual and the physical which I have not properly visualized, and without the inner sense I could not keep them apart. So even if I commit errors in forming concepts of color, sound, light, and intangible phenomena, I must always try to preserve equilibrium between my outer and inner life. Neither can I use my sense of touch without regard to the experience of others and respect for it. I should otherwise go astray or else go round and round in a blind circle. I have always been especially helped by this sentence from Swedenborg's "Arcana Coelestia":

"It is the interior man that sees and perceives what goes on without him, and from this interior source the sense-experience has its life; for from no other than this subjective source is there any faculty of feeling or sensation. But the fallacy that the sense comes from without is of such a nature and so common that the natural mind cannot rid itself of it, nor even the rational mind, until it can think abstractly from sense."

When the sun of consciousness first shone upon me, behold a miracle! The stock of my young life which had perished, steeped in the waters of knowledge grew again, budded again, was sweet again with the blossoms of childhood! Down in the depths of my being I cried, "It is good to be alive!" I held out two trembling hands to life, and in vain silence would impose dumbness upon me henceforth! The world to which I awoke was still mysterious; but there were hope and love and God in it, and nothing else mattered. Is it not possible that our entrance into heaven may be like this experience of mine?

Several years later my life enlarged when I learned to speak. I can never cease to marvel and be excited by that event of thirty-six years ago, it stands out so isolated, miraculous, baffling. Think of transforming mute, soulless air into speech in the midst of midnight silence. Literally, I had no concepts of speech, and my touch did not suffice to convey to me the thousand fine vibrations of spoken words. Without physical hearing I had to exert the utmost thought of which I was capable until I succeeded in making myself not only heard but understood! It is only by sheer force of mind even now that I keep my speech anywhere near intelligible. When I speak best, I am at a loss to fix that degree of perfection because I cannot fully sense the tones going forth from my lips. What surprises me is not that I fail, but that the subconscious part or the spirit enters so often into my clumsy speech, and my friends say earnestly, "Why can you not talk as well as that always?" If I could develop that psychic power more fully, I feel sure that my victory would be complete. The pain and disappointment I have endured are incalculable; but they are a price worth paying for the joy I have in being able to keep this living bond between the outer world and myself. As I learned to articulate and to put feeling into what I

said I sense more and more the miracle of all time and eternity—
the reality of thought! Thought, out of which are wrought books,
philosophies, sciences, civilizations, and the joy and the woe of the
human race! Even as if the lonely blind man who has travelled
many years in midnight gloom should suddenly stumble upon the
sun and all the glories of a sunlit world, so it was with me when the
light of understanding flooded my mind, and I realized that words
were precious symbols of knowledge, thought, and happiness. The
normal human being is familiar with the use of words, and he cannot remember when he first began to use them. I have had a different experience. I was nearly seven years old when I began to
acquire language, and I remember distinctly the feelings I experienced. I learned each word as a hand sensation years before I
learned the sound of it. With most people the sound and the perception of the meanings of the word are, I suppose, simultaneous.
The significance of thought-symbols came to me suddenly.

My teacher, Anne Mansfield Sullivan, had been with me nearly a
month, and she had taught me the names of a number of objects.
She put them into my hand, spelled their names on her fingers and
helped me to form the letters; but I had not the faintest idea what
I was doing. I do not know what I thought. I have only a tactual
memory of my fingers going through those motions, and changing
from one position to another. One day she handed me a cup and
spelled the word. Then she poured some liquid into the cup and
formed the letters w-a-t-e-r. She says I looked puzzled, and persisted
in confusing the two words, spelling cup for water and water for
cup. Finally I became angry because Miss Sullivan kept repeating
the words over and over again. In despair she led me out to the ivy-
covered pump-house and made me hold the cup under the spout
while she pumped. With her other hand she spelled w-a-t-e-r emphatically. I stood still, my whole body's attention fixed on the motions of her fingers as the cool stream flowed over my hand. All at
once there was a strange stir within me—a misty consciousness, a
sense of something remembered. It was as if I had come back to
life after being dead! I understood that what my teacher was doing
with her fingers meant that cold something that was rushing over

my hand, and that it was possible for me to communicate with other people by these signs. It was a wonderful day never to be forgotten! Thoughts that ran forward and backward came to me quickly—thoughts that seemed to start in my brain and spread all over me. Now I see it was my mental awakening. I think it was an experience somewhat in the nature of a revelation. I showed immediately in many ways that a great change had taken place in me. I wanted to learn the name of every object I touched, and before night I had mastered thirty words. Nothingness was blotted out! I felt joyous, strong, equal to my limitations! Delicious sensations rippled through me, and sweet, strange things that were locked up in my heart began to sing. That first revelation was worth all those years I had spent in dark, soundless imprisonment. That word "water" dropped into my mind like the sun in a frozen winter world. Before that supreme event there was nothing in me except the instinct to eat and drink and sleep. My days were a blank without past, present, or future, without hope or anticipation, without interest or joy.

> It was not night—it was not day.
> But vacancy absorbing space,
> And fixedness, without a place:
> There were no stars—no earth—no time—
> No check—no change—no good—no crime.

It was but a step for me from the wonders of nature to the wonders of the spirit. When Swedenborg's message was revealed to me, it was another precious gift added to life. I will try to clothe my emotion in words. It was as if light came where there had been no light before, the intangible world became a shining certainty. The horizons of my mind widened to bright destinies where the race would still be swift, the battle strong.

Heaven, as Swedenborg portrays it, is not a mere collection of radiant ideas, but a practical, liveable world. It should never be forgotten that death is not the end of life, but only one of its most important experiences. In the great silence of my thoughts all those whom I have loved on earth, whether near or far, living or dead, live and have their own individuality, their own dear ways and charm. At any moment I can bring them around me to cheer my loneliness. It would break my heart if any barrier could prevent them from coming to me. But I know there are two worlds—one we can measure with line and rule, and the other we can feel with our hearts and intuitions. Swedenborg makes the future life not only conceivable, but desirable. His message to the living who meet the might of death with its attendant separation and sorrow sweeps across the heart of humanity like some sweet breath from God's Presence. We can now meet death as Nature does, in a blaze of glory, marching to the grave with a gay step, wearing our brightest thoughts and most brilliant anticipations, as Nature arrays herself in garments of gold, emerald, and scarlet, as if defying death to rob her of immortality.

The difficulty man has in believing this arises not so much from the unprovableness of it as from his own incredulous attitude. His egoistic desires tend to overwhelm his spiritual strivings, or, perhaps, it is nearer the truth to say, his inner faculties have not yet reached the point of conscious experience. They are still too feeble to function effectively. He is unable to realize the pernicious influence of acquisitiveness upon his character. He does not understand the true significance of his spiritual being. He believes that only material things are real. Our civilization is a failure in the degree to which we are indifferent to the teachings of philosophers like Swedenborg and the visions of the great thinkers of the world.

With thoughts wide as the universe, deliberate, with wisdom in his hands, Swedenborg tells us how angels led him from realm to realm of the spirit-world, showed him the life that comes after death and the reality of things immortal. Angels were his teachers, his guides. He lodged his soul in heaven; he sensed the magnitude of the Divine Providence, the tremendous circumstance of life eternal. He was permitted to walk the sky and the winding course of stars.

I am aware that some learned critics will break me on the wheel of their disdain. They will try to mend my poor philosophy on the anvil of their keen mirth with the hammer of reasons culled from science. "All creation crowns itself in this invisible atom of matter.

It is the beginning and the end." Perhaps; but there is still a dew-drop in the lily's cup; there is fragrance in the heart of the rose, and under a leaf a bird folds its wings! I cannot understand the poor faith that fears to look into the eyes of death. Faith that is vulnerable in the presence of death is a frail reed to lean upon. With steadfast thought I follow sight beyond all seeing, until my soul stands up in spiritual light and cries, "Life and death are one." When I review my life, it seems to me that my most precious obligations are to those whom I have never seen. My dearest intimacies are those of the mind, my most loyal and helpful friends are those of the spirit.

I cannot imagine myself without religion. I could as easily fancy a living body without a heart. To one who is deaf and blind, the spiritual world offers no difficulty. Nearly everything in the natural world is as vague, as remote from my senses as spiritual things seem to the minds of most people. I plunge my hands deep into my large Braille volumes containing Swedenborg's teachings, and withdraw them full of the secrets of the spiritual world. The inner, or "mystic," sense, if you like, gives me vision of the unseen. My mystic world is lovely with trees and clouds and stars and eddying streams I have never "seen." I am often conscious of beautiful flowers and birds and laughing children where to my seeing associates there is nothing. They skeptically declare that I see "light that never was on sea or land." But I know that their mystic sense is dormant, and that is why there are so many barren places in their lives. They prefer "facts" to vision. They want a scientific demonstration and they can have it. Science with untiring patience traces man back to the ape, and rests content. It is out of this ape that God creates the seer, and science meets spirit as life meets death, and life and death are one.

PERSONAL SURVIVAL: DO WE LIVE AFTER DEATH?

Anthony Standen

The writer of the following essay, taken from a book not yet published at the time of this compilation, is a scientist and a humanist, Anthony Standen, born 1906 of a Boston American mother and an English father. He was educated in England (Wellington and Oxford) and the Massachusetts Institute of Technology. He is an American citizen living in New York where he has just completed several years' work as assistant editor of the Encyclopedia of Chemical Technology, which appeared from 1947 to 1956 in fifteen volumes. He is the author of the book Science is a Sacred Cow, and an earlier book Insect Invaders. He has a degree in entomology but scientifically is primarily a chemist and was on the research staff of the Imperial Chemical Industries for which he did insecticide work in Spain and Brazil.

For three years he taught at St. John's College, Annapolis, Md., the school of the "100 Great Books," and his reading there stimulated him to a number of articles in Life and other magazines on insects, life, death and man's relation to science and the world around him.

Man is a rational animal. That is a very ancient belief, dignified by the adherence of most of the greatest minds of classical antiquity and of Christianity.

It provokes a storm of protest nowadays—for it is regarded as "old fashioned." Probably there was never a time when people were so concerned to convince others, and themselves, of their own irrationality.

"But most people are terribly irrational!" the protest goes. And the speaker will quote the behavior of his brother, or sister, or wife (or husband) or offspring, or of strangers, and will easily make a good case for irrational behavior, sometimes.

But the phrase does not mean "and people's behavior is calculated to their own best advantage, all the time." It means no more than "capable of rationality." It refers to no more than the ability to have an abstract conception, and to assemble thoughts in a logical order, even if only once in a while. This is far more than the beasts can ever do.

But if man has a rational soul, a host of enormous questions crop up in front of us at once. One of them, certainly not the least, is the really tremendous question—Does the soul survive after death?

It has been the all but universal opinion of mankind that the answer to this question is yes. On the other hand, all the "trends" and "influences" from the not-too-distant past, beginning with rationalism, going through evolution, to psychology of all kinds, have been making an indirect but concentrated onslaught directed precisely against this thought. But it is by no means necessary to follow modern trends and influences; they use reason at times, but they are capable of going flatly against reason when it suits them. Often the best thing to do is to go flatly against the trends and influences.

In the first place, is there anything *contrary to reason,* and therefore impossible, about the idea of a man's soul surviving the death of his body? Is it thinkable at all that there should be a soul without a body? If a glass tumbler is smashed, or a lead soldier melted down, the shape is destroyed entirely, for there is no such thing as "shape" by itself, there are only shaped pieces of matter. Is the soul a thing like "shape" that cannot possibly exist by itself, or is a "soul" the kind of thing that *could* exist entirely by itself?

The best way to think of this is to think of what a spirit (that is to say, a disembodied soul) could possibly be doing. For if there were nothing, nothing whatever, that a spirit could *do*, it could scarcely be said to *exist*.

There is one simple answer to this right away—a disembodied spirit could play chess! (Not a very inspiring ability, admittedly, but for the time being we are only clearing the ground.) Chess is not really played with a board and wooden, material chess men. Chess is played in the "head" (really the mind). Skilled players can dispense with the board entirely. And if chess is too much for you—almost anybody can play tic-tac-toe without pencil and paper, and with his eyes shut. But in sharp contrast to this, you cannot play a ball game of any kind, football, baseball, basketball, volley ball or any other kind of ball, without a physical ball. Nor could you challenge a competitor to race a hundred-yard dash in a spiritual manner.

Animals cannot play chess, or even tic-tac-toe. Whether they can play ball games is extremely doubtful. The nearest approach to it is polo ponies. By long experience they can often anticipate their riders' wishes, and may even become more adept than their masters at judging the speed and direction of an approaching ball. Polo, like all other games, is played in accordance with "the rules": the ponies become accustomed to the way of playing the game, but they do not understand the rules. If a change were made, you would not be able to *explain* the new rules to your string of ponies!

But since we have seen there is at least something, even if it is trivial and unimportant, that a man could do without his body, then there is nothing inherently impossible about a disembodied spirit, or the soul of a man surviving the death of the body. But just as it would be exceedingly disappointing, and hardly worth talking about, if the souls of the dead could do nothing but play endless games of chess or tic-tac-toe, according to their ability, or perhaps rehearse the multiplication table, or extract square roots, so also is it an empty thought, a hardly thinkable thought. It is not even thinkable that any entity should be able to "grasp," intellectually, abstract ideas, and yet not be able to *do* anything about them. If we survive the death of our bodies with intelligence, we also survive with will.

The question of human survival, with intelligence and will, becomes clearer by comparison with the same question, referred to animals. Animals have will, of a kind, too. They *want* things. There is no question that a pet dog *wants* its food when it is hungry; it wants out, or in; it is pleased to see its master, and may be angry if a bone is taken away from it. Does this qualify the animals for eternal life? For the matter of that, a dog is a fairly smart animal, as animals go. It is smarter than, say, a beetle, and most beetles are at least smart enough to get out of the way if you try to catch them. There is certainly something, call it "smartness" even if it is not pure intelligence, that a dog has more of, and other animals a little of. Does this make it thinkable that the animal soul should survive after the death of the animal?

The question again is, What could a disembodied animal soul be *doing?* It couldn't want out, or in, because it wouldn't *be* either in, or out, physically. A live dog may want a real bone, but a bodiless dog couldn't want the abstract idea of a bone. All of the dog's desires are directed to *things*. It is the same with the dog's "understanding," as far as it goes. A dog recognizes familiar scenes and objects, and knows by experience that when his master reaches for his hat, he is probably going out. A polo pony recognizes familiar situations in a game that it has played dozens of times before. The dog recognizes smells, and perhaps realizes that a bone that has been hidden away for several days smells even better than a fresh one. The dog, too, may like fighting, and may snarl in his dreams at the thought of a good scrap. In all these things that the animals do, their *senses* are involved. But one cannot imagine the ghost of an animal doing anything that involves the senses, because actual physical eyes, ears, noses, etc., are needed in order to sense anything.

Now we have all the animal abilities, and we can recognize familiar scenes and smells, and we want things that the animals want, food and sensual gratifications. We also have other abilities, and it is important to see the immense difference. We can think of a genuine abstraction, such as "perfection" or "existence," or if you like, "shape" which is clearly distinct from "color." When we do this the senses are not involved in the least. It is true that they were involved, in arriving at these abstractions originally, but the abstractions that we have formed are removed from matter. To see, feel, or taste anything, there must be a physical object and a physical interaction between it and our physical body. But to understand "shape" or "color" or "existence" does not involve any physical object, or any physical interaction. It is not a physical, material process at all. It is quite strictly a spiritual action.

It is the same with willing as with understanding. We can will "spiritually" as well as sensually. ("Spiritually" means, in effect, "away from matter.") We can will "the good" entirely in the abstract. We can will "justice tempered by mercy"—and no animal is capable of willing this. We can will "tolerance" or "cooperation," which are entirely different from wanting a beef steak or a cocktail. We can will forgetfulness, or forgiveness. We could will vengeance —deliberately willing harm to someone, and not willing any particular harm, such as pinching him or frying him in deep fat, but any kind of harm, willed as revenge for some act of his. We can also will love and though there are many kinds of love, at least one of them is an act of will, directed to another person, and entirely abstracted from material considerations. It is, in the highest sense of the word, a spiritual act.

For the word "spirit" or "spiritual," like the word "soul," is commonly used with much less than its full meaning, but with, as it were, the better part of its meaning. "Soul" is used almost invariably to mean "rational soul" or "human soul." Animals, and also plants, have souls too (according to the usage of the word "soul," started by Aristotle, and continued in the Christian tradition). But they only have non-rational souls, and these are so much less important as to be hardly worth mentioning. "Spiritual" is often used to mean almost the same as "Divine," and certainly God is a Spirit, since He is not material. But for the same reason the devil, if he exists, is a spiritual being. A mathematician, when he thinks of space in four, five or six or more dimensions, does so in a spiritual manner. But you can't eat apple pie spiritually. You can't want apple pie spiritually, even if you want it not for yourself but for someone else. But if you *love* someone else, apple pie or no apple pie, if you wish well, or will the Good, for someone else, that is a spiritual act. You could do it without a body. You could do it after death. And this, at last, shows us that survival after death is by no means an empty thought. It is entirely possible, and it is in the highest degree meaningful.

But to show that a thing is possible is not the same as to prove that it does happen. The next step is to examine the reasons for believing that the soul really does survive. There are several reasons for believing this. Some of them have been beautifully expressed by Plato, but Plato or no Plato, they are to be taken for what they are worth in themselves. Some of them are not absolutely watertight and conclusive, against anyone who argues the other side as firmly and strongly as he can, but they are to be taken together and cumulatively. Moreover, anyone who argues the other side with exceptional determination is in reality expressing his own wishful thinking, and not, by the way, that he wishes to disbelieve in personal immortality (on the contrary, his real wish is to believe in it) but that he wants to be quite sure that he is not being seduced into this belief by inadequate arguments.

In the first place, the enormous prevalence of the belief in the immortality of the soul is strongly indicative. *All* religions believe in it, explicitly or implicitly, in some form or other. They do not agree as to what happens to the soul after death; Mohammedans have a very explicit kind of heaven, while Buddhists have the soul incarnated again either in human form or as an animal. The Chinese venerate their ancestors, which would not be worth doing if they supposed that their ancestors had vanished, at death, like a candle flame when it is blown out. Prehistoric men buried their dead with weapons, garments or little bits of food, and present day primitive peoples, although they differ tremendously in their ways of life, agree together in some sort of "animism" or belief in spirits, including ghosts of the dead (sometimes extended to animals). And in this country, here and now, at any rate a very large number of people believe in the immortality of the soul, so that, taking all times and places into account, those who do not are most decidedly in a minority.

What are we to make of this near-agreement, this near-unanimity? There are two ways of looking at it. One is to say that prehistoric men and primitive tribes don't count, while among more civilized races, such as our own, there are many people who are misled by "superstition." According to this view, it is hard to explain why, if we are such advanced, civilized people, so many of us should fall for such irrational superstition. The other way is based on a higher opinion of the general intelligence of mankind, and suggests that what vast masses of people have believed throughout all ages is quite likely to be true—at any rate that the near-unanimity in this opinion is a definite argument for it, not against it.

It is not a conclusive argument, quite clearly. There was a time, long ago, when one could have appealed in the same way to the general opinion of mankind to support the belief that the earth is flat. One would have been discussing, at that time, a matter to which nobody had given very much thought. Probably the first to enquire seriously about it were the Greeks, and they soon discovered clear and cogent reasons for believing that the earth is round, not flat. At any time in the interval between the ancient Greeks and not so long ago, if you had taken a census you might have found flat-earthers in the majority, but they would have been mostly people who had not thought about it, and would not be able to produce any arguments to refute a round-earther, while those few who had carefully studied the subject knew the reasons why we know the earth is round. The immortality of the soul presents another picture, for it has never been a matter of indifference. Believers in it have been in the majority at all times, and they included those who have thought about the subject most carefully. Unbelievers in the immortality of the soul are sometimes intelligent men who have given thought to the matter, but they are not able to produce one single cogent argument against it.

A more cogent argument, and a more subtle one, starts not from the all-but-universal belief in the immortality of the soul, but from the universal longing for it. We cannot believe without strain in our own destruction. People who say they are convinced that, when they die, they fade into nothingness as if they had never been, say so either with a certain gritting-the-teeth intensity or with a touch of wistful resignation. Everything in the entire universe tends to its own preservation. Animals act to maintain their lives with their animal will (which is not a free will), and even inanimate objects, with no will at all, tend to maintain themselves in being. (A principle of physics, known as Le Chatelier's law, formulates this: when an external cause acts on a system, the system reacts in such a way as to counteract the external cause. For example, when you compress the air in a bicycle pump, the pressure of the air increases, thereby opposing your compressive force; or when you boil water, the vaporization of the water absorbs heat, thereby opposing the tendency of the applied heat to raise the temperature.) Our own bodies, as physical objects, act in accordance with Le Chatelier's law; with our animal will we act for the preservation of our lives, and with our own special, human, free will we *will* (that is, we want, we desire, we long for) our own continued existence, alive if possible, but at any rate as disembodied souls, even if the body should perish. Furthermore, we will and yearn very strongly for the survival after death of our loved ones. Only a suicide wills his own destruction, and he is considered an irregular, abnormal, thwarted human being, for the desire to live, and to go on existing after death, is utterly normal and natural to mankind.

Now if the desire for immortality is *natural* to everyone, we can draw conclusions from this. For, considering every other desire that is natural to everyone—food and drink, and a certain amount of the pleasures of life, including love and/or sex—we can note that our wise Creator has provided us with the *possibility* of satisfying these desires. So it would be surprising if this other universal natural desire had been implanted in us, without any possibility of ever fulfilling it! It would be more than surprising, it would be horrible. For it would mean that the Creator, after giving to us, as He does to the animals, all manner of material pleasures, both the desire and the means of satisfying the desire, had made us (but not the beasts) of such a nature that we can exist without our bodies, had given us enough intelligence to see that this is so, and had implanted in our breasts a longing for the life after death—and then denied it to us! It would mean that the Creator granted us all that is temporal and trivial, and denied us the eternal after permitting us to see it! It would impute to God a vile malicious practical joke! And so, if you think you can believe that human beings, when they die, vanish into nothingness, you will do well not to face the logical consequences of this belief, for they would be too horrible to contemplate. You must either refuse to bring your reason to bear on this important question, or be an intellectual masochist. But if you believe that our intelligence was given to us not in vain but with the intention that we should use it, and that it is to help us, not mislead us, (maybe this is an act of faith, but if it is, go ahead and make it) you will have to conclude that our souls are immortal, and that there is such a thing as survival after death.

This argument is subtle, and attempts have often been made to bring it to ridicule by showing that modifications of it—in reality caricatures of it—lead to absurd results. The argument emphatically does not mean that anything that you want you may have. It does not mean that anything you would like to believe necessarily is true. It certainly does not mean that whatever you might like to do is necessarily permissible for you to do. If you want to steal something from someone you do not have the right to do it. The argument refers to a *universal* and *natural* human desire, and says that for every such desire there is the *possibility* of its fulfillment. To own a certain minimum of personal property is indeed such a universal and natural human desire, and accordingly there exists the possibility of fulfilling this desire. (At least this possibility exists naturally, and is preserved in any well-ordered state. Some states are so organized that certain people cannot own any property at all; such a state is a slave state, and can be condemned for depriving people of a natural right.) But if you covet a million dollars, although you may be able to achieve the possession of this sum or even more, you can claim no universal *right* to such wealth, because the desire for wealth is not a universal human desire. Some people lack it entirely. If you long for, say, a particular pearl necklace, belonging to someone else, yours is a longing that many people do not share. If you wish for a mate, there is certainly the possibility of finding a mate. But if you covet your neighbor's wife (or husband) or if your chosen ideal mate prefers to mate with someone else, or not at all, you are not being deprived of anything to which you have a right. Similarly, although some people may wish for the Mohammedan heaven, with houris, their wish does not make it true, for it is not a universal wish, neither is the Buddhist idea of Nirvana necessarily true just because some people wish for that. But we all of us desire happiness, both in this life and the next, and the argument just given refers to the possibility of achieving both of these.

The soul, then, is something which is not destroyed by the death of the body. We can see this in yet another way by noticing that a disease, or an accident, that causes harm to the body does not necessarily harm the soul. A man who has lost an arm or a leg has his soul just the same, and his soul is not harmed by the loss. A wheel chair case, from polio, can go on to be President of the United States. It often happens that people suffering from a serious disease are cheerful, courageous, friendly, loving—in other words that they have splendid souls, though their bodies may be wasting away and even approaching death. Other people become grumpy, unpleasant and disgustingly selfish as a result of some minor distress. A blind man can be not only a good poet or a good musician, he can be a good man. A lame man may curse God (he might call it cursing "his fate"), or he may count his blessings and praise God. Harming the body does not harm the soul; the effect on the soul of a bodily injury may be either way, and is entirely incidental. The body is harmed by physical agents including disease. The soul is harmed entirely differently, by envy, malice, pride, greed, etc.—in other words it is harmed spiritually, and by things that it *does*, not by things that are done to it. Now the things that harm the body are things that can destroy it. We can see this anywhere we look. If something can destroy in strong doses, it can harm in smaller doses. The same things that can cause death, that is, destroy the body, can also harm it. But they don't harm the soul at all. How then can they destroy it?

We can see, then, by reason, that the soul is immortal, and from this conclusion we can go on to ask the most important question of all—What are we here for?

Everyone has to face this question, at some time at least in his or her life. Many people struggle with it all the time, as a constant preoccupation. Some people are able to come to a satisfactory answer, others never are, while still others drift from one answer to another, never finding anything in which they can rest content, and build their lives.

It is a question whose answer, of course, depends profoundly on the immortality of the soul. For if, at the end of our lives, we fade out completely as if we had never been, then there is no point in doing anything but follow our own inclinations all the time. We can do exactly as we please, subject only to the limitation that other people are doing the same, and it will be prudent not to interfere with other people too much, or they will start interfering with us. On the other hand, as Samuel Butler put it, if there is a life after death, then it stands to reason that we should try to make the best of both worlds.

What are we here for? This is the most important question of all. Unfortunately in our climate of opinion it is particularly difficult to answer. All the trends that obscure reason make it harder to answer this question. The misunderstandings about ourselves, the entire neglect of "soul" to the point where we have forgotten what it means, make it more difficult still. The whole influence of materialistic thinking is thrown directly against any clear understanding of this question.

To begin with one of the minor difficulties, there is a verbal, semantic difficulty in the way in which it is often asked, Does Life have any *Meaning*? The question is put in this way by people who, owing to the cloud of intellectual muddle which surrounds us all the time, have not been able to focus on it really clearly. The form—Does Life have Meaning?—though it often serves to communicate the thought from one person to another, does not serve to clarify the question precisely, either to him who hears it or him who asks it. For, strictly and literally speaking, Life could not in any case have a meaning; words have meaning, or sentences may have meaning. We use the word loosely in conversation when we ask, What is the meaning of this or of that? We use the word loosely, too, when we ask the meaning of Life. More precisely, we can ask whether Life has a Purpose. Or to put it still more clearly, are we here for some Purpose? Or is it a matter of indifference what we do with our lives? Is there anything that we *should* be doing, while we live on this earth? And what happens if we don't do it? And if we are here on earth for a purpose, Who is it that has this Purpose for us?

Further difficulties come from the enormous prestige of modern science. It is often said that the overwhelming modern discoveries in astronomy and physics—which have nothing to do with the case —force us to take an entirely different view of the importance of man in the universe. We know so much about the universe nowadays, and it is so staggering and amazing that people have come almost to worship it. They speak of "the world mind" or "the world soul," sometimes "the infinite" which is equally vague, and they wonder what is our relation to this world mind, or soul. These people confuse the vitally important question, What are we here for? by turning it into What is our relation to the Universe? This seems to make things easier for some tender minds to whom the three-letter word G-o-d is almost terrifying. But God is not the universe. God created the universe. He is not the same as His own creation. Our relation to the universe is perfectly simple. We are part of it. We can look at it, admire its marvellous beauty, complexity and order, study it, and use it for our own purposes as far as we have been able to master it. There is no mystery at all about our relation to the universe. It is our relation to God that is important.

Another way of confusing the issue is to call attention rather wistfully to our own puny size, which is so utterly negligible in comparison with the sum total of created things. It all seemed very different, it is said, way back in the days when the earth was believed to be the center of the universe, and man the noblest creature on the earth. But that was hundreds of years ago. Copernicus, in the sixteenth century, showed that the earth goes round the sun, not *vice versa*, and thereby deprived man of his central position. The Copernican revolution also made the universe very much larger, and man by comparison smaller, than had been thought before. According to the geocentric Ptolemaic system, the largest thing in the universe was the "sphere of the fixed stars" which was so large that the earth was negligible in comparison. This was admittedly fairly large, but according to Copernicus the distance from the earth to the fixed stars had to be so great that the entire orbit of the earth round the sun was negligible in comparison! More modern astronomical discoveries have made the universe larger and larger and larger, until we speak of "astronomical" to express anything so immense that our imagination can get no grasp of it. At the same time physicists have discovered the atom, which is inconceivably small, so that one human body is comprised of an unimaginably large number of atoms. All these things, it is said, show the insignificance of man. How, it is asked, can we believe that man has any significance in comparison with the Cosmos, which is so inconceivably vast?

To argue this way is to confuse size with importance. Even in the old Ptolemaic system, man had no size worth talking about. Man's body is minute in comparison with the earth, and the "sphere of the fixed stars" was enormously larger still. Certainly man is insignificant in size, you have only to compare him with the earth to see that, you don't need the entire universe. But who cares what the universe thinks of us? The universe doesn't think. It isn't our relation to the universe that is in question, but our relation to God, and God is not fooled by size—why should He be? He made it Himself. He made the atoms, inconceivably small, and He made aggregates of atoms constituting everything in the material world up to the largest galaxies, but of all these things that He made there is only one (barring possible life on other worlds) to which He gave the gift of intelligence. God made the entire universe, but only we humans (again, possibly excepting other planets or stars) are able to know something about Him. The universe is simply an immense aggregate of matter, but we are able to know something about our own Creator. We have an important relation to Him. We can realize and understand that He has a purpose, and when we ask, Does Life have a Meaning, or a Purpose? we are enquiring about God's purpose.

And finally, there is the quite special branch of confusion contributed to this subject by the theory of evolution, which was devised with the express purpose of denying any Purpose in the universe. George Gaylord Simpson,* who is a typical evolutionist, summing up his conclusions from his lifetime study, declares that man "stands alone in the universe, a unique product of a long unconscious, impersonal, material process, with unique understanding and potentialities. These he owes to no one but himself, and it is to himself that he is responsible."

You may wonder and puzzle indefinitely about the meaning of responsibility to *oneself*. It has no meaning. Responsibility necessarily implies some one *else* to be responsible to. Responsibility only to oneself isn't responsibility. It is irresponsibility.

Even stranger is the acknowledgment of man's unique understanding and potentialities. He got these through evolution, which Simpson himself describes as an unconscious, impersonal and material process. If the evolutionists are right, it was a series of mutations that led from ape-like creatures through sub-men up to men, and mutations are changes that happen in the germ plasm; we cannot summon them by taking thought. Man did not evolve from an animal by his own effort; the mutations did it for him, and man owes his evolution to whoever or whatever made these mutations possible. And this means—even if we accept the theory of evolution at its own face value, we still can't get away from it—that man owes his unique position to God, and it is to God that he is responsible.

Any way we turn, we find that, What are we here for? becomes What did God put us here for? What is our relation to God? What does He want us to be doing?

In order to answer this question properly, it is necessary to go beyond reason. There is only one step beyond reason, and that is

* *Life of the Past*, Yale University Press.

Revelation. God has revealed Himself to mankind, in order to help us find answers to the questions: What is the Purpose of Life? What are we supposed to be doing here on this earth? How ought we to be living? Almost everyone in this country would accept, or at least pay lip service to, the Ten Commandments. These are a revelation from God, who gave them to Moses on the mountain. God made one more Revelation to us mortals in our Lord Jesus Christ, and very many people in this country, including me, who is writing this, accept this Christian revelation. In some things, mostly matters of detail, the Christian revelation is interpreted differently by the various Christian sects. But whatever you accept, it is most important to be clear about the relation between reason and revelation, that revelation supplements reason, and does not contradict it. Anything that we learn by revelation must always be in conformity with reason, in the sense that it is not contrary to reason. For if it were *contrary* to reason we *couldn't* believe it! Suppose a man were to say, in effect "I have a very wonderful new religion, and I would like to tell you about my new religion," and if he were then to tell us something self-contradictory, something that clearly, on the face of it, couldn't possibly be true, how on earth would that man ever make any converts?

There is only one kind of truth, true truth. God gave us our intellect in order to find out many things that are true and in order to guide us in practical life. But, as we are in this world, we do not have enough intellect to find out everything—far from it! God has revealed to us further truths that we would not have been able to find out by our unaided intellect. These are the truths of Revelation, and we believe them through Faith, which is the gift of accepting Revelation. But the truths that we can reach by reason alone, and the truths of revelation, are all part of one and the same true Truth.

Revelation tells us of miracles, but miracles are not contrary to reason. Miracles are contrary to experience; to all *ordinary* experience, that is, but miracles are in any case extraordinary events. The miracle of the Resurrection of Jesus Christ, which is central to the Christian revelation, is not contrary to reason, and neither are any of the innumerable miracles that support the Christian faith without being central to it. Conversely, none of the discoveries of modern science (the genuine, proved discoveries, not some of the interpretations) are contrary to the Christian revelation. If ever there should appear to be a conflict, an out-and-out contradiction, between Faith and Reason, then this conflict *must* be resolved. It will turn out either that an alleged conclusion of reason is not watertight, has not been genuinely proved, or that revelation has been misinterpreted. And in the last analysis, reason must win. For to believe anything contrary to reason is impossible.

Reason tells us of the immortality of the soul. The Christian revelation confirms this. It also adds to it, or at least gives it a curious change of emphasis. The phrase "immortality of the soul" has the flavor of the Greek philosophers. The Christian tradition speaks rather of personal immortality, of "eternal life." It does not make the sharp split between "body" and "soul." It says rather that you will survive after your death. The Christian Creed speaks of "the resurrection of the body," so that at the end you, and not just your soul, will be saved.

Faith, by which we accept revelation, complements reason and does not contradict it. Faith is a gift of God. If we do not have faith, we can pray for it. But since there are many different interpretations of the one Divine Revelation, there is always this peculiar difficulty about praying for the gift of faith, namely, that you do not know exactly what you are praying for until after you have it! Should you go into a Church to pray, or a Synagogue, or even possibly a Mosque? Or is it perhaps the Lord's will that you should become a Buddhist? This is a very troublesome perplexity, but if you find yourself in this difficulty, there is one thing that you can do—you can pray that God will make his will known to you. And go on praying.

THE KNOWN AND THE UNKNOWN

J. Krishnamurti

J. Krishnamurti is a native of South India, born in 1897, educated in England and now a resident of California. He is the author of numerous poems and essays reflecting his Indian outlook on life.

The long evening shadows were over the still waters, and the river was becoming quiet after the day. Fish were jumping out of the water, and the heavy birds were coming to roost among the big trees. There was not a cloud in the sky, which was silver-blue. A boat full of people came down the river; they were singing and clapping, and a cow called in the distance. There was the scent of evening. A garland of marigold was moving with the water, which sparkled in the setting sun. How beautiful and alive it all was—the river, the birds, the trees and the villagers.

We were sitting under a tree, overlooking the river. Near the tree was a small temple, and a few lean cows wandered about. The temple was clean and well swept, and the flowering bush was watered and cared for. A man was performing his evening rituals, and his voice was patient and sorrowful. Under the last rays of the sun, the water was the color of new-born flowers. Presently someone joined us and began to talk of his experiences. He said he had devoted many years of his life to the search for God, had practised many austerities and renounced many things that were dear. He had also helped considerably in social work, in building a school, and so on. He was interested in many things, but his consuming interest was the finding of God; and now, after many years, His voice was being heard, and it guided him in little as well as big things. He had no will of his own, but followed the inner voice of God. It never failed him, though he often corrupted its clarity; his prayer was ever for the purification of the vessel, that it might be worthy to receive.

Can that which is immeasurable be found by you and me? Can that which is not of time be searched out by that thing which is fashioned of time? Can a diligently practised discipline lead us to the unknown? Is there a means to that which has no beginning and no end? Can that reality be caught in the net of our desires? What we can capture is the projection of the known; but the unknown cannot be captured by the known. That which is named is not the unnamable, and by naming we only awaken the conditioned responses. These responses, however noble and pleasant, are not of the real. We respond to stimulants, but reality offers no stimulant: it *is*.

The mind moves from the known to the known, and it cannot reach out into the unknown. You cannot think of something you do not know; it is impossible. What you think about comes out of the known, the past, whether that past be remote, or the second that has just gone by. This past is thought, shaped and conditioned by many influences, modifying itself according to circumstances and pressures, but ever remaining a process of time. Thought can only deny or assert, it cannot discover or search out the new. Thought cannot come upon the new; but when thought is silent, then there may be the new—which is immediately transformed into the old, into the experienced, by thought. Thought is ever shaping, modifying, coloring according to a pattern of experience. The function of thought is to communicate but not to be in the state of experiencing. When experiencing ceases, then thought takes over and terms it within the category of the known. Thought cannot penetrate into the unknown, and so it can never discover or experience reality.

Disciplines, renunciations, detachments, rituals, the practice of virtue—all these, however noble, are the process of thought; and thought can only work towards an end, towards an achievement, which is ever the known. Achievement is security, the self-protective certainty of the known. To seek security in that which is nameless is to deny it. The security that may be found is only in the projection of the past, of the known. For this reason the mind must be entirely and deeply silent; but this silence cannot be purchased through sacrifice, sublimation or suppression. This silence comes when the mind is no longer seeking, no longer caught in the process of becoming. This silence is not cumulative, it may not be built up through practice. This silence must be as unknown to the mind as the timeless; for if the mind experiences the silence, then there is the experiencer who is the result of past experiences, who is cognizant of a past silence; and what is experienced by the experiencer is merely a self-projected repetition. The mind can never experience the new, and so the mind must be utterly still.

The mind can be still only when it is not experiencing, that is, when it is not terming or naming, recording or storing up in memory. This naming and recording is a constant process of the different layers of consciousness, not merely of the upper mind. But when the superficial mind is quiet, the deeper mind can offer up its intimations. When the whole consciousness is silent and tranquil, free from all becoming, which is spontaneity, then only does the immeasurable come into being. The desire to maintain this freedom gives continuity to the memory of the becomer, which is a hindrance to reality. Reality has no continuity; it is from moment to moment, ever new, ever fresh. What has continuity can never be creative.

The upper mind is only an instrument of communication, it cannot measure that which is immeasurable. Reality is not to be spoken of; and when it is, it is no longer reality.

This is meditation.

Meditation

He had practised for a number of years what he called meditation; he had followed certain disciplines after reading many books on the subject, and had been to a monastery of some kind where they meditated several hours a day. He was not sentimental about it, nor was he blurred by the tears of self-sacrifice. He said that, though after these many years his mind was under control, it still sometimes got out of control; that there was no joy in his meditation; and that the self-imposed disciplines were making him rather hard and arid. Somehow he was very dissatisfied with the whole thing. He had belonged to several so-called religious societies, but now he had finished with them all and was seeking independently the God they all promised. He was getting on in years and was beginning to feel rather weary.

Right meditation is essential for the purgation of the mind, for without the emptying of the mind there can be no renewal. Mere continuity is decay. The mind withers away by constant repetition, by the friction of wrong usage, by sensations which make it dull and weary. The control of the mind is not important; what is important is to find out the interests of the mind. The mind is a bundle of conflicting interests, and merely to strengthen one interest against another is what we call concentration, the process of discipline. Discipline is the cultivation of resistance, and where there is resistance there is no understanding. A well-disciplined mind is not a free mind, and it is only in freedom that any discovery can be made. There must be spontaneity to uncover the movements of the self, at whatever level it may be placed. Though there may be unpleasant discoveries, the movements of the self must be exposed and understood; but disciplines destroy the spontaneity in which discoveries are made. Disciplines, however exacting, fix the mind in a pattern. The mind will adjust itself to that for which it has been trained; but that to which it adjusts itself is not the real. Disciplines are mere impositions and so can never be the means of denudation. Through self-discipline the mind can strengthen itself in its purpose; but this purpose is self-projected and so it is not the real. The mind creates reality in its own image, and disciplines merely give vitality to that image.

Only in discovery can there be joy—the discovery from moment to moment of the ways of the self. The self, at whatever level it is placed, is still of the mind. Whatever the mind can think about is of the mind. The mind cannot think about something which is not of itself; it cannot think of the unknown. The self at any level is the known; and though there may be layers of the self of which the superficial mind is not aware, they are still within the field of the known. The movements of the self are revealed in the action of relationship; and when relationship is not confined within a pattern, it gives an opportunity for self-revelation. Relationship is the action of the self, and to understand this action there must be awareness without choice; for to choose is to emphasize one interest against another. This awareness is the experiencing of the action of the self, and in this experiencing there is neither the experiencer nor the experienced. Thus the mind is emptied of its accumulations; there is no longer the "me," the gatherer. The accumulations, the stored-up memories are the "me"; the "me" is not an entity apart from the accumulations. The "me" separates itself from its characteristics as the observer, the watcher, the controller, in order to safeguard itself, to give itself continuity amidst impermanency. The experiencing of the integral, unitary process frees the mind from its dualism. Thus the total process of the mind, the open as well as the hidden, is experienced and understood— not piece by piece, activity by activity, but in its entirety. Then dreams and everyday activities are ever an emptying process. The mind must be utterly empty to receive; but the craving to be empty in order to receive is a deep-seated impediment, and this also must be understood completely, not at any particular level. The craving to experience must wholly cease, which happens only when the experiencer is not nourishing himself on experiences and their memories.

The purgation of the mind must take place not only on its upper levels, but also in its hidden depths; and this can happen only when the naming or terming process comes to an end. Naming only strengthens and gives continuity to the experiencer, to the desire for permanency, to the characteristic of particularizing memory. There must be silent awareness of naming, and so the understanding of it. We name not only to communicate, but also to give continuity and substance to an experience, to revive it and to repeat its sensations. This naming process must cease, not only on the superficial levels of the mind, but throughout its entire structure. This is an arduous task, not to be easily understood or lightly experienced; for our whole consciousness is a process of naming or terming experience, and then storing or recording it. It is this process that gives nourishment and strength to the illusory entity, the experiencer as distinct and separate from the experience. Without thoughts there is no thinker. Thoughts create the thinker, who isolates himself to give himself permanency; for thoughts are always impermanent.

There is freedom when the entire being, the superficial as well as the hidden, is purged of the past. Will is desire; and if there is any action of the will, any effort to be free, to denude oneself, then there can never be freedom, the total purgation of the whole being. When all the many layers of consciousness are quiet, utterly still, only then is there the immeasurable, the bliss that is not of time, the renewal of creation.

THE MIRACLE WITHIN US

Jean Hellé

Jean Hellé is a French writer and his contribution is taken from his book Miracles, *translated by Lancelot C. Sheppard, and published by the David McKay Co., Inc., New York.*

> A little science estranges men from God, much science leads them back to Him.
>
> —PASTEUR.

Beyond the venture into the domain of the miraculous lies the Divine Presence. A man may believe in God or deny him; in both camps honorable, upright, sincere men are to be found. But one who has never asked himself the question, who has never interrogated heaven with fervor or anxiety, such a one, whatever the length or the fame of his earthly span, is a nonentity, less than a nonentity, a more or less foolhardy nonentity clinging to the walls or the floor of his prison.

—J. H.

The more the world advances in time and the greater the progress of what is called civilization, the less does the soul act as a window overlooking creation. From those far-off times when life was natural, when a pastoral people led their flocks over the vast grassy expanses, down to our modern days when the machine is interposed like a screen between our eyes and the natural elements of the cosmos, a revolution has occurred; the senses have become specialized, sealed off in compartments; it seems agreed that men shall see only with their eyes, think only with their brains, touch only with their hands. We have departed from that primitive wisdom according to which man formed one whole, thinking and seeing with his entire body. In this connection the poet Lanza del Vasto reminds us that this power is now to be found in the East, which is nearer than we are to primitive times. Thus some of us require the visible signs of God's presence on earth to strike us forcibly, almost roughly. We do not go out to meet them; we demand that they come to us. We want them to swoop down like a thunderbolt through the superficial structure of our dwellings. The heavens must open, the sun must leap from its zenith to the horizon, from one horizon to another, the paralyzed must rise and walk. And prodigies as striking as these are still not enough to convince us.

Miracles do not always convince. Each one reacts in accordance with his temperament. The uncultivated mind will adapt itself to any wonder, cry miracle at the sight of any hysterical, vanity-obsessed woman, whereas the skeptical mind will refuse to admit even the instantaneous ossification of an aperture in the skull; some superior or honest-minded men recognize that the universe is not entirely a laboratory specimen, holding no secrets, to be observed or dissected at will, that Nature, treacherous to her own self, mocks at Nature. But in either case neither those who peacefully await another life nor those who believe in final extinction in an everlasting nothingness will change their position, for neither will make the necessary effort.

Bernadette was right: to contemplate infinity there is no need to look at an exceedingly high point. To the fleshly eyes of man the heavens appear unchanging and limited, a gray, an azure vault wherein move the clouds which he has tamed to his own uses. The Christian God is no Jupiter seated on a mountain, flinging down his childish thunderbolts and, by way of recreation, busying himself inciting martial men to battle. God breathes in the smallest particle of the universe and His presence absorbs every one of our thoughts, every act of our life. How should we not be His intimates since not only did He create us but He became one of us. In one of his novels Graham Greene wrote that for him (or rather for one of his characters who was obviously expressing the author's view) the Crucifixion and the sufferings of the Passion were only additional sufferings to that inconceivable torture by which God took on our poor human frame with its difficulties and infirmities. Before making the journey up to Calvary, jeered at, scourged, crowned with thorns, and a reed thrust mockingly into His hand, God was that child in swaddling clothes described by Catherine Emmerich, wailing, crying, and undergoing all the hardships of earthly life. He shared the very lowest state of bondage with us. And He continues to share our life, at its good times and its bad, with us mortals. He has said so, He has proclaimed it, and He has even instituted a Sacrament to confirm it. Now ordinary reason—it has nothing to do with mysticism, it is just common sense—should be sufficient to prove to us that a God so closely bound to us, dwelling in our flesh, does not require to be contemplated from afar. In His manifestations He emphasizes His own Word, when He desires to do so; and then He chooses a witness to the miracle and this chosen one—pledged inexorably to be humbled on this earth—will surely possess virtues that we most certainly have not. But each one of us, day by day, is steeped in some particle of grace—and even in the entirety of grace. When we break bread, when we plane wood or plough land or write books, when after our work we fall asleep at night, God is there. The conscious Christian relates all things to God. His own unworthy life is adorned, illuminated with the infinite perfection of Heaven.

A blind man goes to Lourdes and asks God to restore his eyes. Near him one suffering from incurable Pott's disease promises, if he is healed, to offer his orthopedic jacket as an ex-voto to Our Lady; that is a natural and a moving gesture. It is normal for a man to ask God to end his sufferings. But if the blind man or the sufferer from Pott's disease should be cured, will it be considered the first and most wonderful miracle granted them by God? The grotto at Lourdes is full of these ex-voto offerings proclaiming men's and women's gratitude for deliverance from their ills—and now they are dead and reduced to an intangible dust. For some years they lived with less discomfort; their last days were less clouded with suffering; the blind were given the time to glance about them, the paralyzed to try a few steps. Then they died, and now it may be believed they contemplate the Creator of all things. But in contemplating Him they contemplate themselves as well. Their whole life is spread out before their profound spiritual gaze like a marvelous film of which human memory is but a wretched caricature; in a flash they see all, the important moments of their life—the landmarks—as well as the forgotten and supposedly insignificant minutes. They see again that moment when the miracle occurred which they remembered until their death and which their descendants will continue to remember, that moment which in some sort was historic. But it is hardly that moment which they now dwell on or hold important, although it was important, important for themselves and for those who witnessed it as a proof of the mercy of God in their regard. Yet that mercy itself was conditional, and they showed themselves in the years to come perhaps unworthy or unmindful of it. And so, the provisional cure of their bodies in itself, the reprieve from suffering, with the necessity of dying ever awaiting them at the end, counts only a little more than the preservation from other hazards—some germ, some bullet, perhaps. But what counts most for them now is the thread of their life, the texture of their destiny: some intuition which turned them away from evil, some supposedly chance encounter with an earthly companion which revealed them to themselves, some bestowal of grace which brought them nearer to God; a joy occurring at the right moment, some salutary suffering. For it may well be for a pain, an infirmity that cries of thanksgiving go up in Heaven: "I thank you, my God, for not having heard my prayer."

In this sense the miracle is a daily phenomenon. It can be achieved within each of us.

TRANSLATED FROM THE FRENCH
BY LANCELOT C. SHEPPARD

THE EDITOR AND HIS BOOK

WHITNEY EWING BURNETT, a long-time newspaperman, foreign correspondent, author and editor, was born in Salt Lake City, Utah, on August 14, 1899. His education took him to the University of Southern California, the University of Utah, and the University of California at Los Angeles. His newspaper career started in 1916 in Salt Lake City where he worked for the Telegram, the Herald-Republican, and the Tribune. Two years later he went to Los Angeles to work as a reporter for the Evening Express and then joined the Associated Press in 1919, working in Los Angeles, San Francisco and New York. In 1927 he went to Paris as city editor of the New York Herald's Paris edition, going to Vienna two years later to organize the Balkan news service for the New York Sun and Consolidated Press. While in Austria, in 1931, he founded the magazine, Story, with his first wife, Martha Foley, and transferred this venture to New York in 1932, publishing the magazine until 1954. He was founder and editor of The Story Press, an editor with J. B. Lippincott, E. P. Dutton and other publishing houses, and for many years has taught courses in short story writing at Columbia University and other colleges. He is editor of A Story Anthology (Vanguard Press, 1933), Story in America (Vanguard Press, 1934), and The Flying Yorkshireman (Harper & Brothers, 1937), all in collaboration with Martha Foley; This Is My Best (Dial Press, 1942), Two Bottles of Relish (Dial Press, 1943), The Seas of God (Lippincott, 1944), 18 Great Modern Short Stories (Avon, 1944), The Story Pocket Book (Pocket Books, 1944), Time To Be Young (Lippincott, 1945), American Writers Today (with C. E. Slatkin) (Ginn & Company, 1947), The World's Best (Dial Press, 1950), This Is My Best Humor (Dial Press, 1955), The Spirit of Adventure (Henry Holt, 1956), Animal Spirits (Lippincott, 1956), This Is My Philosophy (Harper & Brothers, 1957), This Is My Funniest (Pocket Books, 1957); in collaboration with Hallie Burnett, he edited Story: The Fiction of the Forties (Dutton, 1949), Story: The

Magazine of the Short Story in Book Form, Nos. 1, 2, 3, 4 (*David McKay, 1951; A. A. Wyn, 1952, 1953, 1953*), Sextet (*David McKay, 1952*), The Tough Ones (*Popular Library, 1955*), 19 Tales of Terror (*Bantam Books, 1957*), Crazy Youth (*Bantam Books, 1958*). He is author of The Maker of Signs (*Smith and Haas, 1934*), The Literary Life and the Hell With It (*Harper & Brothers, 1938*), and Immortal Bachelor (*with John Pen*), (*Story, 1942*).

THE SPIRIT OF MAN (*Hawthorn, 1958*) was *designed by Betty K. Crumley and completely manufactured by H. Wolff Book Manufacturing Company, New York. The body type is Electra, designed for the Linotype by W. A. Dwiggins, one of America's best-known typographers and designers.*

A HAWTHORN BOOK